J.W.G. Bruce

IN THE STEPS OF MOSES
THE CONQUEROR

Books by LOUIS GOLDING

FICTION

FORWARD FROM BABYLON
SEACOAST OF BOHEMIA
DAY OF ATONEMENT
STORE OF LADIES
THE MIRACLE BOY
THE PRINCE OR SOMEBODY
GIVE UP YOUR LOVERS
MAGNOLIA STREET
FIVE SILVER DAUGHTERS
THE CAMBERWELL BEAUTY
THE PURSUER
THE DANCE GOES ON

SHORT STORIES

THE DOOMINGTON WANDERER

VERSE

SORROW OF WAR
SHEPHERD SINGING RAGTIME
PROPHET AND FOOL
THE SONG OF SONGS, RENDERED AS
 A MASQUE

TRAVEL

SUNWARD: ADVENTURES IN ITALY
SICILIAN NOON
THOSE ANCIENT LANDS: A JOURNEY
 TO PALESTINE
IN THE STEPS OF MOSES THE LAW-
 GIVER
IN THE STEPS OF MOSES THE CON-
 QUEROR

BELLES LETTRES

ADVENTURES IN LIVING DANGER-
 OUSLY
LETTER TO ADOLF HITLER
JAMES JOYCE

SHEPHERD ON MOUNT NEBO

IN THE STEPS OF MOSES THE CONQUEROR

By

LOUIS GOLDING

LONDON
RICH & COWAN, LTD.
37 BEDFORD SQUARE, W.C.1

First published 1938

MADE IN GREAT BRITAIN

PRINTED AND BOUND BY THE CAMELOT PRESS LTD., LONDON AND SOUTHAMPTON
FOR MESSRS. RICH AND COWAN LTD., 37 BEDFORD SQUARE, LONDON, W.C.1

ACKNOWLEDGEMENTS

I MUST again record my deep indebtedness, before all others, to my friend, Dudley Jones. To these also: Colonel Peake Pasha; Sir Ronald Storrs and the much-adventuring Storrs letter; Major C. S. Jarvis and his amiable patience with my questionings; Dr. Nelson Glueck, of the American School of Oriental Research in Jerusalem; Flight-Lieutenant Sims, of the Royal Air Force in Amman; Abdullah Bey Rihani, of Tafileh; Father Dunn, of the Latin Mission in Kerak; Dr. Neville Whymant, for his invaluable help with proofs; my secretary, S. R. Hopwood.

LIST OF ILLUSTRATIONS

(*The photographs were taken by the author, except in the cases otherwise listed*)

CHAPTER ONE

§ 1

THE last candle had only just gone out in my high-hung cell in the Convent of Mount Sinai, when the first camel entered.

He entered not by the door, but by the right hand wall, and though it was a small room, he found no difficulty in picking his way between the foot of the bed and the wash-stand. His head high in air, he padded contemptuously towards the left hand wall, and disappeared. Another camel and another followed him; the caravan was stretched out along the steel-grey horizon. Without pause the tawny river, humped with yellow waves, heaved along its uneven channel. Then it reached the lee of a high mountain, which was altogether on smoke, because the Lord descended upon it in fire: and the smoke thereof ascended as the smoke of a furnace, and the whole mount quaked greatly.

And a voice at the head of the caravan cried out: Mount Sinai! Mount Sinai! All change! This way for Hazeroth and all stations for the River Jordan! All change!

Then the cloud that had hung stationary over the head of the leading camel moved, the trumpeters blew their silver trumpets, the standards went forward; and the host went after the standards, and the four winds of heaven blew; and, as they blew, all the valleys were filled with the odours of myrrh and frankincense.

So the host moved out of the plain of Er Rahah into one of the narrower wadis, and the tumult died down, saving only for the sound of the camel-bells. Far and delicate, like rocking pin-points of sound, the voices of the camel-bells thrilled across the cold air.

The cold air . . . I became aware of a sudden that my shoulders were slabs of ice. With the dream still heavy on my eyes, I reached out to lift the bed-clothes over me, but they had slipped, they were not there. I was awake now. I was aware the door of my cell was wide open. I had not latched it properly and the stark wind from the summit of Gebel Ed Deir had swung it open. I was aware also that I heard the sound of bells, though they were not the camel-bells of my dream.

It was not many bells but one bell, the bell that summons the monks of the Convent of Mount Sinai from their cells for their first devotion. It rings at two-thirty in the morning, first three notes, low pitched, then louder, again three times, five minutes later.

It was only two-thirty, then, and it was icy cold. I got out of bed. The floor was like rimy steel plates on a ship's deck. I latched the door properly, then got back into bed again. Then I gathered up the bed-clothes and pulled them over my head. The sooner I went off to sleep again the better. It would be several hours before I could see the *Oikonomos*, the Bursar, about the camels.

Oh, yes, the camels. I knew now why my dream had been full of camels.

Perhaps there won't be any camels, I comforted myself. I don't want camels. Lucas doesn't want camels. He'd rather walk. Only Jim wants camels. In a little time the camels were in the room again, picking their way between the foot of the bed and the wash-stand.

It was bright hot morning when I awoke again. The strip of sky raced like a blue river between the tops of the rust-red cliffs.

§ 2

We had eggs for breakfast that morning, fried in olive-oil. I don't think I have ever seen tinier eggs. I suppose the Sinai fowls can't help being a little discouraged by that combination of high sanctity with low temperature.

Then I went down to the *Oikonomos*. Will there be any camels for us, I asked. The *Oikonomos* regretted. The Convent

camels were all in Tor, down on the west coast of the peninsula. A Bedu had come in that morning with a message from
the monks there. They would have to keep all the camels, as
they were so busy with the Muslim pilgrims making the *haj*
to Mecca.

"So you see?" I turned to the others. "Let's tell Mustapha
to get the cars ready."

§ 3

We had made a journey between the Nile and Mount Sinai
in the steps of Moses the Lawgiver. We were setting out that
day on a journey between Mount Sinai and the Jordan in the
steps of Moses the Conqueror. It was not the second part of
a journey we were making, but a new journey, different in
mood, with different fellow-travellers.

We had been three living men moving with the multitude of
Israelite ghosts, though there had been moments when we had
felt that we were the ghosts and those others the living men.
We had till this moment of departure from Sinai been engaged
upon an Exodus, fugitives from the terror of Pharaoh. And
the terror had not completely gone out of our bones, though
the road to Sinai was long, and wild with miracle; though we
had crossed a sea cloven by a great wind, and when the wind
died, we had beheld the bodies of the Egyptians with their
raiment, and their horses with their bridles and saddles, tossing
lazily in the trough of the sea.

But now, now that we were moving forward from Sinai, we
were not a rabble of fugitives any more. A great thing had
happened to us, no greater has ever happened to any host of
men. We were a People. We had been brought forth out of
our camp to the nether part of the mountain to meet God;
we had beheld Mount Sinai altogether on smoke, because the
Lord descended upon it in fire. We were bound together by
a Covenant. For the first time in the history of the dwellers
on this planet, the instinctive yearnings of men upward from
the brute, upward toward goodly and godly living, had been
rendered into a code, as limpid as water, as final as death.

That was the thing that had happened to us. The Exodus of the rabble was over. The Advance of a People towards its promised heritage was about to begin. We were not the same people as we had been, nor was our leader, Moses, the same leader. He had been chiefly a Lawgiver, codifying and teaching the law he had during long years meditated in the solitude of the wilderness of Midian. From now on his rôle was to be changed. If the promise was to be fulfilled and the heritage won, he must be Moses the Soldier, the Conqueror. It is possible he had once already been a soldier, in those " veiled years " of his youth regarding which the Old Testament breathes no word, and the New Testament, in the person of St. Stephen, tells us one pregnant thing: he was " learned in words and deeds." It may have been in Ethiopia, as Josephus recounts, that he acquired the experience in the art of war which he was to put to good use in the series of campaigns that swept him across Moab and Edom to the plain of Jordan. But he had actually fought quite recently, on the journey between the Egyptian frontier and Mount Sinai, the first of this long series of battles. That was at Rephidim, where he defeated the Amalekites. And though the text seems to suggest that he did no more than pray on a hill-top, while Joshua did the actual fighting in the valley below, whatever the nature of his participation, it was clearly necessary to the victory of Israel. For the very next battle in which Israel was engaged, the first after the departure from Sinai, was once more against these same Amalekites, in alliance this time with the Canaanites. But Moses (as it is written) departed not out of the camp; wherefore was Israel smitten, and beaten down, even unto Hormah.

There was to be no victory without Moses, then, Moses the Conqueror. It was in the steps of that new Moses we were setting out that day, on the road that began under Sinai with the trumpets of a myriad angels blowing, and ended on Pisgah, with no sound at all save the grass-blades rustling in the evening wind.

DESERT OF THE WANDERING

§ 4

Where, then, were we to make for—what was to be the first stage of our journey? We opened the Book of Numbers and read these words: " And it came to pass . . . that the cloud was taken up from over the Tabernacle of the testimony. And the children of Israel set forward according to their journeys out of the wilderness of Sinai; and the cloud abode in the wilderness of Paran."

That " wilderness of Sinai " we read of was here, where we found ourselves, in the plain of Er Rahah, as it is called to-day, under the flank of the Holy Mountain. We were to go hence and make for the " wilderness of Paran." Which wilderness was that, west, north, or east? It sounds a little strange to speculate might it be west. It was, after all, from the west they had fled, from the marches of Pharaoh's land that now lay west of them. Yet actually west of them, and only a little north, lay the wadi Feiran, the longest in the peninsula, and wilderness for most of its length. It is not impossible that Feiran and Paran are the same word; and, even, that both are cognate with the word *Pharaon*, Pharaoh, for the terror of that word threw its shadow over great distances far removed from its bases.

If Paran is Feiran, our journey lay westward for a time, along the way we had come, by the wadi es Sheikh to the wadi Feiran. Doubtless, by some route still to be ascertained, the road would then turn north and east towards the fringe of Canaan, the land of the promise.

But is Paran Feiran? On the whole the scholars believe not, despite this similarity of names. Unless egress from Er Rahah were barred in every other direction, Moses might well have felt that a return towards Pharaoh, if for no more than a day or two's march, would be an infelicitous initiation of a journey sanctified by Jehovah's most hallowed auspices. Further, the events that took place in Paran, of which we learn as the narrative evolves, seem almost certainly to have taken place in the region to-day called the " Negeb," over towards the southern border of Canaan, and that is a long way from the wadi Feiran. No. For the most part the scholars take Paran to mean the great limestone plateau of Et Tih, which stretches east and west of the Peninsula, northward from these granite and porphyry ranges at the heart of which we found ourselves, here at Gebel Musa.

To sum up, the first stage of the journey must be either to Paran-Feiran or Paran-Et Tih. And yet were the two totally incompatible, we asked ourselves, when so many of the names mentioned in the narrative are shadows overlapping shadows, merging with shadows? Was it impossible that the experience began with Feiran and faded into Et Tih? In this inquiry nothing is impossible. Does the text itself indicate, however dimly, the line of route? Does any faint taper shine across the hieratic mist?

" And they set forward from the mount of the Lord three days' journey," we are told, " and the ark of the covenant of the Lord went before them three days' journey, to seek out a resting-place for them." *And the name of that place was called Taberah*. But it was only called Taberah, *after* the host had rested there, not before. " The name of that place was called Taberah, because the fire of the Lord burnt among them." The wanderers carried the name on with them in their records. They did not leave it behind them, impressed into the slope of a hill, a spring in a wadi.

Taberah is no taper, then. It does not help us. We read shortly that the people abode in a place called Kibroth-hattaavah. Exactly the same is the case here. " And the name of that place was called Kibroth-hattaavah, because there they buried the people that lusted." It is, in fact, much less the name of a place than the description of an episode. It is, moreover, not at all clear whether one place is meant, or two. Burning and burying may well have happened in one and the same place, so much of the aboriginal devil remained unexorcised in the hearts of these stiff-necked ones, despite the incomparable privilege and matchless glory of Sinai.

We go further. " From Kibroth-hattaavah," we read now, " the people journeyed unto Hazeroth; and they abode at Hazeroth."

How then of Hazeroth? What pointer, if any, have we here? None, says one scholar, glumly. " It is impossible to identify the site. The name denotes ' enclosures ' and might be applied to any spot where nomads were accustomed to stay with their flocks." But most scholars are not so glum. They note that in the opening verse of Deuteronomy, when we are promised the words " which Moses spake unto all Israel beyond Jordan in the wilderness," it is stated that it was in the Arabah he spoke, " over against Suph, between Paran, and Tophel, and Laban, and Hazeroth, and Di-zahab."

Di-zahab? they ask themselves a little less helplessly, Di-zahab? The word might mean " place of gold," as the Vulgate implies, or it might not. But there is, in fact, a place with a name vaguely similar to it, somewhere vaguely in these regions: a minute beach called Dahab, due east from Gebel Musa on the shore of the Gulf of Sinai. But that is not all. About fifty kilometres north of Dahab is a well the tribesmen call Ain el Hudhera.

Hudhera! Hazeroth! And not hopelessly remote from Dahab—Di-zahab! It is enough. We have picked up the traces of the host of Israel moving northward to its destiny! What is the way from Gebel Musa to Ain el Hudhera? And what transport do we use to take us there?

Well, we had to use camels to get there, Lucas and Jim and I were well aware. We could take our two cars back a little distance along the wadi es Sheikh, but from that point we must have camels to take us north-eastward by the wadi Saal towards Ain el Hudhera, this very speculative Hazeroth which had been worked out for us.

Camels. I did not want to travel by camels, which are a form of transport I dislike. Lucas did not object to them, because, being a person of strenuous habits, he would walk,

Bc

and carry some of the luggage, too, if the camels made any difficulties. As for Jim, he was the enthusiastic one. He said, once mounted on a camel, he would not get off, he would sleep on it at night.

I agreed to camels, provided, of course, we could get them —the monks at the Convent had made it clear from the beginning it might not be easy. But I was a little troubled about what we should do when we got to Ain el Hudhera. What would be the next step? We could return to the wadi es Sheikh and pick up our cars. We could go on with the camels a long way northward and pick up the *haj* road at some point in the howling desert between Suez and Akaba. Or we might even go south to Dahab, we had thought at one time, and pick up a felucca in which we would beat north-ward to Akaba.

All these possibilities bristled with difficulties, most of all that felucca. To begin with, there would be no felucca, it was a dream; and if there were a felucca, it might be a long time before we would find the right wind to take us to Akaba. The other two possibilities involved keeping the cars hanging about a long time. We could not do that; they had to report at their headquarters in El Arish before long.

The camels were going to cause a lot more trouble than they were worth, I told myself. None the less, I inquired of the *Oikonomos* could he arrange some beasts for us and learned without grief he could not provide them. I am sorry, I said. There will be no Ain el Hudhera and no Dahab. And perhaps that is as well; we are saved from a scholars' snare and etymologists' delusion. It is really very unlikely that the one is the Bible's Hazeroth and the other its Di-zahab.

We must go by the cars that brought us here, I said, and make straight for Paran, which is Et Tih, often called the Desert of the Wandering. Well, not quite straight, I admitted. We would have to go all the way back to Suez, for it is impossible to go anywhere else by car from Gebel Musa, except-ing to Tor, which is further south and irrelevant to our journey. From Suez we will have to turn due east again,

along the *haj* road to Nekhl and Akaba. But we have at least
this consolation. If Feiran and Paran are really the same
word—

" I would have liked those camels," murmured Jim.

" Anyhow we have Mustapha," I pointed out, " and
Mohammed and Hassan."

Jim's eye brightened. Yes, we still had Mustapha and
Mohammed and Hassan. To me any one of them was worth
more than all the camels of Tartary.

§ 5

Mustapha was an *umbasha*, a corporal, in Camel Corps,
number four company. Hassan and Mohammed were *askaris*,
private soldiers. They drove the two Ford trucks which the
authorities in Cairo had put at our disposal. They were
Sudanese. Their uniform was a khaki turban, a khaki over-
frock, a green sash round the frock and puttees under it.
There was a diamond-shaped flash of leopard skin on the side
of the turban. Mustapha was large and round and nearly
coal-black. Mohammed was small and sinewy and quite
coal-black. He had a startling gold tooth. Hassan was as
handsome as any film star. He had all the social graces. He
seemed to have gone to El Arish by way of Eton and Magdalen.

I went to Mustapha and Mohammed and Hassan and
reported the news to them. We were beginning our new
journey that very day. They were to take us to Suez. Thence
they were to take us in the track of the wanderings of the Beni
Israel so far as the frontier, which was at Akaba. Alas, from
Akaba they must return to their headquarters. For our part,
we would continue across the emirate of Abdullah, to the
banks of the Nakhr el Ordonn, the River Jordan.

" To Suez, Mustapha! " I said, up there, in the icy courtyard.

I never saw faces grow more suddenly radiant, with a warm
white-toothed radiance, than the faces of the *umbasha* and his
two *askaris*. It had been rather grim for these children of the

torrid Sudanese desert, among the frigid sanctities of Sinai. They shook my hand till I thought it would drop from the wrist.

" *Quais! Quais!* Good ! Good ! " they cried in chorus. Mohammed's gold tooth winked delightedly, like a seventh eye.

CHAPTER TWO

§ 1

WE would have to go back on our tracks then, on our journey in the steps of the host. Very well then. The host had done a great deal of that same thing in the forty years' wandering between Nile and Jordan.

So we left Mount Sinai behind us, and the Convent under the Mountain, and the cypresses in the Convent garden, the cypresses that are like a mirage refracted all the way from green Tempe to cindery Sinai. And we turned aside from the Plain where the host had abided so long in its station. " Mount Sinai! Mount Sinai! " I heard a voice cry faint and far as we turned right-handed into the wadi es Sheikh.

Where, where, had I heard that voice, a little nasal, slurring the consonants, protracting the final vowel? Where? " All change! " the voice continued. " All change! "

Then I remembered. In my dream last night . . . the voice at the head of the caravan crying out: " All stations for Hazeroth and the River Jordan! All change! "

Yes, true enough, all had been changed, all, excepting only the stiff neck of Israel.

The wadi es Sheikh sweeps round in a vast arc from the plain of Er Rahah to the wadi Feiran. It is all vast, the mountains, the sky, the solitude, so vast that though in a car you move over the uneven wadi floor in as many hours as its other travellers move in days or weeks, it does not seem as if the time you existed in is computable in any of these terms. There is a near broken rhythm of jolt and jar, there is a far smooth rhythm of dipping centuries. Between the far and near, the broken and smooth, the mind weaves unceasingly, numb with starry fatigue.

11

I became conscious of words addressed to me, this time from without, not within.

" What have you done with it? Do you hear? Has Jim got it? "

" Got it? " I repeated stupidly. My eyes were bleared with sun and space. " Got it! " I was content to let it go at that.

" The camera! " the voice said insistently. " All the gadgets! "

The gadgets! My heart jumped. I at once envisioned the sly gadget, the lovely gadget, gadget *par excellence*—the angle view-finder. There were a dozen other gadgets in the gadget-bag, a photo-electric exposure-meter, filters, telescopic lenses. They were there for duty. The angle view-finder was there for the joy of it. It gives you eyes at the side of your head. You become superhuman, a creature of myth. You behold faces that would veil themselves in swart veils, if you had not this lateral pair of eyes; you become a partner of joys and sorrows, of loves and hates, that would stay fast-bolted behind their doors, if you had no angle view-finder.

" What? " I cried in dismay. " The gadget-bag? Where is it? "

" It's what I've been asking you for half a wadi," said Lucas.

" Jim! Has Jim got it? Stop the other car, Hassan! "

We were driving in front for the time being. Hassan braked and bumped obliquely across Mohammed's bonnet. No, Jim had not got the gadget-bag.

" What are we going to do? " I asked faintly. It seemed as if I could not hope to glimpse Moses without an angle view-finder. Manna had lost something of its savour.

" What was the last photograph we took?" asked Lucas. " We must have left it there."

I could not remember taking photographs that day. But the others remembered. A camel and a tree, they said, in the opening to a narrow gully. It was about two hours' drive back. The camel will not be there any more, I said hopelessly. But the tree will, they insisted, and the gully will.

Mustapha, Mohammed and Hassan were looking very grieved and contrite. "*Mish* quais! Not good!" they were intoning, like a sinner saying "Peccavi!" Then Mustapha, *umbasha*, rose to the exigencies of the situation. He said a quick word to Mohammed. Mohammed jumped into the car and slewed it round.

"Wait one moment! I come!" exclaimed Jim. He vaulted into the seat beside Mohammed.

Mustapha evicted a deep breath from under his moustaches. With his hands he made a swift winnowing movement. It was indicated that Mohammed would go and come back like the wind.

The thunder of Mohammed's car dwindled along the ravine and died down. It was very hot and quiet here, among the fallen rocks under the cliff. Lucas and I walked round the next head of the wadi. There was no faint flicker of any greenness in the join of the cliffs where you will sometimes find it. The air was like a bar of metal put down by a crane, and it is big and solid, and no one can move it. We took our things off, and moved about, like earliest men engendered out of the egg of heat.

"There's shade here," Lucas's lips went. "And it's cooler." He padded over to a bay in the cliffs, and I followed. We lay down. At once a noise rang out upon the noiselessness like a tiny hammer on a bell. We lifted our heads.

"Where?"

"There!"

A bird stood perched on a rock, the beak opening and shutting, as it emitted and checked the bell-noises. It was a mourning chat, a bird rather bigger than a swallow, glossy black, with a white spot on its head and a white under-carriage, a bird, I think, of a species known only in these deserts. It continued this crying out for some time, as if in the hope of producing some result, which it did not achieve. It moved off to another rock, and another, still crying. Clearly its nest was somewhere close by, and it hoped to attract us away from where we were. Soon its mate arrived, the he-bird, I suppose, a slightly larger bird. They conferred with each other for a minute or two, then the male moved further and higher, and bent its head, and looked down on us. But we did not move.

There was silence for a time, we were deathly still, the two birds, the two men. Then the she-bird uttered a low long tentative whistle. There was a note of inquiry in it. You intend no harm then, after all, to us and ours, O most strange of bipeds?

Lucas replied. He can whistle well. He, too, uttered a low long tentative whistle, but there was no inquiry in it, there was a statement of fact. Please believe it, O much more gracious bipeds. We intend no harm to you and yours.

He stopped. The bird replied, first in single notes, then more confidently, in long trills of sweet sound. Then the bird stopped, and Lucas began again. Then the bird broke in. They continued so for a few minutes, each anxious to make his point, neither waiting for the other to say his say. The he-bird listened for a time, then flew off, as if he felt confident his mate could hold her own, without any help from him. Then at last the she-bird, too, flew off, though we had a feeling she was still somewhere not far away, still regarding us.

" Let's go ! " breathed Lucas. " It will be kinder to them." His eyes were brushed over with a sort of bliss like dew.

" The ghost of Zipporah," I murmured, " who once sat by a well, somewhere in these parts. Don't you remember? That's what the word means: *zipporah*, little bird? And that was the ghost of Moses, on the rock higher up. And in the nest the young ones, Gershom and Eleazar."

" What? " he asked. " Who? " The names had lost all meaning for him. I think he was still continuing that silver debate in his head.

The camel and the tree and the gully where, as we had decided, we had left the gadget-bag, were about two hours' drive back along the wadi. Jim and Mohammed were with us again in rather less than three hours. It was good going over such a surface. Mohammed's gold tooth shone reassuringly from the centre of the advancing pillar of cloud. They've got it, I realized. They would not have come back without it. My angle view-finder. Oh thank the Lord!

But it hadn't been so simple as it seemed. No, said Jim. We hadn't any difficulty at all in recognizing the place. There was the gully right enough, and the tree. The camel wasn't there, and the gadget-bag wasn't either. Somebody had come along and carried it off.

"No!" I said. "Is that true? Are you sure it's all there now?" I took the gadget-bag from his hand. It was all there —extra lenses, filters, cases of film, the precious angle view-finder.

"You should have seen Mohammed," said Jim. "He got down with his nose to the ground like a dog and found a track. The ground's hard there. I couldn't see a thing. It was like Red Indians," Jim insisted.

"Yes?"

"The track didn't go up the gully where the tree was. We'd have been back half an hour sooner, if it had. It went over to the other side of the wadi, and then up another small wadi about ten minutes away. Then we came on it suddenly, just where the wadi makes a twist. The gadget-bag, I mean. The chap had made a little cairn for it in the middle of the wadi. He didn't intend you to miss it. I suppose he knew we'd come after it," Jim speculated. "Didn't he?"

"But how strange!" I exclaimed. "Why did he take it at all, if he took so much trouble to put it where we'd see it?"

"With only a little more trouble," said Lucas, "he could have put it back where he found it."

"That's true," I agreed. "It's strange. It beats me."

"Don't you think," asked Jim diffidently, "he was frightened?" Jim was always most diffident when he made his most acute suggestions.

I hit my left palm with my fist.

"Frightened!" I said. "Frightened! That's exactly it! The poor fellow thought it was all magic! He thought it might all go off any moment, like a bomb!"

" Yes," Lucas agreed. " That sounds very likely. Or "
—he paused—" or it may have been pure conscience. Jarvis
Bey," he said briefly.

That seemed to me just as likely. During his tenure of office,
Major C. S. Jarvis, the late Governor of Sinai, established so
wholesome a respect for the Decalogue, (partly, perhaps,
because it was first issued in his own territory) that he has
become the discarnate conscience of the peninsula tribes.

" I like the idea," I said. " I like to think of the poor Bedu
sloping along, with the *djinn* of Jarvis Bey coming up behind
him, and the bag growing heavier and heavier in his hand.
I like to think of him building a little cairn to propitiate the
Big Spirit. It is very comforting. It is also comforting," I
added, " that I have my angle view-finder."

§ 2

We drove on. Hour after hour went by. We were making
for Abu Zenima, a small anchorage on the coast, where we
would spend the night in a Government rest-house. We had
been driving for a great many hours now. The wadi es Sheikh
was behind us, the wadi Feiran, the wadi Mokatteb. Sunset
was sliding between the walls of the wadi Sidre like a sluice.
Sooner or later, we would come out upon the plain of El
Markha, and there the sea is. Sooner or later. It did not
matter when. Nothing mattered, as the car jerked into a pit
or over a boulder.

Nothing mattered. Time did not matter. It was outside
myself, like the rose and lilac on the hill-tops, like Hassan at
the wheel, like my own body. All outside myself. I was
drugged. Heat and sunshine had drugged us, and the whisper
of a word. " Hashish ! " Hassan had whispered. That was in
the wadi Mokatteb, I think. Thereafter I felt the heat and
sunshine not merely hot and bright, but narcotic. They were
poppies.

It happens that I am unusually sensitive to the imaginative
idea of narcotics. It is a sensitiveness unrelated to my actual

experience of them, which has been brief, and unpleasant. I once tugged at a couple of mouthfuls of *kif* in a Tunisian café and was sick. I have three times been injected with morphia before operations and have hated the impertinent abrogation of my faculties. On the other hand, I become numb when the names of narcotics are recited to me. It may be only a sort of horror, I do not know. Once, some months after an operation, someone came to the back of a chair and tapped lightly on the base of my skull three times. It evoked so completely the tapping of the anaesthetist on his chloroform bladder, I went under for some half-minute, I went outside myself.

So it happened there, in the wadi Mokatteb, on that circuitous journey between Sinai and Paran. I was half-drugged already, with all that sunshine and heat. And then Hassan uttered the narcotic word. And I succumbed exactly as I had done that other time when someone came to the back of my chair and tapped lightly on the base of my skull.

It happened like this. I noticed, but with no more than a sleepy interest, a herd of four or five camels billowing ahead, with two camel-men plodding beside them. Then suddenly, as we came alongside the second camel, Hassan braked the car. He slewed his head round.

" Hashish ! " he whispered in my ear.

I slumped. I went under. I emerged soon, but all my veins were sluggish with poppy and mandragora.

Now Hassan, as I have said, is an *askari* of the Camel Corps. It is a very infrequent duty with Hassan to transport pilgrims in the steps of Moses the Conqueror. He is more often on the hunt for smugglers. A great quantity of narcotics is smuggled annually across the desert frontiers of Egypt, into that already somnolent land. There would be a good deal more smuggled over if not for Hassan and his kind—hashish for the low people in town and village, opium for the grand people in town.

" Hashish ? " I asked dimly. Had we come across a convoy of hashish-smugglers in the open wadi ? But they usually keep out of sight away from the tracks before they come down to the lonely beaches, where the fishing-boats wait off-shore, innocently casting their nets. And the smugglers travel at night, usually. My pulses quickened a little. Hashish-smugglers! Would there be shooting?

"Look!" said Hassan. I don't know whether he recognized the rump of the camel, or its walk, or whether he knew it was in the possession of these men. The animal he pointed out was distinguished from the others by a sort of satchel of hair hanging lop-sided below the spine. "Inside!" explained Hassan. He made an action like a woman stuffing things away into a hand-bag.

Then I remembered. I had both read and heard that one of the smugglers' tricks was to cut away a square of the camel's hair, stick a slab or two of hashish on the bare skin and then glue the hair to the slabs.

"Bang!" said Hassan. He stretched his left hand out towards the barrel of the rifle on the seat beside him, and put his fingers affectionately round its waist. "Dead!" he went on. The Bedu smiled at him. He smiled back at the Bedu.

There wasn't going to be any shooting now; the shooting had already been done. It was easy to see what had happened. The smuggler had been shot while trying to get away with his load. The camel came through all right. The Bedu had either bought the camel or got it as part of his reward for laying the information. The cut in the beast's side had not healed as well as usual; but that harmed nobody.

"Sa'ida!" said Hassan. "Happy night!" and got into gear again.

"Sa'ida!" said the Bedu.

We moved off again, into the sunset, into the heat-haze, hour upon hour again. But I had left something of myself behind me, folded up in the shrunken folds of the camel's false pouch. I had taken something away, too. Hashish was in my nostrils, the smell of the slabs the Camel Corps had con-fiscated that day, on their way to the coast of Sinai and the coast of Egypt, and the little back-alley cafés where they sell the stuff. Some little clerk in Cairo would have to go short of his ration. He would be very miserable for a few days, till the next lot came through. He would feel no more than his own size, instead of feeling ten foot high to the other fellow's four foot. People's faces in the cafés and trams wouldn't look so uproariously silly any more; you wouldn't be able to see the dog or cow or pig under the skin. Yes, he would be very miserable for a few days.

Or would he? Would he need to? We had talked to a man about hashish in Cairo. He said he had only to hook his finger at any street-corner and half a dozen vendors would come hurrying up to him and let him have as much as he wanted. He was a rather cynical person. He insisted that the police and the smugglers were in league with each other. I argued with him rather acrimoniously on the matter. It happened that I had just come from a Government office where they had been talking about the traffic in narcotics. They had information about a load a gang was trying to smuggle across the plateau of Et Tih. At that very moment the gang was approaching a carefully prepared ambush. There in the office they had the maps spread out before them and went over the ground step by step. Without knowing it, the gang had been forced from point to point like game driven up by beaters. "What's the time now?" a voice said from above the map. "In an hour the first gun will go off."

It was all very thrilling to me, however matter-of-fact it was to those others. There was no doubt either of their immense efficiency or their whole-heartedness in the job. If it was humanly possible, they had sworn, they were going to sweep out the whole stinking traffic from the wadis of the peninsula, sinuous though they were, full of ambuscade.

I said as much to the man in Cairo. He smiled and put his finger to the side of his nose.

"Yes," he said. "That's true of the high-up ones. But not lower down. Oh no." Last year, he said, only twenty tons of the stuff had been stopped at all the customs and frontiers, that is, one third of one per cent of the quantity that had got through. They always let the smuggler go, but now and again they confiscate a few kilos of the stuff itself, for the government pays a good price, and the police and smugglers share the profit.

There in the wadi Mokatteb I recalled that conversation, and looked sideways at Hassan, a monument of simplicity and honour; I felt, if I would ever see him again, I would like to hit the head of the wise gentleman in Cairo with one of the boulders that lay around us.

The hashish is made out of a sort of hemp, said the wise gentleman, which is grown in Greece and Syria, chiefly. They might stop that. I don't know. Never take it after meals, he cautioned, it paralyses the stomach. It will make you bring your food up. Between five and six in the evening is the ideal time. As for the opium—that, of course, grows in China mostly. You can't do anything about opium. The League of Nations is knocking its head against a brick wall. I met a priest coming from Indo-China who induced me to try some. He had himself taken five pipes a day for twenty years. His mission was in a part of Indo-China where you'd be dead of dysentery in three months if you didn't take any. It wasn't bad. You've got to know when to stop.

When to stop. Know when to stop. The car did not stop. My narcotized fancy, silly with warm waves of sunset, floated anywhere, anywhere in space, anywhere out of time. Smugglers. Chickens.

Chickens! What on earth had chickens to do with it? Enormous cartloads of mimosa! Clumps of pinks as large as a barrel!

Oh yes! Ventimiglia, where they sell mimosa and pinks by the cartload! The way they used to smuggle liras across the frontier to Mentone. They rolled them up very tight and stuffed them down the gullets of chickens. I remembered that other time, the other way round, into Italy, not out of it. I was coming from Austria. The third-class wooden coaches seemed to have false sides. They took out a screw or two when they

got across the Italian frontier, then removed a panel, and a
wave of fine lace foamed out.

Then I was on another frontier, the frontier between
Belgium and France. It's the second-class carriages there
which are fixed up, to take flat aluminium cases of cocaine.

Who told me? Oh yes. I remember. That was in Montmartre, in that little café-bar behind the Place Pigalle. I
happen to know Jo, he's an old friend of mine. I asked
Jo what that young fellow was looking so glum about. Jo
snuffed up an imaginary powder from between finger and
thumb.

" He's not been able to get any," said Jo. " He's trying to
give it up. He's having a hard fight. Poor Marcel! "

" Fine," I said. " Call Marcel over. Will he have a
Pernod? " No, the thought disgusted Marcel. He would have
a glass of Vittel. He drank it; then he started talking. He
talked in a monotone; he sounded as if he wanted to get things
off his chest. We manage to smuggle through a lot in the
upholstery of the trains. And of course, cars. We make special
cases which fit under the foot-boards of certain makes of cars.
That's for the big loads. It's different here in Montmartre; we
go in for little tubes, like aspirins. Sometimes the police are
tipped off, see? Then we drop it into ladies' handbags. Oh no,
the ladies don't know anything about it . . .

" I hope you're going to manage," I said. " You know—to
keep away from it all." He smiled palely, the sad youth.

" It is going well. If it keeps like this, I will make a camping
next week-end at Bois-le-roi."

At Bois-le-roi by the Seine. Any amount of water. No water
in the Wadi Sidre. Dry as a bone. The only water is colour,
the ebbing tide of sunset drawn along the cliffs and leaving
them dark crimson, dark violet. A long way off the plain opens
out, the plain of El Markha. There is a fine blue line stretched
like a cord between cliff and cliff at the end of all the cliffs.
The sea, isn't it? The sea is in sight at last, and in between, the
boulders blazing like nuggets of dark gold and the acacia
throwing off drops of light like a fountain.

Then suddenly I felt the car jerk forward so violently, it was as if the whole front part of it, the bonnet, the dash-board, the steering wheel, had gone ahead and left us yards behind, cushioned on empty air. I heard a cry, and realized only because it was so close to my ear that Hassan had emitted it. I turned my head sharply. I saw the mask hesitate, then drop clean, like a thing made out of papier-mâché. One moment he was still handsome Hassan, Hollywood Hassan. Then he was a primitive Negro from the Sudan, with thick lips protruding, the whites of his eyeballs flaring yellow in the horizontal sunset flame. In his sudden frenzy of excitement, the car was for some moments out of control. Then we resumed contact again, the gears with my knees, the steering wheel with his hands; or, to be exact, with his right hand. With that, he swerved the wheel over to Mustapha's car, with the other, he seized the rifle. He shouted something to Mustapha.

" Hashish ! " he cried. " Smugglers ! " Or that is what I thought he cried. For hours now hashish and smugglers had thudded in my head like drums. What else could it be he cried out to Mustapha? He waited for no reply. He tore a cartridge-clip out of his bandolier and stuck it in his mouth. He looked like some sabre-toothed man-eater. The car raced forward as if the smell of blood and hashish were in its carburettors.

I stared wildly along the riven wadi as far as the tipped-up cauldron of the setting sun. I saw scrub, rock, a few trees. Nothing more, nothing.

" Where smugglers? " I cried to Hassan. " Where hashish? " I was still outside the chase. I could not see the quarry. My contemptible eyesight. I could have wept with chagrin.

Hassan emitted a few animal syllables. " Um! Um! Um! Um! " They meant nothing. They would have meant nothing if his mouth had not been stuffed with that cartridge-clip. We were going at the maximum speed of the car, plum straight forward, straight as a Roman road. Usually one drives through a desert wadi with the sinuosity of a serpent,

CAMEL-LINES, EL KUNTILLA

avoiding this trench, that boulder. He removed his right hand and pointed. He made that same noise again. It was like the noise of a dog who has been trying to dig a rabbit out of his burrow for some time, and he gets no further and still the rabbit refuses to come out and be killed.

Then I saw the thing we hunted at last. It was not smugglers. It was not hashish. It was a gazelle, the loveliest creature, it seemed, my eyes had ever fallen on. It had dark speckles on its pale fawn body, with a white underside. It bounded lightly and graciously from rock to rock, seeming not to touch the earth before it was in the air again. Then it stopped and looked at us, without alarm, with a certain almost humorous curiosity. Then it was away again. On each side the enormous mountains soared. On the western edge of the world the sea was a thin rod of blue steel.

The hunt continued for some moments, the quarry with nothing but its fleetness, the huntsman with his roaring bumping thrashing engine and the dickering gun. I did not like the gun, poking about all over the place, with its barrel coming to rest every two moments two inches from my nostrils. I did not like the way half of me got savage with the hunt-lust.

"Hassan! Hassan!" I heard myself shouting. "Go it, Hassan!"

And some of me, thank God, remained aware of the creature's inconceivable beauty, ached for its peril, prayed desperately no harm should come to it . . .

And no harm came to it. Perhaps Hassan's sense of law and order reasserted itself, for he was about to commit a misdemeanour, and he had always been the most exemplary of *askaris*. Perhaps the gazelle was merely making a fool of him, and he realized it at last. Perhaps the car began to murmur a little. Or it may be that he was not really going to shoot it at all, as he told me later, in a subdued voice. It may be that. At all events, there were no gazelle-steaks for supper that night at Abu Zenima.

Cc

§ 3

The journey between Mount Sinai and Mount Pisgah arranged itself for us under two aspects. It was first an experiment in evocation, being an attempt to recall the experience of Moses the Conqueror and his host. Under that aspect, the journey divided itself into two sections, Mount Sinai to Kadesh-barnea, Kadesh-barnea to Mount Pisgah. Where we found ourselves impelled to locate Kadesh-barnea, and for what reasons, need not for the moment concern us.

Under another aspect, the political, the journey was divided between two territories, Egypt and Transjordan, with a frontier-post at Akaba. It had been arranged that our Camel Corps trucks were to take us as far as the frontier, from which point they were to return to their headquarters in El Arish, on the coastal railway-line between Egypt and Palestine.

We could, of course, go with them, and had been earnestly advised to do so; for if we did, we could make things much easier for us in Transjordan, by presenting our letters first in Jerusalem, and subsequently in Amman.

It had been no less an authority on these regions than Dr. Weizmann, President of the World Zionist Organization, who had pressed this route upon us. It happened that we had met him in Cairo, a day or two before we set out for Mount Sinai. He was looking a little grey and worn. He had been giving evidence before Royal Commission then sitting in Jerusalem, and one way or another it had been strenuous. I told him about our journey, and he speculated rather sadly how much less strenuous it would have been if Moses had led the children of Israel to Panama, or Madagascar, anywhere in the world but Palestine.

" Tell me. Which way do you intend to go? " he asked.

" The way Moses and the host went," I said. " How else? "

" Of course," he agreed. " That means you propose to enter

Transjordan somewhere on the wadi Arabah, by Akaba, I suppose? "

" Yes. By Akaba."

" But whatever you do," he insisted, " you should find your way to Jerusalem first, and they will tell Amman about you, and Amman will——"

" Please," I begged. " What is the idea of that? "

" It's important they should understand how completely innocent the idea of your journey is. Otherwise, they might think anything."

" What on earth could they think? "

" They might think you political servants of the Jewish Agency. Or representatives of some sinister organization of American millionaires, prospecting for fish or oil or gold."

" But that's nonsense! " I cried. " My letters show very clearly what we are about! "

" In the desert," said Dr. Weizmann a little wearily, " sometimes they cannot read. Go to Jerusalem," he said. " Or at least write."

The desert of Transjordan did not seem to be altogether an easy-going part of the world, I reflected. Before we left England, Lucas had written to an important British police-official in Transjordan, at the suggestion of a distinguished mutual friend. The letter had mentioned I was a Jew. The police-officer had written back helpfully and charmingly, but had stated that he thought it inadvisable that I, personally, should enter Transjordan. Seeing that Moses had fought all but one of the battles which made him Moses the Conqueror in the region now called Transjordan, it seemed to me that the book I proposed to write might lack a certain authenticity if I only heard about the country it described at second-hand from my companions. It seemed to me also that an undertaking sponsored by a British firm, for the profit and entertainment (it was hoped) of a British public, and executed by three British citizens, of whom two were Christians and one was a Jew, was entitled to whatever help it might need from the British police authorities. And indeed the British police authorities had by no means intimated they would withhold their help, should the need for it arise. One individual had ventured a private opinion that it was inadvisable for the Jewish member of the party to enter Transjordan—that was all.

" What are you going to do about it? " asked Lucas, keeping his eyes and voice as expressionless as he knew how. If my racial origin should involve me in real danger in Transjordan he did not want to feel he had responsibility for pushing me into it.

" Do about it ? " I said. " Do about it ? Scuttle away from Akaba and wait for you on the Palestine side of the Allenby Bridge at Jericho? No," I said. " Of course not. We go straight on beyond Akaba into Edom and Moab. As the host did before us! "

Then suddenly an idea struck me so forcibly it was almost like the smack of a wind.

" Don't you see, don't you see ? " I repeated urgently. " Transjordan has *got* to be like that! Edom and Moab and Amman have *got* to be like that! It's grand! I don't know how risky it's going to be, or if it's going to be risky at all! But it shouldn't be as safe as Surrey! Or Egypt, for that matter! It would be all wrong! "

" Why would it be all wrong? " asked Lucas patiently.

" Because," I said, " that's how it was with Moses and the host, too. They found it fairly quiet going between the Nile and Mount Sinai. Whenever things looked awkward, there was a miracle. Like the Crossing of the Red Sea, for instance. There was only one battle on that stage of the journey—at Rephidim, you remember, against the Amalekites. But up in Moab beyond the Arabah, the enemies close round, the battles really begin. If we have any trouble, if the tribesmen are suspicious or hostile—it's fine! We get the *feel* of it, the *mood* of it all! Don't you see how lucky we are? "

Jim's eyes were gleaming with delight. He was rubbing his hands together and singing softly. There was a gleam even in Lucas's more reserved eye. He was pleased. He liked the sound of it all. But he was not going to be verbose about it.

"So long as it doesn't interfere with the journey," he said briefly.

"No," I said. "No. It makes all the difference in the world to the journey! It *makes* the journey! Unless——" I stopped. Another idea blew up from another quarter.

"Unless what?"

"Unless—if there should be any *real* unpleasantness . . . I mean, would it be quite fair to you two?"

Each made a disrespectful remark in his own idiom.

On the way between Abu Zenima and Suez, we recalled these conversations, for beyond Suez and Et Tih lay Akaba, and beyond Akaba Transjordan.

"I suppose we ought to find a letter from Jerusalem waiting for us in Suez," said Lucas. We had written to Jerusalem, as Dr. Weizmann had suggested. "It would be pretty sickening if they tried to put their foot down on us."

"Well," I said. "We'd have to dodge the foot."

Lucas continued with his train of thought. "In that case, we could always do the other thing."

"What?"

"Go to Jerusalem and see the High Commissioner. And then go to Amman and see the British Resident."

"In other words we'd enter Transjordan just near Mount Pisgah, exactly where the footsteps of Moses end. Then, with our eyes shut, we'd go backward from Pisgah, across the steppes of Moab and Edom, to Akaba, the point at which we'd cut and run. Then we'd open our eyes, because we'd got a few nice letters in our wallets, and go forward to Mount Pisgah, pretending we hadn't been there at all. Is that what you mean?"

"That's about it," said Lucas.

"It sounds a little complicated. In fact, it's foul. It would smash the whole impetus of our journey into smithereens. I'd rather go back to St. John's Wood. And you?"

" So would I," said Lucas.

" I'd rather go back to Marylebone," said Jim.

That was all right. We all saw eye to eye. The letter from Jerusalem was all right, too. It was duly waiting for us in Suez. We were informed that a task so politically aseptic as a journey in the steps of Moses the Conqueror was not disapproved of by the authorities, despite the unsettled state of the Transjordan tribesmen. The slightly alarmist view of the British police-officer who had suggested that it was inadvisable for me to cross the frontier was shared neither in Jerusalem nor Amman. It was all plain sailing, then. Mustapha and the two cars would take us as far as Akaba and then turn back. We must arrange transport from Akaba.

The recurrent camel question rose like a languid fish at a fly. Then it sank and was not seen or heard of again. We would get a car, a large one, preferably. But everyone we had ever talked to about Akaba was convinced there were no cars in Akaba. There were a few fishing-boats and one coracle, but not a single car, not even a bicycle. Akaba seemed a forlorn, hot, sleepy place at the head of its burning blue gulf. Like a dog wrapped round itself, snoring, with just a few flies buzzing round its muzzle. It had bestirred itself during the War of Arab Independence; the celebrated Colonel Lawrence had prodded it with a sharp stick and it had barked a bit. But there was no Colonel Lawrence any more in Akaba. Not even in England. There it lay snoring, at the edge of the shade of the palm-trees.

" Sometimes a car comes up from Maan," one or two people had said, " and you could perhaps go up to Maan on its return journey."

" How often do cars come up from Maan? "

" There might be two cars in two days. Then there mightn't be another car for weeks."

" Akaba seems a hard enough place to get to and a harder one to get away from. What are we going to do? " I asked. We were sipping beer in the Anglo-American Stores, in Suez, in the rue Colmar. The vendors of pigs' heads passed unceasingly up and down the tables, their tin trays balanced on their heads.

" Chance it," said Lucas. " We can dump our things on the beach and wait. Something's bound to turn up."

" Perhaps there's a car leaving Suez direct for Akaba," speculated Jim. " They sometimes do, I gathered, in the bar at the Bel Air."

" Fine. We'll ask at the Bel Air."

We did. We were rather lucky. They did not know of a car that was actually setting out for Akaba, under its own steam, as it were. But they had a Greek friend, an owner-driver, a scholar and a gentleman. They thought it possible that their Greek friend might be happy to take us, not merely to Akaba and Maan, but all the way up country to journey's end at Mount Pisgah. He would come in on the strength of the expedition, in a manner of speaking, at cost price, or just a little over, to pay him for his time, as it might be. It all seemed quite attractive, and I asked might we meet the Greek friend. By all means, they said, and produced him.

The Greek gentleman squinted rather badly, but he was none the worse for that. His estimate of cost price was rather terrifying, but he was, after all, an owner-driver, not a mere chauffeur. Then he asked us how big our police escort was going to be when we started out from Akaba.

" Police escort? " I cried. " Who said anything about a police escort? It's the first I've heard about it! "

The upper eyelid of his left eye quivered uncontrollably. " No police escort? But you cannot travel in that country without an escort! I was expecting, of course, that you would find me a police escort to take me back to Akaba!"

I began to feel that we were not likely to fix things up with the Greek owner-driver.

" No! " I said. " I'm sorry! It looks a nice car, too! "

" It is a wonderful car! " he said. " There is no finer car in Suez! But why go by car at all? "

I was not going to have all that brought up again. " It has been arranged," I said with finality.

" And why go in the steps of Moses? " he continued. " Moses, after all, is very out of date."

I thought he was presuming on his status as owner-driver.

" Some may think so," I said coldly.

" Do not misunderstand me," he begged. I wished I knew whether he was looking at me or at Jim or at Lucas. " What I mean is, it would be so much more exciting to go in the steps of Mohammed."

" I see. Would you take us? In your car? "

" Excuse me." He signalled to us to approach as closely as we could. " If you want," he whispered, " I could arrange you should go in the *haj* to Mecca. It would be very original. You could write a wonderful book."

" In your car? " I repeated incredulously.

He brought his lips even closer to my ear.

" No," he whispered. " No. I could arrange a disguise for you. You would have to stain yourselves a bit; not you so much, but your two friends here."

" I think my Arabic might betray me," I ventured.

" You could go deaf and dumb. I could arrange it. It would not cost much."

" It has been done," I said. " And even if it had not been done, it would be too difficult."

" You mean it might be dangerous. Excuse me. I could arrange it. I have my agents. I could arrange everything."

" No," I objected. " I said difficult, not dangerous. My friend there "—I pointed to Jim—" he could be deaf for a long time, months on end. But he could not be dumb. Sooner or later, he would sing, and that would give everything away. Excuse me. It is very kind of you. No, I think we will go with Moses for the time being. Thank you. Good night. We will meet again some time, I am sure."

" Good night," said the scholar-gentleman owner-driver. He looked quite put out.

" There we are! " said Lucas. " Where we were! "

" We'll have to chance it, that's all, over in Akaba."

" There's plenty of water anyhow," said Jim.

" And plenty of sharks," I pointed out.

" We'll have to chance the sharks, too," said Lucas. " I'm going to bathe, sharks or no sharks. They're all right if you only take a firm hand with them."

I made a joke. It was the sharks that took the firm hand with them. Both laughed briefly. Then we fell into meditation again.

It was Jim who made the bright suggestion, as ever.

" Why not telephone to Amman and ask them to telephone to Maan to send a car to Akaba? "

We looked at each other incredulously. " He's right! " we breathed. " Dead right! Fancy not thinking of the telephone before! "

I ran over to the booth and asked the telephone-operator to get me the British Residency in Amman. I need not have run fast, for it took several hours of false alarms and etheric cracklings before we made the connection. But we made it at last, with a very refined Residency voice, unimaginably far and faint.

" Are you Amman? " I shouted. For it seemed to me the voice must be Melbourne, Australia, at least.

" What? " the refined voice asked.

" Are you Amman? The British Residency? "

" What? "

I screamed for several minutes more, till the sweat ran in streams down my cheeks. It was very hot indeed in that telephone-box.

" Yes, this is Amman," the voice finally admitted.

The rest of the conversation was not easier. However, it was fixed up at last. A car would come down from Maan on a certain date, and pick us up at Akaba. I staggered over from the telephone-box and slumped like a sack into a chair.

" A little water," I whispered faintly. " With ice! "

§ 4

We did not linger in Suez. It was not that we reproached ourselves for turning back in our traces. The host did the same thing continually. But we felt that we were definitely on the wrong side of the Et Tih plateau. There is nothing to tell us how far west the Israelites went in their penal wanderings, but it is likely that Moses saw to it they kept well away from the side over towards Egypt.

So, crossing the Canal at El Kubri, we made straight east by a good macadamized road across the strip of intervening desert between the coast and Et Tih, and entered the plateau country at the wadi el Haj. We were in fact, taking the old *haj* road, the road the Egyptian pilgrims used to take for Mecca, before they were carried direct by steamer from Suez to the port of Jeddah on the Arabian coast. We proposed to call a halt in a government rest-house at Nekhl, one of the three fortresses the Ottoman Sultan Selim had set up four centuries ago to protect the pilgrims from Egypt, one behind us, at Ajrud, near Suez, the second at Nekhl, the third at Akaba. We were taking the road to Mecca, after all, though we had turned down the kind offices of the Greek owner-driver. But we were not going the whole way. We should not join up beyond Akaba with the other great caravan coming southward from Damascus. We should turn northward instead, in the steps of the earlier Prophet.

From the wadi el Haj some twelve miles from Suez the road turns southward a little to enter the main plateau region by the Mitla pass. It then turns northward again for some miles and thereafter almost without deviation goes east and slightly south for Akaba. It is a disheartening country. In every direction the biscuit-coloured plateau stretches endlessly, with curved bastions of hills, stepped and scored by the rain, thrust out of the haze at intervals. Beside the road lay the ruin of a burned out car. A little farther lay the arched skeleton of a camel. The death of both must have been equally

fiery in that ovenny glare. Nothing grew save a few charred
thorn-bushes and mops of white broom in the gashes of the
wadis. The mirages were a charity. Now the whole desert
was pitted with brimming pools, now the pools cohered
into one vast lake. Once I saw Como clear, with greenery
lush on its many islands, once a great marsh tufted with
feathery reeds. The hills of the plateau in Sinai saw their
own images as clear as the hills on Windermere do on a
windless day.

There must always have been a track connecting the head
of the Gulf of Suez with the head of the Gulf of Akaba, whatever the names of the terminal towns were, Clysma and Aila,
Suez and Akaba. From time to time during their wanderings
the host of Israel cannot have failed to come astride this track
and to have moved some distance along it. Some sort of a
cloud went before them, that in the night had the appearance
of fire; and once, on the eastward horizon, we saw a column
of smoke spiralling blue into the blue air, as if the host were
wandering still.

The host of Islam that set out from Egypt twenty centuries
later, carried a gaudier furniture before them at the head of
their caravan: there would be camels bearing the brightly
caparisoned Mahmal, or litter, and the Kiswa, a carpet
specially woven in Egypt, to cover the tomb of Mohammed
in Medina. And there would be horsemen going behind,
beating drums, and sheikhs on foot, wearing turbans coloured
according to their sects, and green and white and yellow
banners behind these, inscribed with texts from the Koran,
and wise men and soldiers and the rank-and-file pilgrims.

A picture of these things was much in my mind as we
rumbled eastward along the desert road, for we had found
the air in Cairo full of the talk of Mahmal and Kiswa, which
were being sent forth to Mecca again for the first time since
1926, when a quarrel between the Mecca soldiery and the
Cairo guards led to a remission of the holy courtesy. It was
considered, I remembered, a good omen that the Litter and
Carpet were being sent out again during the first year after

the signing of the Egyptian Treaty of Independence. But they no longer went by the road to Akaba. The Muslim *haj* was dispersed out of the desert as completely as the Israelitic Wandering. The caravan we saw, a great herd of black goats and their goatherds, seemed to be coming up towards us out of an antiquity compared with which both Prophets were striplings.

At last among all the mirages, one remained, being no mirage. Against the barren distance Nekhl blocked itself out like a thing of papier-mâché built out on location within an hour's drive from Hollywood. They looked real enough, real papier-mâché, the single mosque pointing a blunt finger at the heavens, the block-house, the soldiers' lodgings; as we came closer we saw they were made of tough desert stone; newly rebuilt, we learned later, since the British blew it up during the war to deny it to the Turks.

The lean-shanked *umbasha* of Camel Corps, number three company, as lean and comfortless as our Mustapha was fat and comfortable, came out and welcomed us gravely, and took us to a cool rest-house of white stone and green-painted doors and windows, where we lunched pleasantly on Bel Air chicken and eggs, cheese and fruit and tea. Thereafter we paid a state visit, like travelling potentates, to the almost completely derelict fort. The soldiers occupied a few rooms on the inner side of a courtyard. We duly commended them on the folding of their blankets and the polishing of their brass, and admired still more fervently an ancient cannon they had clamped on a small mound in front of the fort. The rest of Nekhl was like death itself, hard and white and absolute. We wandered among the deserted houses where the *haj* pilgrims had once lodged, and nothing stirred there now but the shadow itself, which seemed to shift on the hot stone from one haunch to the other. On the edge of the compound the immaculate camels gargled at their tethers. Beyond, a vast covey of blue-black brown-necked ravens fed lusciously on the camel-dung, with a small white cur at their centre disputing their right to it, sharply but without success. We said good-bye to the men of Camel Corps, number three company, with a pity in our hearts we hoped we did not show. If the heat was like this now in early spring, what would it be like in summer? Good-bye, they said, peace be with you. They looked a little wist-fully after their retreating companions, Mustapha, and Mohammed and Hassan; or I thought they did. Perhaps they had emerged from heats no less formidable in the Sudan, and would go back to end their days contentedly there, as English countrymen might go back to Somerset.

We made across the dead plain still on a slightly southward line, towards two or three white hills poking up into the horizon like teeth. The scrub twanged like wires in the heat. The small stones that littered the plain were like pieces that had crumbled away from the edges of the baked air. An hour later we saw a cavalcade of four cars coming up towards us each in the centre of its own cloud. They were the only cars other than our own we had seen in all the peninsula. At about two hours distance from Nekhl we came upon a huge flock of black and white goats, in the charge of a tall goatherd, extra-ordinarily handsome in his flowing robes. When Mustapha slowed up and saluted him he turned away, twitching his robes over his shoulder. He called his dogs and moved his flock north and east from the track. Mustapha's eyes wrinkled up like a hurt child's. He did not know how a desert man, or any man at all, could be so discourteous. Then he remembered. "Ah!" he said. "Ah!" The puzzle had resolved itself. He pointed along the line the goatherd was taking with his flock. "Bir el Themed!" he said. "Themmedi *mish quais*!"

I racked my brains, and remembered in my turn. It was to the men of Themed in Arabia that the prophet Saleh, the forerunner of the greater prophet, Mohammed, had been sent on a mission; and the sign he had shown them was the Naga, the she-Camel of God. He had bid them let her go and feed in God's earth, but they had hamstrung her, and great evil had befallen them. And it seemed that here in Sinai was a shoot of that stock, which gave to the well north and east of

us here the name of Bir el Themed. And here was one of the
hamstringers of God's she-Camel, stalking away from us with
his fine head in the air.

" Mustapha knows Koran ! " I said approvingly.

Mustapha changed the subject. Not even Mustapha was
comfortable with the name of his Prophet or the Prophet's
Book on the lips of a *rumi*.

A few miles further we swung northward from the direct
road to Akaba on to the track for El Kuntilla, where we were
to spend the next night or two. In an hour or so dusk came
down on us. All the harshness went out of earth and sky. The
sky was speckled with a rosy down like the breast of a great
bird. The cooling earth seemed so gentle you would have only
to climb the next rise, or the rise beyond that, to look down on
a glade of grass and winking water. The first stars slid into
the sky-channels. Then it was night and all the stars came
flooding through the sluice-gates and the sky was one broad
estuary of stars. The hills were smooth and black as cloth.
We came upon El Kuntilla quite suddenly, round the bend
of the wadi ; or upon the steep conical hill on which the rest-
house is lifted above the torrid plain. High on its peak someone was swinging a lantern to welcome us, right-left, right-left,
in steady half-circles. We pressed the accelerators with a leap
and roar and circled the hill three times and came to rest on
the small plateau on the summit, within an inch or two of the
swinging lantern.

The *farrash*, the bedmaker, put his hand to his heart gravely
and bowed within his lantern's brief circle. Then he conducted
us into our sitting-room. A fire of thorn-wood was blazing
merrily under a curved chimney-piece. There were bright
chintzes in the windows and over the furniture. There were
easy-chairs, and a white cloth on the table. We felt that
nothing less festive than our tinned steak and kidney pudding
would suit the occasion, and the remnants of a Châteauneuf
du Pape we had found among our straw-padded bottles.
We could not decide whether it had been packed inadver-
tently or with intent, like Joseph's gold in Benjamin's bag of

corn. It seems unlikely that that vineyard ever turned out a
bottle which received such fierce shakings during the course
of its career, or one of which the lees were savoured with so
tender an appreciation.

After supper we went out and looked from our hill-top upon
the surrounding plains. A few twitch-fires burned by Beduin
tents, but they seemed almost smothered in that excessive
purity of air, as if fire needs some measure of impurity to
feed on. I lay awake in my bed for an hour or so. Now and
again a flagpole creaked. Now and again a dog barked.
They were like registers by which the silence could be
measured. Then even these ceased. I listened for them,
but they did not recur. I listened for my own heart-beats,
but could not hear them. Here at last was sound's zero. I
was conscious of a growing terror; in silence so absolute I
could not, dared not, sleep. Then at last I heard footsteps
far off, and the hooves of horses. It was like traffic which
has been barred from a city entering the gates at last. It
was the advancing traffic of sleep I heard, heard for a time,
and did not hear again.

We rose and breakfasted and looked out from our private
hill over Et Tih. On a flat-topped hill east of us rose the twin
buildings of the Camel Corps Headquarters, walled and
battlemented and crenellated with an almost grotesque
newness and rectangularity like a scene out of a Foreign Legion
film, *Beau Geste* perhaps. Immediately below the Beduin
women were scraping water-holes in the gritty sand. In the
shallow circular pits they had made, a brown stain widened.
They scooped the brown stain up with jugs and poured it into
tin basins for their donkeys. Other women led up their
scraggy herds of goats from the edges of the plain to partake
of the refreshment, their children rolling behind them like
small black hedgehogs. " Come, come! " they called. " Do
you come? " The children twittered like swallows. There
were no other sounds than the women and children crying out
and the harsh grating of crows. It seemed that from far off

and from close at hand sound came equally clear, thin and direct, like sunrays from behind a cloud. Every raven was attended with ghost-like fidelity by its own shadow. They were black. The robes of the women were black. All else was fawn and yellow, the fawn camels in the camel-lines picked out with small boulders in the yellow sand, the undulating yellow and fawn flats of the desert, the yellow and fawn hills on the horizon. Beside us stood a yellow and fawn desert dog, looking out into a hungry world which even our egg-shells had momentarily enriched for him.

" Fil-fil! " the *farrash* called out to his dog.

Fil-fil? The word sounded familiar. " Fil-fil? " I asked. " What is the meaning of that word? "

The *farrash* slid away silently into the dining-room and came out with a pot of pepper. This, he pointed. Fil-fil!

Fil-fil! Pepper! I remembered now. My father sitting at the table of our kitchen in Doomington. He was pointing to the Hebrew word-book he had made up for the use of the boys. He has a butcher's skewer in his hand with which he descends the ranked columns of Hebrew words.

Lechem	Bread
Sackin	Knife
Pilplim	*Pepper*

Then he takes the same butcher's skewer in his hand and goes over to the chart framed in maple-wood, on which is traced a thick red line, the line of the wandering of Moses and the Israelites. " And the cloud was taken up from over the tabernacle," he says, " and abode in the wilderness of Paran."

Yes, I remembered Pilplim, I recognized Filfil, looking down on the pepper-coloured map of Paran spread out under my feet.

You shall make a meal of more than egg-shells to-night, Filfil, when we come back from our journey to Kadesh-barnea. You will need it. We shall have been there twice

AIN KADEIS

before we return, and in between we shall have wandered for thirty-seven years and five months across the desert you look on so despondently now.

You will have a whole tin of bully-beef to yourself, Filfil.

§ 5

So standing upon the truncated cone of Kuntilla, I looked southward towards the visible limestone bluffs of Et Tih, the invisible granite ranges of the Sinai massif. Then I turned and looked northward. Once more the limestone bluffs of Et Tih, and further north, the invisible dry watercourses of the Negeb, the southland, the border of Canaan. If Paran was anywhere, Paran was here, we were at the centre of it. " And the cloud abode in the wilderness of Paran."

But between Mount Sinai and Paran, the cloud had come to rest three times, in the three intervening stations of Taberah, and Kibroth-hattaavah, and Hazeroth. Much had happened in those places. We had not without scars advanced so far into the wilderness of Paran. For once more, and in each of these places, the evil heart had arisen amongst us. " And the people were as murmurers speaking evil in the ears of the Lord : and when the Lord heard it, his anger was kindled, and devoured in the uttermost part of the camp. And the people cried unto Moses ; and Moses prayed unto the Lord, and the fire abated. And the name of that place was called Taberah : because the fire of the Lord burnt among them."

Now I said earlier that the scholars are quite at sea regarding the whereabouts of this place Taberah ; they point out it is not the name of a place at all, but a description of the thing that happened there. My father was troubled by no such doubts. He would rise from his chair under the cupboard where the holy books were kept, and go over to the wall where the chart hung, the chart of the Wanderings.

" And this place," he would say firmly, pointing out with the point of the butcher's skewer, " this place is Taberah, where the fire of the Lord burnt among our fathers.

Dc

" For they had not been long gone from Sinai," he stated, making his way back to his chair, " when certain of them remembered their bulls and cows and calves which they had worshipped in Egypt. And when they raised their voices, so did their neighbours, and the neighbours of their neighbours. And in the encampment thereafter to be known as Taberah, a cry to the Lord rose from the whole host. ' Give us a bull to be our god ! ' they cried. ' Or a cow ! Or a calf ! ' And for my part," (my father considered), " it might well have been a sheep rather than a bull. For what sheep-heads they must have had to provoke the Lord so sorely when He had lately shown them such surpassing kindness, on the Holy Mountain !

" And the Lord sent the consuming fire upon them, which is that same fire of which all mortals behold a single spark in the moment of their death. And this fire took heavy toll among all the tribes, but chiefly the tribe of Dan, which was of them all the most addicted to idols. And it raged fierce and far among the mixed multitude that had added itself to the host on the departure from Egypt. So the elders of the people turned to Moses and cried out : ' Rather hand us over as a sheep to the slaughter, but not to a heavenly fire that consumes earthly fire ! '

" And Moses raised his hand to the Lord, and the Lord said : ' Spread ye bundles of wool upon the devouring fire.' And Moses said : ' How can such a thing be, oh Lord, that bundles of wool shall assuage and not increase a fire ? '

" And certain ones that heard him emptied goatskins filled with water upon the fire, and the fire waved and licked the branches of the sky, and these doubters were burned into cinders for their disbelief and arrogance. And then Moses took the bundles of wool, as the Lord had commanded him, and the fire waned and burned no more.

" That," said my father, " was how it fell out at Taberah. And the cloud moved and rested at the place thereafter to be called Kibroth-hattaavah. Let the others see where this thing was," he commanded me, and put the butcher's skewer into my hands ; and I went over to the chart and laid a finger upon a point one quarter of an inch northward from Taberah. " That is the very place," he said, and smiled, as if I had used fine instruments to attain such precision.

" And in that place, as often before, once again it was the mixed multitude that brought woe upon Israel, and those same idolaters of the tribe of Dan. For they had become weary of manna and the taste of it, the celestial food the angels ground nightly in their granaries, so that it might fall fresh and sweet each morning in the way of the host. ' Who shall give us flesh to eat! ' they complained. ' We remember the fish, which we did eat in Egypt for nought; the cucumbers, and the melons, and the leeks, and the onions, and the garlick.' "

Now for my part, young though I was, the enumeration seemed inconceivably wistful, most of all the garlick, savoury implacable garlick, the climax to that dream-menu they scratched out for themselves on the unappetizing sand. And I could hardly restrain my tears as the dirge continued. " But now our soul is dried away; there is nothing at all. We have nought save this manna to look to."

But my father took them up sharply for those last words. " This manna, indeed! " he protested. " The ingrates! For as I have often told you, the sublime and special virtue of manna lay in that to each it had the taste he most desired, according to his condition. To children it tasted even as milk, to youths like bread, to old people like honey, to the sick like barley prepared in oil and honey. It is indeed true that the property of tasting like any of these five vegetables, the cucumber, the melon, the leek, the onion, the garlick, was denied to manna. Which but illustrates more notably the glory of the Lord, for these five growths are noxious, to be eschewed, and sit like stone upon the stomach.

" Moreover, they complained this manna could in no wise be a good thing, seeing the body did not discharge it. For that was a further quality of this substance. Of so delicate a tissue it was, and so exactly adapted to the body's needs, that it entered the blood-stream and so fed bone and brain."

Yet so it was. They were tired of manna, they mourned;

their soul was dried away. So Moses making a round of the camp, heard them weeping throughout their families, every man at the door of his tent. And at the sound and sight of it, something broke of a sudden in his heart. He did not read them homilies, as he did at Marah. He was not ablaze with anger, as he was when he came down from the Mountain to see them worshipping the Golden Calf. He went utterly to pieces for the first and the last time.

" I am not able to bear all this people alone, because it is too heavy for me. And if thou deal thus with me, kill me, I pray thee, out of hand, if I have found favour in thy sight! "

" But the Lord did not do so," my father said, " for if Moses had been even by one moment sooner than the appointed time taken from his place in the world of men, the Law would have crumbled, even as a heap of sand, and there would have remained not one grain of it. And it was this same Law which was the whole reason for the complaining of the people, for they found its yoke irksome to them, having been restrained by no Law in Egypt nor on the journey from Egypt, all the way to the Holy Mountain.

" And this was the reason for the extreme loneliness of the Prophet in Kibroth-hattaavah. For until lately there had been a company of seventy elders to support him on his going and coming, but these had behaved ill, and they were numbered among the murmurers, and the fire consumed them at Taberah, in the great burning. And the Lord seeing the Prophet weary and lonely, appointed that another and worthier company of elders should be chosen, to be brought unto the tent of meeting. And there the Lord took of the spirit of prophecy that lay upon Moses and put it upon them, that he should not bear it alone. But the spirit of Moses was not lessened by this, for he was even as a burning candle from which many others are lighted, but it is not thereby diminished.

" So the Lord bade the Prophet go to the tent of meeting and the seventy elders that might bear the burden with him. And He requested his servant to prophesy to them, saying: ' Sanctify yourselves against to-morrow, and ye shall eat flesh:

for we have wept in the ears of the Lord, saying, Who shall give us flesh to eat? for it was well with us in Egypt: therefore the Lord will give you flesh, and ye shall eat. Ye shall not eat one day, nor two days, nor five days, neither ten days, nor twenty days; but a whole month, until it come out at your nostrils, and it be loathsome unto you.'

" And so, as it is written, there went forth a wind from the Lord, and brought quails from the sea. And the less impious ones withdrew into their tents, but the more impious ones remained out of doors; and the quails covered the orb of the sun, and blew down like a hail of stones upon the unsheltered ones, so that they fell dead where they stood, with their skulls cracked. And the creatures did not fall upon the ground, but fell no further than two cubits measure above ground-level, so that the less impious ones, coming from their tents, did not need to stoop to gather them, but gathered them where they stood, and spread them all abroad for themselves round about the camp.

" And while yet the flesh was between their teeth (as it is written) ere it was chewed, the anger of the Lord was kindled against the people, and the Lord smote the people with a very great plague. And the name of that place was called Kibroth-hattaavah : because there they buried the people that lusted."

It seemed to me there was a note of satisfaction in his voice, when he told this tale of the doom of the quail-eaters. Perhaps he thought it a little unjust that his ancestors should have had quails laid out for them on the north side and south side of their camp, on each side a day's journey, while he himself had never had the flesh of a single quail between his teeth, not even the leg of one.

From Kibroth-hattaavah, by which is meant literally, " the graves of lust," the host journeyed to a place called Hazeroth, which may have been, and may well not have been, the spring called at this day " Ain el Hudhera." It was at Hazeroth that certain difficulties in the immediate family circle of Moses, which may have been smouldering under the surface for some time, came to a head. " And Miriam and Aaron spake against Moses because of the Cushite woman whom he had married: for he had married a Cushite woman."

Who was this lady then? Where was Cush? Cush has usually been taken to be the same word as the Kesh or Keesh of the Egyptian hieroglyphs, by which was meant the region later called Ethiopia, and still later Abyssinia. Further, Josephus tells us that Moses married an Ethiopian king's daughter, Tharbis by name, when he was fighting Pharaoh's wars in the black land up the river. It is possible that this text in Numbers is all the warrant that Josephus had for his pretty embroidery. It is also possible that this same story is based on some scriptural authority now lost to us.

In that case Tharbis was this Cushite woman concerning whom Miriam and Aaron spake against Moses at Hazeroth. Their brother had been married to her a great many years by this time, but perhaps they felt that he should have put her away from him, now that the children of Abraham, Isaac and Jacob had been unified in the covenant granted on the Mountain. It was the mixed multitude that had been responsible for most of the trouble at Taberah and Kibroth-hattaavah. Miriam and Aaron may have felt the Cushite belonged rather to that company than to the tent and bed of their brother, Israel's prophet.

Or does Cushite not mean Ethiopian, after all? The place-name, Kusi, has been recently identified in a number of Assyrian inscriptions. Perhaps Cush is not far removed from that region of Midian whither Moses fled from the wrath of Pharaoh after he had slain the Egyptian. In that case the Cushite woman may be none other than Zipporah, the daughter of Jethro, whom Moses served so devotedly during his exile. The mere fact that she was the daughter of Jethro may have been enough to provoke the jealousy of Aaron and Miriam. Only quite recently, shortly before the departure of the host from the Holy Mountain, a curious little episode had occurred, which illustrated the high esteem in which Moses held anything connected with Jethro.

We read as follows: " And Moses said unto Hobab, the Son of Reuel the Midianite, Moses' father-in-law: We are journeying into the place of which the Lord said, I will give it you: come then with us, and we will do thee good: for the Lord hath spoken good concerning Israel . . . for thou knowest how we are to encamp in the wilderness, and thou shalt be to us instead of eyes." But Hobab refuses, he wishes to depart to his own land.

It has been argued that Hobab is not the son of Jethro, but Jethro himself; in which case it is easy to sympathize with him. He is an old man, unfitted to an adventure so long and perilous. It is indeed time he made due east, to be gathered to his fathers in Midian, on the opposite side of the water. If he was Jethro's son, he might well have felt that despite his father's friendship with the Israelite leader, his own destiny lay with Midian rather than Israel. However, whether he yielded to the entreaty of Moses and went north to Paran, or whether he went to his own kindred, is not made plain. It is only made plain that to Moses about to wander in the desert, Jethro, or the son of Jethro, was the eyes with which he begged he might see it.

It is, as I say, a curious little episode. The Talmudic mythmakers have little to say about it. But it is significant of the diffidence of the Prophet, more often called his " meekness." And it also illustrates a devotion to Jethro and all that pertained to Jethro which may have been the well-spring of the reproaches against Moses uttered by Aaron and Miriam in the encampment at Hazeroth.

That is, of course, if the Cushite woman was the Midianite woman, Zipporah, Jethro's daughter. Yet whatever she was, Midianite or Ethiopian, the woman was no daughter of Israel.

" Let her go! " cried Miriam and Aaron. " She is not of us! "

They had another complaint against Moses, his sister and brother, there at Hazeroth. " Hath the Lord indeed spoken only with Moses? " they cried. " Hath he not spoken also with us? " It was a touch of natural jealousy, by no means unknown in families less exalted, which it is possible to forgive. What we find less easy to forgive is Aaron's habit of involving other people in his misbehaviour and of extricating himself from all its consequences, while his associates pay, and pay heavily. It was Aaron who put up the Golden Calf, though he was ready with satisfactory explanations of his part in the matter. But he was not of the three thousand that fell when the sons of Levi girded every man his sword upon his thigh, and went to and fro throughout the camp using it mightily. He seems to have been as much to blame as Miriam, there in Hazeroth, in the murmuring against Moses. For while the priestly editors of the Text dared not go so far as to omit mention of Aaron's sins, they contrive somehow to omit the effects of them. So it is Miriam, not Aaron, concerning whom we learn she became leprous, white as snow.

This punishment, the Talmud points out, was of the Lord, not of Moses, because Moses was very meek—" above all the men which were upon the face of the earth." Only the angels are meeker than he, for when they are assembled together to sing the glory of the Lord : " Do thou sing first," each bids the other throughout the countless host, " for thou art worthier than I."

The Talmud is a little troubled by this exclusion of Aaron from the punishment. It always finds itself a little troubled by the part assigned to the High Priest in the narratives, and is forced to exercise on his account its maximum of ingenuity. On this occasion it goes so far as to suggest that Aaron, too, was afflicted with leprosy, which is the punishment assigned to those who speak ill of their neighbours, but that Moses looked upon it, and it lasted one moment only. He was less successful with Miriam. " Hear her, O God, I beseech thee," he cried, drawing upon his inexhaustible stock of loving-kindness. And he made a circle round about himself, to increase the potency of his prayer; but it availed nothing, the leprosy was not lifted from her. " If a king had but spit in her face," the Lord said, " or her own father, would she not be ashamed and hide

herself from men's eyes? How much the more shall she be
ashamed when it is I, the first King, and the first Father, who
have spit upon her with the white spittle of leprosy? But seeing
it is thou, Moses, who askest, she shall hide herself, not for the
due fourteen days, but for seven days only. Bid her betake
herself beyond the edge of the encampment. Seven days shall
go by, but she shall come forth at the end of them, cleansed
and shining."

And it was as the Lord said, and Miriam came forth out of
her tent of exclusion, and the cloud removed from above the
Tabernacle, and moved into the wilderness, and the stream
followed whereat the marching host quenched its thirst.
"And the people journeyed from Hazeroth, and pitched in
the wilderness of Paran."

. . . That wilderness of Paran, of which we at this later day
stood at the centre, on the truncated cone of Kuntilla, looking
northward over the limestone bluffs of Et Tih, looking still
further northward, towards the invisible dry watercourses
of the Negeb, the southland, the border of Canaan.

CHAPTER THREE

§ I

WHITHER was our journey now to take us, from the hill to-day called Kuntilla at the heart of the desert once called Paran?

The next episode in the narrative is the tale of the spies whom Moses, at the Lord's command, sent to spy out the land of Canaan. " Get you up this way by the South," the Prophet bade them, " and go up into the mountains: and see the land, what it is." It is clear that the host is no great distance from the border of the land, though there are mountains in between. Perhaps they are still in the open plain, more likely they are somewhere in a hollow of the mountains, they are afraid to issue from the tangle of valleys.

Where are they then? The place from which the spies set out is not stated. The place to which they return, is. They are doubtless one and the same place. " And they returned from spying out the land at the end of forty days. And they went and came to Moses, and to Aaron, and to all the congregation of the children of Israel, unto the wilderness of Paran, to Kadesh."

We must find this place called Kadesh, then, the Holy Place, that is to say, if we would fare further, for after Sinai, it was the most important point in the wanderings of Israel between Nile and Jordan. It was the furthest point reached by the host in the attempt to penetrate into the land by the direct route. It was the place from which the spies went out and whither they came again. It was the place from which the host went forth on their desolate penal wanderings which endured decade upon decade. It was the place where, on their return, the Prophetess Miriam died, where Moses struck the rock twice, and water came forth abundantly. Lastly, it was from Kadesh the host set out a second time on that final assay which was to lead them at length to the land of the promise.

Where, then, is Kadesh? Is it the same as the place called Kadesh-barnea, later in the book of Numbers, where it is indicated as a mark of the southern boundary of the land Israel is to inherit? Perhaps it is. It has been conjectured that Kadesh means rather a region, and Kadesh-barnea a point in it. Is it the same as that Kadesh, to which is also given the name of Enmeshpat, the Well of Judgment, in the fourteenth chapter of Genesis? Perhaps it is. Few and obscure are the signposts set up to lead us to it. " And Abraham journeyed from hence toward the south country," we read, " and dwelled between Kadesh and Shur." Or we read in Joshua : " And the border passed along to Zin, and ascended up on the south side to Kadesh-barnea." It is not easy, I say, to find the way.

More than three millenniums have gone by since these dim events of the spies going forth and Miriam dying happened there. The place then was dim, in its trackless cirque of mountains. It remains dim to this day. Pious and indefatigable scholars have examined all that wide waste of rock. They have pored in museums over ancient charts and modern ordnance surveys. They have rendered one Kadesh-barnea after another to us, wrapped round in thousands of closely printed leaves. But to this day it cannot be said that any of their Kadeshes is startlingly more credible than any of its competitors.

Yet a word was mumbled a hundred years ago by one Bedu lip to another, and it chanced that an attentive ear heard it. " A well," it said, " a well up the wadi. We can water our camels there. Ain Kadeis," the lip shaped. Ain Kadeis . . . Kadeis . . . There is something familiar in the sound of that. Kadeis? *Kadesh!* But of course ! We have arrived ! We are at Kadesh-barnea !

Is it true there is but a phantom resemblance between the two words? Yet it is true also that it is a well very much where you would look for it, a well on the border of the southland, on the line of march north from the Holy Mountain, and heeling over slightly eastward to the frontier of Canaan. It is, moreover, approximately at the distance from Mount Sinai where Deuteronomy places it for us . . . " eleven days' journey from Horeb by way of Mount Sinai."

We are there. We have arrived. We are at Kadesh-barnea.

So the scholars, very rare at first, and the sparse caravans of pilgrims, set out for Ain Kadeis, approaching either from Gaza or Akaba. It is the traveller, Rowlands, who first describes the spring in 1842. Palmer in 1870 gives a minute and exact account of it. Less exact is the account of an American traveller, a certain H. C. Trumbull, who spends a pleasant Sunday afternoon there in 1882, and produces a large volume on the subject, painting a portrait of the place so glowing the reader thinks himself transported to Mr. Hichens's " Garden of Allah." Later visitors are more modest. But a general sense of unease is spread abroad. What? This little stony basin under the parched hills, with its two water-holes and three stunted wild figs, is this then after all the Kadesh of the wanderings? Can a city, yes, in truth, a *city*, have been contained in so strict a zone (for it is so Moses speaks of it when he sends messengers to the king of Edom: " Behold, we are in Kadesh, a city in the uttermost of thy border ") ?

And then at last, in 1914, a traveller appears on the scene, with a keener eye than most that have preceded him, a man slight in build, of low voice, so featured that if he were wearing the head-cloth and cloak and sandals of the local sheikhs, it would be hard to distinguish him from among them. He is, in fact, within a year or two, to assume those very garments for that very purpose, of seeming a sheikh among his fellows. During this journey in the steps of Moses the Conqueror, this is the first occasion we come on the superimposed print of these later feet; but we are so often from now on to be reminded of them, we sometimes find ourselves thinking: is not this a journey in the steps of Lawrence the Conqueror?

And indeed, this is he, this acute shade darkening briefly the sun-scoured rocks of Ain Kadeis, this is T. E. Lawrence. He is accompanied by one of the most distinguished of living

scholars, Mr. C. Leonard (now Sir Leonard) Woolley, but he
rises to the stature of his company, as he always does, whether
the company be of great artists, great soldiers, or great camel-
riders. They are engaged in an archaeological report for the
Palestine Exploration Fund, on " The Wilderness of Zin."
But already, we learn from the prefatory note to the report,
" both the principal authors have been called to Egypt, for
Special Military Service." It is interesting to compare those
two Lawrences, the scholar flickering like a lizard from stone
to stone in the frightening silence of Ain Kadeis, the soldier
conducting one of the most spectacular guerrilla campaigns in
military history, drawing upon himself more and more inexorably the eyes of a whole world. It is interesting, too, to
speculate which was the happier Lawrence.

Mr. Lawrence, a note informs us, is chiefly responsible for
the fourth chapter of the report, which is a well-documented
(and, it need not be said, extremely well-written) description
of Ain Kadeis and the surrounding country, with a last
section devoted to the Kadesh-barnea question. It is reasonable therefore to attribute to Lawrence the damaging footnote regarding the derivation of Kadeis. " The word," we
are told, " in Hejazi Arabic, is a scoop or bailer used in the
bath for purification. The Sinai Arabs use such scoops (of
wood) to lift up water from a shallow well. It does not mean
' holy ' as Trumbull and other writers have assumed."

To us it was a discouraging footnote. It looked as if it
might disintegrate this section of the journey rather badly.
Why prefer " Ain Kadeis " to its principal competitors, Ain
Gedeirat, Ain el Weibeh, and Petra, when *kadeis* means nothing more holy than a wooden water-scoop? But, on reflection,
we found we ought not to be so discouraged, after all. The
fact the word *kadeis* to-day, in one of the many Arabic dialects,
means one thing rather than another, does not in the least
preclude the word from having had some entirely different
affiliation in its remote past. In fact Lawrence himself upsets
the inference of his own footnote towards the end of this same
chapter. " The similarity between the names Kadeis and

Kadesh," he writes, " need not be a mere coincidence, for the former is just as likely to be of ancient as of recent origin."

Moreover, on renewed examination, the competing Kadeshes did not seem too winning. The identification that Major Jarvis makes of Kadesh-barnea with Ain Gedeirat five miles to the north of Ain Kadeis seemed less a new suggestion than an amplification of the old one. For while it is true, as we were shortly to confirm, that Ain Kadeis is now merely " an insignificant spring," while Ain Gedeirat is a " strong little stream that flows through the valley for a distance of a mile and a half," it is possible that in three thousand years the quantity of water given out by the two springs has altered. It is also possible that the ratio of water has not changed, but that the spring now called Ain Kadeis was in the time of Moses the holy spring *par excellence* of all that region, having been already a holy spring before Moses reached there, the " Enmishpat " we have read of in Genesis, the Well of Judgment, and that the sanctity of that small spring may well have sanctified the whole area, so that they called all of it " Kadesh." It seems much more likely it was called " Kadesh," *before* the host arrived there, because some earlier deity than Jehovah had sanctified it, than after, for nothing can have been less " kadesh " than the host's behaviour all the time they were there.

Major Jarvis goes on to say that there are " traces of extensive cultivation and irrigation, and amongst other things a very fine stone reservoir, twenty-five yards by twenty-five and nine feet in depth. The reservoir is of great antiquity. . . . From the nature of its construction it is obvious the work is not Roman, and it is just possible that the Israelites themselves may have made it."[1]

Yes, that is possible. But it does not mean to say that because there are no traces of reservoirs now at Ain Kadeis, five miles away, there always were none. On the contrary, we,

[1] I should observe Major Jarvis has since reconsidered his opinion. He is now inclined to think the work is late Roman.

in fact, learn that certain travellers, who went on pilgrimage in 1483, en route for the Holy Mountain, came south from El Arish and crossed a sandy plain to " Chawatha, called Cades by the Latins, where there were large cisterns in ruins."

Another school of inquirers prefers to remove Kadesh-barnea from the Sinai uplands and demote it into the enormous depression of the wadi Arabah, which is less a wadi than a colossal gulf cloven between the Et Tih plateau and the southern spurs of the Transjordan mountains. For there Robinson found a mournful little well under the Sinai cliffs called Ain el Weibeh, but it was discouragingly pointed out by Stanley that the identification was unpropitious to at least one important element in the Bible narrative. Its " stony shelves three or four feet high " nowhere soared into such a high-hanging " cliff " (to translate the word correctly) as Moses struck to bring forth water.

It can be said, however, that it is fractionally easier to credit that a city in the uttermost of the borders of the king of Edom might be placed rather on the edge of the wadi Arabah, commanded on the east, as it is, by the Edomite Mount Seir, than up on the steeps of Sinai. In that case, the Desert of the Wandering is likelier to have been the wadi Arabah than Et Tih, though it is beyond belief that a people should have plodded year in, year out, up and down the steam-heat of that aquarium, without thrusting upward for air into the cooler mountain places.

Stanley goes to the opposite extreme from the Ain Kadeis theorists. He would identify Kadesh-barnea with the rock-hewn city of Petra, over on the Transjordan side of the Arabah, a site so much in the heart of Edom that it would have been very hard for Moses to describe it as being in the uttermost of its border. It is true that Petra is watered by the copious stream of the Ayun Musa; it is true that over the egress from one of its defiles hangs Jebel Harun, the traditional site of the death of Aaron. This also is true, that whereas the other Kadeshes would seem to offer neither a large nor a small host comfortable house-room for a period extending over several months, Petra, with all its greenery and waters, could have entertained them indefinitely and without stint; so much is this so, that it is not at all easy to imagine Moses, all other sources failing, being under the necessity of striking a rock to produce water. As for the fact that the water is called after his name, very little water in these regions is not. While Jebel Harun may have been the site of the death of Aaron, it by no means need have been. But last and chiefly, the very shelter and richness of Petra are the chief argument against it. It is hard to believe that once there, the host would ever have wanted to get out again, or, if they wanted to get out, that their enemies would have let them.

To conclude this slightly arid matter. After a rather disheartening overture, Lawrence had determined there was no reason to wipe Ain Kadeis from the slate, though he preferred to identify the " city " of Kadesh with the fortress of Ain Gedeirat, a few miles to the north. Later writers of authority took Kadesh-Kadeis in their stride, as it were. " We had gazed wonderingly at the little trickle of water flowing from Ain Kadeis, the Kadesh of the wanderings," writes Professor Bentwich, without more ado, in the account of his Palestinian journeys. We had the warrant even of the exigent Peet. " This place is almost certainly to be identified with Ain Gadis on the southern border of Palestine, a place distinguished in modern times as having been for some time the railhead of the Turkish army in its attack on Egypt during the war."

What was " almost certain " for Professor Peet was certain enough for us.

" Ain Kadeis, Mustapha ! " I said confidently that morning in Kuntilla.

" Quais! Quais! " agreed Mustapha, more heartily than usual, as if he could have told us from the beginning there was no other thinkable Kadesh-barnea.

WATERS OF AKABA

§ 2

For the first few miles going northward from Kuntilla, it was as difficult as it ever had been to envisage a host moving with its standards and companies, so hopeless, so characterless, the country was. But this was the Desert of their Wanderings. If they did not wander here, they wandered east of us, west of us, it was all the same desert.

A few miles further, however, there is a first flickering of spring in the air, a sense, rather than a sight, of sprouting grass in the wadis. Out of a hole in the baked earth a first snake flickers, as if this same sense of the coming spring had summoned it. He is ringed with black rings round his pale grey body. His forked tongue darts delicately out towards us as he crosses our path. He is black and pale grey like the wastes between the wadis, which seem irrespective of season, neither to be freshened by spring nor cooled by winter, immune from weather, like the fields of the moon.

The Bible, as I recalled earlier, describes Kadesh, and Kadesh alone among all the stations of the Wandering, as a " city." In a later major event of history, as we learned from the pages of Peet, Ain Gadis was again some sort of a city; at least it was used for some time as the railhead of the Turkish army. These facts had implanted the feeling in us that Ain Kadeis would be a simple place to find. We knew that nothing at all remained of the earlier Kadesh but a well, perhaps even some barely distinguishable relics of the cisterns noted by the fifteenth-century pilgrims. But a well is enough and a good deal in these parts. Further, a place can hardly be a railhead without leaving some signs about; it must be an easy place to get to as well as to get away from. Ain Kadeis should be easy to find.

But Mustapha did not share our confidence. He asked one or two Beduin on the road, and as far as we could make out, they were completely non-committal. They may have thought we wished to impound their water, or dispute grazing-

Ec

rights they had in those parts. Perhaps, in fact, they did not know, because we were quite a distance from Ain Kadeis and it is not a very important well when you get there. It is too small, Lawrence found out, to water the flocks of other than the few poor families who live near it, and too remote from all roads to come to the notice of such Arab guides as live at any distance. Had we not been forewarned by him, we too might have taken this native ignorance as deep-seated policy, and come to believe that the spring had remained, from the time of Moses, still a holy place—some great head of water in an oasis too beautiful and too precious to be disclosed to infidel eyes.

The fact remains that the Beduin to whom Mustapha addressed himself were not helpful. It therefore seemed to him we would have to take somewhat more decisive measures than merely asking. When next two Beduin approached, leading their camels, he got out of the car and with great gentleness confiscated one of them, and put him at the back of the truck. He looked a little bewildered, like the nanny-goat and the kid she had given birth to some hours earlier, whose heads were lolling helplessly down from a large straw basket slung from the hump of the leading camel. After an hour or so, I presume when he had recovered from the shock, he must have extended his hand to the right, for we duly turned right, though there was no vestige of a track, not even a goat-track. The impressed Bedu may have felt the shorter the route he took us, the sooner he would be back with his new-born kid; or he may have felt this was a good way to get his own back on the machines which had impressed him. There was a phantom sort of track, we discovered later, on our return from Ain Kadeis; that was some few miles further, along the wadi Gaifi.

Here where we turned east the going was grotesquely difficult, littered with boulders and whip-corded with scrub. For some time we managed either to push aside the boulders or to climb them; but the scrub would have none of us; if the camels had accepted its immunity what right had we to

challenge it? We tried two or three times to induce Mustapha
to desist, lest we find ourselves impaled on a rock or corded up
in the scrub. But the light of battle was in his eyes. At the
heart of this primordial litter he saw a golden oasis of soft
sand shaded over with a thicket of broom. He extracted from
tyre, from engine, from axle, their ultimate iota of discipline
and service. Grrr! went the rocks one moment. Hush! Hush!
Hush! went the sand the moment after. I have never known
such swansdown sand.

Hassan spread out a rug under the tallest bush of broom.
Mohammed got busy with our lunch. In an annexe of broom
Mustapha set himself to making tea. It was warm. We were
in a pocket of the hills protected from the north and from
winds. Somewhere under the evening-primrose sand a secret
trickle of water flowed from Ain Kadeis, where once Israel
had slaked its thirst. It was fresh. It was spring. There were
flowers. There was a low-growing four-petalled whisky-yellow
flower winking up from the sand it pretended to be and was
not. There was a plant the men called *mekhnan*, a sort of
amber-yellow groundsel growing on a thick cactusy stalk.

Lucas was some fifty yards afield eastward, Jim some fifty
yards afield westward. " A crocus! " cried one. " A daisy! "
cried the other. We suddenly lost our heads. We forgot Ain
Kadeis and Moses and Israel. We remembered only spring,
and flowers. Excepting for a single purple and yellow night-
shade under a rust-red cliff in the wadi Sidre, we had seen no
flowers in the wilderness till now. We were like three nostrils
twitching, scenting out a quarry. Nose close to ground we
slid from point to flowery point. The three Sudanese stared
open-mouthed at us for a full half-minute, a thing they had
been too courteous to do before, and then went on with their
duties, a little preoccupied, perhaps a little alarmed.

" Is this grass? " I cried. " Is it a corkscrew? Is it green
hair? " It looked like all of those, rolling round itself its treble
strands. Jim scored with a four-petalled purple star with a
yellow centre, Lucas with more crocuses, blue and purply-blue.

We ate lunch but were more aware of the minute guests we

entertained than the food we were eating: a solemn tribe of ants who were levering off to their larders crumbs of cheese as high as houses; two beetles who had a long conversation about a piece of orange-peel and decided it was no use to anybody; a spider who swung at the end of his thread and merely looked on. Then we turned from our guests to the desert that had bred them, the desert that had first seemed an empty page, and then developed characters under our eyes as we stared at it, like secret writing held up before a lamp. Desert? It was populous as the city itself. Here was the track of a fox once and again muffled by the smother of his tail; here was the track of a lizard with the tail dragged clear behind it, and, before it, the mark of the splay feet. This was the track of a Bedu boy with one sandal; here a bird had delicately passed, here a scarab had trundled away. As for these empty white shells, did they not prove that once the sea . . .

Mustapha touched me with one finger on the elbow. With a finger of the other hand he pointed skywards. " *Shemsh!* " he said. " Sun! "

" Quite right! " I endorsed, disentangling myself from the corkscrew grasses and vaulting over the edge of the empty white shells. " We must look for those other tracks now! " I called to the others, " the railroad tracks to the city! " I turned to the Bedu. " How far now? " I asked him.

" One! " He held up one finger.

" One kilometre! " amplified Mustapha.

" I should say so! " said Jim sceptically. We all knew quite a lot by now about Bedu distances. They were like Biblical censuses, untrammelled flights of the imagination rather than sordid statements of fact.

" I don't mind if it's five," I said, " or even fifty. I mean I metaphorically don't mind."

What I meant was this. By the time we had covered whatever distance lay between us and Ain Kadeis, and had come back to our cars again, we would have covered a great deal of time and space, in our attempt at an imaginative recreation of the host's wanderings. In the scale of times worked out by

Blunt we would have covered some part of the two and a half months the host took on the journey between Sinai and Kadesh; we would have spent three and a half months during the first encampment in Kadesh itself; we would have gone wandering round the desert for thirty-seven years and five months, setting out from Kadesh and at the end of that time going back there again; finally, we would have spent at least another month or two there, before leaving it for ever and setting forth across the passes eastward, and down into the Arabah. We would have spent, as I say, a good long time there.

As for the amount of space we would, in this secondary manner, have covered, that is beyond all computation, and no scholar has ever attempted to compute it. All we could tell ourselves was this: that for the sin the host had sinned, crediting the false and not the true reports regarding the land of Canaan, they were condemned to wander in the wilderness for forty years, which presumably means forty years *additional* to those the journey between Nile and Jordan must in any case have involved them in. Forty additional years—and they must have covered a great deal of space during that time.

But here again this eternally recurrent number holds us up—forty. Is forty forty? Presumably not. All we can say is, the wanderings lasted years rather than months, probably many years rather than few years. In many years of wandering, even under settled conditions, a nomad tribe covers a good deal of ground. Harried by Amalekites and Canaanites and Edomites and God knows how many other half-settled tribes, the Israelites must have covered a great deal more. It was no exaggeration to say, there in the wadi Gaifi, that by the time we had been to Ain Kadeis once and a second time, and come back again to our motor-cars, we would have had our bellyful of wandering.

So we moved up the wadi Gaifi en route for Ain Kadeis. The valley rose slightly, between flat-topped gravelly hills. There was more than one kilometre of it, or two, or three. It was a long way, but we did not mind. We saw half a dozen stonechats, six lizards, one more snake, three partridges and five new sorts of flower.

There was one other thing we looked for, but did not see. Ain Gadis or Kadeis (Professor Peet had said) had been a Turkish railhead during the war. The rail-tracks must have run along this wadi. It could not have approached Ain Kadeis from the other side, because there were hills there, and they were quite steep. Where were the rail-tracks, or the places where the tracks had been, or the blastings in the hillside, or the embankments? We turned an angle of the wadi twice and a third time, and at last came to a sort of arena. Here were patches of turf. Here were several stagnant blankets of water. Here, nearer the hillside, was water flowing, making grass tremble as it moved, water that came together out of three separate streams. Twenty feet higher up the bank from which the three streams issued, was the well which fed them, a well about five feet deep, loosely parapeted with rough stones. These, and a small camel-trough below the well, were all the relics of old Kadesh, or modern railhead. There had been no railhead, evidently. The eminent scholar had somehow been led astray. (And perhaps that is not surprising. How shall a scholar, however erudite, not go astray in this formless region if he has not been there, when erudite scholars, who have in fact been there, differ? This uncanny railhead haunted me. I have since tried to lay its ghost. The Turkish railhead? At Auja Hafir, Professor Bentwich specifies. At Ain Kossaima, Major Jarvis pronounces, some fifteen miles away.)

However, the presence or absence of new railhead did not in the least invalidate the identification of Ain Kadeis with old Kadesh; yet the trivial error had the effect of mitigating during the rest of the journey the almost religious awe we had till now entertained towards the scholars.

We knew that Mustapha, Hassan and Mohammed were not well informed, either on the subject of their Prophet or ours.

But the Bedu we had brought with us was a local product. If anyone knew what connection, if any, there was between Ain Kadeis and Moses, it was he.

"Water of Musa, this is?" I asked.

"*La! La!* No! No!" He threw back his head in such vigorous negation that I suspected he was merely being sulky about it; he was remembering his poor nanny-goat and the new-born kid from which he had been so roughly divorced.

"Water of Musa, this is?" I asked again. This time I handed him a cigarette.

"Ain Musa?" he asked. "Oh, Ain *Musa*!" as if he had not heard properly the first time. "*Aiua! Aiua!* Yes! Yes!" He nodded his head in the most vigorous affirmation.

"See?" I turned to the others. "Doesn't that prove it?" It was agreed that was as good a proof as any. In the meantime, the memory of the nanny-goat had come back into the Bedu's mind. Mournfully he opened his wallet, took out a steel and flint and tinder, and lit his cigarette, much as the spies who were sent out from this place might have done, if they had been served with a cigarette ration.

"Never mind, Saleh!" I comforted him. "We won't be long! We have a few journeys to make, but they won't take more than forty years. Then we get on the road to Kuntilla again and we'll see how poor nanny is. She'll be all right, I'm quite sure. That young man with the eyes like damson-plums seemed entirely competent."

And we also puffed at our cigarettes, a first, and a second, and a third cigarette, and looked round about us for some minutes, and then went backward into time, and outward into space, into desert space.

It was hard to conceive there was ever any room in this small arena for a city, or even for a good-sized encampment. It seemed to me it could be so easily surrounded, it would have been a first-rate trap. The reverse holds, too, I suppose; that it would have been easy to plant guards on the surrounding summits, while the host rested up in the valley below.

But they would not have been well off for water, unless they had access to Ain Gedeirat, and a few other wells in the neighbourhood.

Nevertheless, with much water or little, they spent three and a half months in Kadesh the first time they encamped there, and liked it so much they came back again many years later and spent another month or two. A good deal happened there, one way and another. There was, it will be remembered, the sending forth of the spies.

" Send thou men," the Lord commanded Moses, " that they may spy out the land of Canaan, which I give unto the children of Israel."

And the spies went up as far north as the entrance of Hamath, between Lebanon and Hermon. They spent forty days in all up in Canaan, and came back with a mixed tale, excepting only the trusty Joshua and Caleb, who were all for an immediate invasion of the country. The remaining ten, the ten timid ones, could not pretend the place was not a fountain of milk and honey, particularly as they themselves had brought back specimens of its figs and pomegranates, and a cluster of grapes so vast that two men had to bear it between them on a staff. (So vast, indeed, the Talmud amplifies, that the wine pressed from its grapes sufficed for all the ceremonial needs of Israel during the ensuing forty years of wandering.) But they had seen giants, said the timid ones, and they felt themselves as grasshoppers in their sight; such gigantic giants, the legend says, that they grew fruit-trees to scale in their orchards; and when on a certain occasion the twelve had taken refuge in a cave, they soon found themselves bodily lifted and cast away, cave and all, for it was not a cave but a pomegranate, which a daughter of one of those same giants kicked out of her path.

These tales were too much for the Israelites, who seemed ready to believe anything. The old murmuring started again. Egypt, Egypt, they murmured! The pomegranates may not be so big, but the Egyptians are not, either. And the Lord was about to smite them with a pestilence, there in Kadesh, but still once more Moses prevailed on Him to abate His wrath, and instead of that pestilence the Lord decreed that the host must turn again from Kadesh and go wandering in the desert for forty years, and at the end of that time, none of all those wanderers should survive to enter the Promised Land, saving only those two exemplary ones, Caleb and Joshua, and the young folk not yet twenty years old.

"To-morrow turn ye," said the Lord, "and get you into the wilderness by the way to the Red Sea." By which, if Kadesh is Ain Kadeis, it is to be understood that the host were to turn eastward, and make for the wadi Arabah, deep down there between the mountain massifs of Sinai and Transjordan. The phrase can mean nothing else but the wadi Arabah, and there, it follows, the host must have spent some part, great or small, of their years of penal wanderings.

But before they turned east and south into the Arabah, they committed further follies. It is reported, for instance, that they rashly went up beyond Kadesh into the hill country to fight the Amalekite and Canaanite, neither seeking nor receiving the Lord's blessing; and neither Moses nor the ark of the covenant went up with them, and the heathen "smote them and beat them down." Yet that they should go up and fight without their leader's support into that country concerning which they had just heard such terrifying reports, seems unusually hard to credit. It looks almost as if the battle were a recollection of some earlier event, or an anticipation of some later one. On the other hand, if some such smashing defeat were actually inflicted on them, they would salve their self-respect by explaining that their enemies were giants; it might also help to explain why they chose to wander in the repulsive deserts for years, rather than come to grips again with so formidable an enemy.

There followed two further rebellions against the authority of Moses in that ill-found encampment at Kadesh-barnea, or it may have been one and the same rebellion. "Now Korah, with Dathan and Abiram and two hundred and fifty princes of the congregation assembled themselves together against

Moses and Aaron and said: 'Ye take too much upon ye, seeing all the congregation are holy . . . wherefore then lift ye up yourselves above the assembly of the Lord?'" And Dathan and Abiram refused to come up when Moses summoned them, and they and their followers were swallowed up in the earth. And Korah protested that the tribe of Levi was not more sacred than the other tribes of Israel, and he was confuted in the blossoming of the rod of Levi, though the rods of the other tribes did not blossom; and the princes of Korah were burned with fire, and without doubt Korah too, though his death is not reported in that place.

" So ye abode in Kadesh many days," Moses records in his valedictory address in Deuteronomy, but he does not tell us how many; nineteen years, the Talmud clarifies, though it is hard to see in Ain Kadeis what kept them there all that time. " Then we turned," Moses continues, " and took our journey into the wilderness by the way of the Red Sea: and we compassed Mount Seir many days."

Now Mount Seir, as most scholars are agreed, means the long line of Transjordanian mountains flanking the wadi Arabah on the east. (It is even held that the word survives in the present name of the range north-east of Akaba— Jebel esh Sherat.)

So the host, unspecified for how long, moved up and down the eastern fringe of the wadi Arabah, gazing mournfully up the deep wadis which cleave the massif from east to west, green and fertile and in the hands of their enemies. The tracks up to the plateau were steep enough, but that way lay Canaan, up the wadis and northward along the plateau, then down again on to the plains of Moab which run down to Jordan, the river of Canaan.

But the time had not come yet. The people of those valleys would have none of them, and they themselves were too weak as yet to dispute the passage. The Lord had imposed on them forty long years of aimless wandering. Yet no, not entirely aimless. He had announced one aim, at least—that the old might die in that time and the young come to manhood.

And that end being achieved, then at length, the Lord said: "Ye have compassed the mountain long enough: turn you northward."

So the host came up from the wadi Arabah up on to the plateau of Et Tih, which is the wilderness of Paran. And they came to a section of the wilderness of Paran which is named Zin, and crossed the dry tracts of Zin and came a second and last time to Kadesh-barnea.

"—Where we are now," I said to my two friends. "So let us stand up from this rock. Our journey is in the steps of Moses the Conqueror, though many years are to pass before he starts conquering. If this is truly Kadesh-barnea, he went up the pass there and climbed the slopes of Gebel Kharuf. Then he descended the wadi el Siq and so went down into the Arabah. But for a variety of reasons we cannot go with him, not the least of which is that we would have to cross a frontier where there is no frontier-post, and that would make complications on the other side, when they came to look into our papers. They would think us spies, the progeny of those twelve that set out from Kadesh a long time ago. Or they would think us smugglers. And it might be amusing in a pale sort of way, but it would be inconvenient. And we are expected in El Kuntilla to-night, and, in any case, Moses will be back here again in rather less than forty years.

" So let us stand up and walk forty paces. Let us then close our eyes for forty seconds. The wandering of forty years will be achieved in that time. Then we will open our eyes again, and walk forty paces back, back to Kadesh-barnea. And the host will be encamped here again, and certain things will happen here, and we will witness them."

I do not think I made so lengthy and coherent a speech; but that certainly was the spirit of it. And we stood up and walked forty paces, as I had asked, and we kept our eyes shut for forty seconds, and came back again to where we had been standing. And Mustapha and Hassan and Mohammed looked at us in astonishment, and then Hassan whispered something to the other two. "It is their religion," he whispered—or so I am convinced. And they turned their eyes away decorously.

Then we sat down again, and looked about us, and recalled certain further events that took place during the second sojourn in Kadesh. The host now was a conspicuously younger congregation than it had been when it was last here. The old people had been dying off like flies; not many survived, though these still included Miriam, and Aaron, and Moses himself. But even as we sat there, a wailing of women arose from one of the tents by the water-side. Miriam is dead! The Prophetess is dead! And the dew of death was already on the High Priest's forehead. Three or four months later, when the host a second time left Kadesh for the Arabah and had reached Mount Hor, Aaron is dead, too. And half a year after that, the tale of Moses is all told. Much happens between now in Kadesh and then on the summit of Pisgah. Much ground is covered. But the foot of Moses will not cover even one cubit of that holier ground on the far side of Jordan.

It was here in Kadesh Miriam died, somewhere beside this stream, which then ran deep enough to quench the thirst of a host. And then the stream ceased. There is not any water to drink, cried the host. It died when Miriam died, the Talmud tells us, for it was the well of Miriam. And the people strove with Moses (for which reason Kadesh is also called Meribah, a striving). And they said: Why have ye brought us into this wilderness, that we should die there? And the Lord commanded Moses to speak unto the rock before the eyes of the people. Perhaps this is the very rock before our eyes now. But Moses in his anger did not speak to the rock but struck it, and struck it not once, but twice. And it was for that reason that, at the end of it all, Moses must not reap where he had sown, but turn his back upon the harvesters.

And one more thing happened here, in this place, Kadesh, as I recalled earlier. It was from here Moses sent messengers to the King of Edom, asking for free passage through his territory. " We will not pass through field or through vineyard," Moses promised, " neither will we drink of the water of the wells: we will go along the king's highway, we will not turn aside to the right hand nor to the left, until we have passed thy border." But Edom said unto him: "Thou shalt not pass through me, lest I come out with the sword against thee."

And Moses and Aaron and the host went down a second time into the wadi Arabah, crossing over the width of the wilderness to Mount Hor, and Aaron died there. And they continued down the plain, by the way of the Red Sea, as far as the Red Sea itself, namely to a place then called Ezion-geber, and now called Akaba.

As for ourselves, we will not be able to follow them down the Arabah any more this second time than we could the first time. We will have instead to walk down the wadi Gaifi where we have left the cars, and make for Kuntilla where we must spend the night. From Kuntilla we will drive down to Akaba to-morrow, and, roughly forty years later, we will join up with Moses again at Ezion-geber. He will be a lonely old man then, his sister dead, his brother dead, most of his old friends dead. But he will still hold his head high. His head will not droop even on the top of Mount Pisgah, though he knows when he lies down to sleep there, he will not rise again.

§ 3

Excepting for the rocks themselves, there is no vestige of those early histories in the small arena of Ain Kadeis. I looked hopefully at a shallow trough near the upper well, which had something of the appearance of a sacrificial slab, and even made a suggestion to that effect to our Muslim attendants, passing a hand across my throat to convey the idea.

"Nebi Musa? Nebi Harun?" I asked tentatively.

Mustapha was all for attributing the trough to the two brothers, for he was a kind person. But the impounded Bedu would have none of it. It was "Turki," and a camel-trough, and I am afraid that was all there was to it.

The point was I had been told to look out for a relic of a really formidable antiquity in Ain Kadeis, and was somewhat disappointed not to find it there. Lawrence, in 1914, had found a worked flint in the valley of Ain Gedeirat, not far away, which might have been a prehistoric one, he thought, in which case the place would be distinguished as the only Stone Age site he noted in that part of Sinai. But a certain Sergeant Ali had told me of a living flint he had come across in these parts, a pure neolith.

We had met Sergeant Ali in Suez and he seemed to know a good deal about the peninsula. He was not strictly a sergeant, as far as we could make out, he was some sort of minor Government official, but the expression seemed a good way to distinguish him from the other Alis of Suez.

" You go Ain Kadeis from Suez? " he asked. " By El Kossaima? Yes. I know. I was."

" You were, were you? What was it like? "

" I see hyena-man."

" Hyena-man? " I asked excitedly. That seemed to be a creature of an epoch much earlier than the Prophet's.

" Government official," he said with dignity. " He look after camel-men water camels there, not quarrel. He has gun. Government give him gun. But he not use it. He frightened. He has axe, instead."

" That sounds very bloodthirsty," I said. " I hope he doesn't have to use it often."

" He not use it on men. He use it on hyena."

" Hyena? " I asked. " Are there many hyenas round Ain Kadeis? "

" Not plenty much. Not enough. Very scarce."

They could hardly be too scarce, I thought.

" He get too little money, not much. He eat hyena."

" *Eat* hyena? "

" Yes. He bait with dead donkey. Then all of a sudden, listen. He hear laugh of hyena. Ha! Ha! He drop gun. He run up hill. He have axe in hand. He throw it. Fifty yard. Seventy yard. Crack! Back of neck. Hyena lie down and die. He take hyena to well. Water for drink, flesh for eat. Very happy."

" What sort of an axe? " I asked. " Does Government give him an axe?"

" No, he make himself. He make big stone sharp. He get curved branch from tree, like handle. He get gut from dead camel, tie together stone and branch. Then he throw. Never miss. Back of neck. Here, feel! " He took hold of my fingers and showed me exactly the part of the neck he meant, below the angle of the skull.

" Very old-fashioned," said Sergeant Ali. Yes, it seemed to me the fashion went back a long time. We duly kept eye and ear open in Ain Kadeis, but neither saw the hyena-man nor heard the laugh of the hyena. We did not even find a worked flint.

" We must make do with Moses," I said to the others, " even though he only goes back to last week. I mean," I added, " compared to the hyena-man."

" Not much Moses," Lucas murmured.

" The word! " I said. " The word! Kadesh! Kadeis!

> *The word, and naught else,*
> *in time endures.*
> *What love doth Helen*
> *or Paris have*
> *Where they lie still in*
> *a nameless grave?*
> *Her beauty's a wraith,*
> *and the boy Paris*
> *muffles in death*
> *his mouth's cold cherries.*
> *Nor Helen's wonder*
> *nor Paris stirs,*
> *but the bright, untender*
> *hexameters . . .*

He might well have added Kadesh," I murmured, " a poem in a not less stately tongue . . . that so strange city, Kadesh. A city of which the remains are so fragile that the remains of Troy and Nineveh are gross beside it. A city of ranked pavilions and coloured tents in rows, and banners flying, the blue flag of Judah, bearing the sign of the lion, and the black flag of Issachar, figured with the sun and moon, and the white flag of Zebulum, with a ship for token. All gone! All gone! The word, and naught else, endures! Kadesh! Kadeis!

" Let us go now. We've had a good deal of this place, all told. Let us get going upon our journeys."

§ 4

The impounded Bedu had plunged us a few miles too soon in the direction of the well, in the hope, perhaps, that we would get impaled on a boulder and so release him a few hours sooner. He underrated the resilience of Detroit, however, and we arrived. On the return journey, the men made a point of sticking as closely as possible to the wadi, and we came out on the track a few miles further north. The thousands of boulders in the wadi were bigger than the millions of stones in the plain, but by quick jerking of the steering-wheel it was sometimes possible to go round them. The Bedu, in a sudden access of amiability, led us up on to a sand-hill and pointed out a few dimly circular groupings of rock. They were graves, I think. They looked very lonely there. It did not seem to me the bodies that had been placed there, if these were indeed tombs, can have been much more private inside the circles than outside them.

" Pharaon! " said the Bedu. But we were not convinced.

And then, when the wadi twisted again and thrust out a broad fan into the gravelly plain, we suddenly came upon a few acres of thin wheat and straggly onions. The planting and the tending of this simple stuff, the faint flare of greenness in all that ashen monochrome, seemed as valiant as a small force in a beleaguered city holding its own against great odds.

" There has been rain this year," said Lucas.

" There was rain three thousand years ago," I said, " when Moses moved down this way with the host behind him."

Akaba

" We agreed," Lucas pointed out, " that Moses moved over the pass the other way, over the Gebel Kharuf and down into the Arabah."

" Nobody knows," I said, a little desperately, " nobody knows. Perhaps he came back this way, and went down by an easier valley. Perhaps this was the Hashmonah, the last of the stations between Hazeroth and Kadesh. Do you remember? One of the scholars said Hashmonah was the same word as Kossaima, which is not many miles up the track there."

A gust of wind blew up a saucerful of sand from a trench under a boulder. Lucas stretched out his fingers towards the spiralling sand. " That's what it's like," he said, " snatching at these names."

Yes, I remembered, so, too, it seemed to Doughty. " Here a word " (he writes) " of the camping grounds of Moses; all their names we may never find again in these countries,—and wherefore? Because they were a good part passengers' names, and without land-right they could not remain in the desert, in the room of the old herdsmen's names. There is yet another kind of names, not rightly of the country, not known to the Beduin, which are *caravanners'* names. The caravanners passing in haste, with fear of the nomads, know not the wide wilderness without their landmarks; nor even in the way, have they a right knowledge of the land names. What wonder if we find not again some which are certainly caravanners' names in the old itineraries? "

We turned southward again over Et Tih, along the way we had come. Those others, the Israelite host, turned often enough, I murmured, along the way they had come. Sunset on our right hand was like the cooling of the red-hot plates of a ship's deck. The green tongues of water that came from the north seemed to scatter in bubbles and go up in steam from the still-hot furnace-flanks. Then at last all colour, of red metal or green water, left the sky. There was no sky. Nor was there any earth. Only, few and far, the twitch-fires of the wandering Beduin wrapped in their cloaks beside their beasts.

Fc

I had forgotten the Bedu we had impressed into our service. So, too, I think, had Mustapha. Mustapha was wrapped up in his own warm black mystery. Where were the stations of his mind's journey? The kraal he was a boy in by the swampy edge of the up-country Nile. Some soldiers' café in Alexandria, where one night he had seen a small Kabyle girl, with heavy silver circlets above her elbows and round her ankles? They were stations of a journey as remote from me, as untraceable, as the stations of the journey made by the Israelitic wanderers three thousand years ago, Rithmah, Rimmonparez, Libnah, Rissah. Where were the stations of my mind's journey? The kitchen in Doomington, the leaping fire, the blank back wall beyond the barred windows? The Greek theatre in Syracuse, where the ghosts of the Greek lads go about, who died so slowly that they are not even yet dead? The Bierkeller in Berlin where they kicked and kicked and kicked my prostrate ribs?

" Hi! Ho! " A cry suddenly came down over the hood to me in Segovia, to Mustapha in Khartum, if those were the places where at that moment we found ourselves.

Mustapha unspread himself from over the steering-wheel. " Hi! Ho! " he called aback again, and braked his car.

" What then? " I asked.

" Home! " Mustapha said. " The Arabi is home! " He stretched his right arm across my chest and pointed to a tiny flicker in the dark wilderness. The Bedu had jumped from his place in the tarpaulin behind us, and stood for a moment beside us, glimmering like a bush of white blossom. I put my hand into my pocket, but before it was out again, he was gone, like a ghost, like a thought.

" How did he know that's his boy out there, and his fire, and his tent? "

" He hear his camels cry to him."

" His camels? I heard no camels! "

Mustapha was not surprised I had heard no camels. But to me it seemed a quite notable thing the Bedu should hear his beasts from a long way off, above the noise of the engine three feet from his ear, and recognize them as his own beasts. So a westerner might recognize his dogs, I thought.

" Now Kuntilla, Mustapha ! " I said.

We plunged almost at once into complete blackness, except for the two booms of light attached to our headlights. It was as if the night ahead of us and each side of us were curtained by black velvet. The ceiling, too, was black velvet, with a rent here and there through which a star shone. Despite the weight and clatter of the cars, so indistinguishable was above from below, and side from side, it felt almost as if we were moving in a middle ether, with the wheels grinding on nothing but packed air. But we were not entirely alone in this odd universe. From time to time a species of living creature was picked up by the beam of the headlights, that trundled side-ways along the edge of things and toppled over; or trundled forward, fascinated by our colossal eyes, and disappeared under the annihilating wheels.

We could not make out what the creature was. It was so disrelated from all perspective it was impossible to decide what its size was. It may have been no bigger than a field-mouse, it may have been as big as a beaver. It seemed to have the gait of a hedgehog, yet it looked more rat-like. It was, I be-lieve, the jerboa rat. Heaven knew what sustenance it drew upon, that it preferred the profitless night to the profitless day.[1]

Into just such a blackness, I mused, the route of the host of Israel across this desert of wanderings had disappeared. A name emerges briefly out of the welter, a little awkward, a little top-heavy. Like these small creatures blinking on the edge of the non-lingering light. " And they journeyed from Rissah, and pitched in Kehelathah. And they journeyed from Kehelathah and pitched in Mount Shepher." And the blackness immediately entombs them again.

So for our part we pitched a second time in the encamp-ment called Kuntilla. Again a second time the *farrash* perched

[1] I have subsequently gathered it eats the corn in camel-dung.

on the peak swung a lantern to welcome us, right-left, right-left, in steady half-circles.

His dog, Fil-fil, the pepper-coloured one, was waiting for us, too. It was as if he had noted the incredible promise that he should have a whole tin of bully-beef to himself, when the host came back from their wanderings about Kadesh. He stood there with a hopeless resignation in one eye, with a wild hope in the other. With one eye he meditated egg-shells, with the other the tin of pressed manna. He fed royally that night.

We did hardly less well.

CHAPTER FOUR

IT was Sunday. A more than sabbatic calm reigned over the Et Tih plateau. There never was a silence so absolute on any other Sunday morning. Even the rock-martins refrained from disturbing it. They clung to their minute ledges in the face of the cliff below us, like carved images of themselves.

It was a Sunday of no bells, and so remained for an hour or two after we had risen. Then from somewhere, incredibly minute and clear, a bell tittered across the distances. It came from everywhere, tiny though the sound was, so permeable was that virgin air. We did not for a long time associate it with the moving black-headed yellow lily that issued from the shack built of kerosene tins a mile or two across the plain. Slowly the lily floated towards our hill. It was a little girl, we saw now. Wizza, the *farrash* told us indifferently, she was his daughter. The *farrash* preferred his sons.

She was the source of the bell-music, we perceived at length. She was the steeple of our Sinai Sunday. The music moved with her, and her yellow gown swung about her. She came closer. She came to the top of the hill. She had a bundle hanging behind her neck, our washing, evidently. The patched rags of her gown swung from elbow and ankle as she set the bundle down with a final flicker of bell-noise. There was a small brass bell threaded on to a string above her left elbow and her left ankle. She had black still eyes like the carved martins in the rock-face. She was about five years old, I suppose.

We were leaving for Akaba that day, where we should meet the host again encamped at Ezion-geber. Akaba and Ezion-geber were both important places on our journey, Akaba because that was the frontier-post where we should leave Egypt for Transjordan, Ezion-geber because it was one of the three or

four stations out of the forty-four, of which it could be said:
this is in all likelihood the place where the host pitched their
tents.

But looking down from the hill-top of Kuntilla that Sunday
morning, on all that blinding whiteness of the Et Tih limestone, it was difficult not to entertain the fancy that Kuntilla,
too, must have been one of the stations of the wandering,
perhaps the one called Libnah, which means " whiteness."
There was water here, at the foot of the hill, which was here
then, too. There was even a few yards of greenness, as
we found out shortly, tucked away against the north slope,
where a minute mitigation of the fierce heat might be hoped
for.

So we found, during the visit of inspection on which we
shortly proceeded. " Camel Corps waits," Mustapha informed us, and we gathered that he would prefer us not to
leave for Akaba without a formal tour round the encampment.
It was the only kindness of any sort that Mustapha had
suggested he would like from us, and it was impossible to
refuse it, though I, for my part, did not see myself very comfortable in the rôle of a visiting G.O.C.: however, the rôle
sat a little easier on the shoulders of Lucas, who had had
more than a respectable military career in the late war.
Lucas pointed out, also, that if Kuntilla were really the site
of the encampment at Libnah, I had no option in the matter.
Jim did not need the warrant of Libnah.

The well of Kuntillah-Libnah that had (we had by now
convinced ourselves) watered the beasts of the Israelites, had
been renovated since then, by a solid parapet of squared
stones. It was surmounted by a double wooden trestle, over
which a metal cable passed, attached at one end to a cluster
of paraffin tins, at the other to the halter of a blinkered camel,
which walked endlessly in a straight line fifty paces forward
from the well, fifty paces back again. It seemed a most
menial task for so high-stomached a creature to perform, and
he showed what he felt about it in the frozen sneer of his acute

hare-lip. The inflating and deflating balloon of his protruded tongue added a touch of horror to his visage, without detracting from his dignity. As the cluster of paraffin tins rose to the height of the trestle, the camel's jerk as it turned, emptied the water into an iron pipe. The pipe led into a twenty foot long cement trough where three straddled camels stood drinking, with expressions of profound disdain, as if by accepting the stuff, they were conferring a kindness on the whole human species. The remaining camels of the company, having filled their own bellies, were being loaded with layers of oblong water carriers, to fill the bellies of the company's motor trucks. The water-lifting camel had her stable ten yards or so from the well. It was, very properly, a good deal better built and more commodious than the two or three hutments in the plain, occupied by mere human beings.

The garden I spoke of was close by, against the north slope, a forlorn garden, irrigated drop by drop from the trough's overflow, as if each drop were tried silver. It was protected from the lateral blasts of furnace-heat by a laboriously raised broom fence, criss-crossed with a lattice of wires from which a rag-market of black rags hung like dead crows, to frighten the living ones. In the edges of the garden, in the branches of the thorny acacias flanking it, the birds squatted, staring mordantly between the scraggy besoms of broom at the scant harvest of cabbage and broad beans and onions. There was, too, a hollyhock type of vegetable. *Bamia*, Mustapha called it. He said it was good. But all the four growths looked a good deal less like themselves than like grey rags drooping listlessly under the black rags that hung over them.

From this woebegone travesty of an oasis in the plain, we drove up to the Camel Corps headquarters on the flat-topped hill to the east. The building did not look less papier-mâché as we approached it; it was like something in Culver City rather than Sinai. The sun had the same effect on the thick whitewashed walls as a car's headlamps have on the gnarled trees of a wood; it robbed them of their third dimension. The fortress consisted of two separate oblong buildings, one storey high, each built round a large interior courtyard. Half-way between the buildings, a flag-staff was planted, from which the flag of Egypt drooped in no wind. Over the first building rose a wrought-iron camel weathercock. There the camel-men and their beasts were stationed. Over the other rose a weathercock shaped like a motor-car. There the cars were garaged and relieved of their frequent ills. Both tokens hung passive in the dead air.

It was in the second of these that Mustapha, being himself a motor-man, invited us to begin our inspection. We passed through a high square vestibule occupying the width of the building and entered the courtyard, where so much fire-fighting apparatus was gathered together, extinguishers, buckets, pick-axes, spades, hatchets, heaps of sand—you felt it was expected the motors might burst into flames any moment. It was, in fact, so hot you would not have been surprised to see an ice pudding burst into flames, if there had been any ice puddings about in Kuntilla. In the shade of a lean-to, a number of large earthenware water-pots diminishing to a point, reposed in holes in a cement bench. In the same corner of the buildings, was a dispensary presided over by a spectacled Egyptian in a voluminous *djellabieh*, whom Mustapha respectfully described as " Hakeem." He bowed to us very fluently a great number of times, in vivid contrast to the soldiers, who, whatever their avocations were, rose and stood at petrified attention the moment we made our appearance. Some were working in the repair shop that occupied one side of the quadrangle. Some were stooping in the kitchen over an enormous iron cooking-stove. Others were putting the final touches to their kit in the dormitory. All sprang to attention, and stood rigid as marionettes.

I found it all a little embarrassing; my neck was hot enough and was getting hotter. Jim was subdued. Lucas, on the other hand, was quite at his ease. You would have thought the war had not stopped, and he was inspecting a new battalion in Etaples. We climbed to the crenellated battlements by one of the iron ladders which were let into each of the four

walls, and inspected the rifle-range installed up there, and
the machine-guns posted at each corner turret. We descended with dignity and entered the kitchen, where they
were cooking a savoury mess of tomatoes, potatoes, onions
and rock pigeons. My insistence on stirring the stew and
tasting it caused the first breach in the general stiffness.
One soldier unbent. Another breathed. The situation
became a little more tolerable.

We went on into the dormitory. The beds consisted of
wooden boards on iron trestles, covered over with army
blankets. In a shelf above the bed, each man had neatly
ranged his reserve blanket, his spare kit and his best boots,
that shone like burnished sunflowers. By each bed a rifle
stood, as it might be the soldiers' *alter ego*. One soldier brushed
a fly from his cheek. Another soldier said something to somebody. A rot threatened to creep into this parade of the
military virtues, when Lucas checked the process, at least
temporarily, by seizing one of the rifles, to inspect it. He
opened the bolt with a curt military click, eyed it sternly, closed
it again, eased the spring and passed it as satisfactory. We
walked on to another bed and another rifle. Lucas was having
a good time. He should not have given up being a soldier.
I wanted to blow my nose but did not dare. Through the
corner of my eye I saw a soldier, several beds away, hastily
slip into his pocket a rosary he had spread out carefully on
his blanket. I suppose he left it out to assure his couch some
form of spiritual protection, but his sense of military decency
got the better of him. On the opposite side three soldiers
stood shoulder to shoulder over against a space of wall.
You might have thought they wanted to cover something up,
if it could be conceived that soldiers so faultless could have
anything anywhere that needed to be covered up.

Lucas opened another rifle with another curt military click.
He liked the sound. I did not. We walked on to another bed.
I walked in his shadow like a very second lieutenant following
a very senior staff officer. At this moment I noticed that Jim
had crossed the room and taken up his position opposite the

three soldiers standing shoulder to shoulder. Somehow some instinct had informed him there was something worth seeing on the wall behind the soldiers. He is of the post-war generation and his sense of military decorum is rudimentary. He approached nearer to the contiguous shoulders and rested his chin on them to get a view of the Thing he had become aware of. A moment later he had pulled the two soldiers aside. In the gap appeared a piece of cardboard tacked on to the wall. On the cardboard frolicked a bevy of maidens, cut out of the pages of magazines. Some were mere advertisements, some were from the text, some were black and white, some coloured. None was more than scantily attired.

"*Bints! Bints!*" cried Jim joyously. "Girls! Girls! *Quais! Quais!*"

The perpendicular troops crumbled as at a whiff of grape-shot. They were all over the place. They forgot me, which was easy; they forgot Lucas, which ought not to have been so easy. They crowded round Jim, chuckling delightedly.

"*Aiua! Bints!*" they repeated. "*Quais! Quais!*" Their black faces gleamed like copper kettles. There was a spatter of gold teeth up and about the grinning mouths, like pomegranate seeds. The military inspection was over. We jostled each other, slapping shoulders and insisting we were *quais*, one and all.

"Come kitchen!" insisted one hearty warrior.

Jim and I tumbled out of dormitory and came kitchen. I preferred this lack of ceremony. Lucas drew up the rear a little morosely.

"Take!" the chef requested, and thrust the stirring-spoon into our hands. We took. It was a good stew, as I have said, of vegetables and rock-pigeon. The troops thrust their naked fists into the scalding pottage.

"*Quais? Quais? Quais?*" the question boomed and rattled like fireworks.

"*Quais!*" we assured them. "*Bints!* Rock-pigeon! Kuntilla! All *quais!*"

It seemed to me, as I stood there, a whole stewed pigeon in

my mouth, the host might not have done so badly for itself, after all, when it pitched at Kuntilla-Libnah.

" Well, Mustapha," I said some half-hour later. " It's all very *quais*, but we've got to think of getting to Akaba some time to-day."

" *Aiua!* " he agreed. He looked a little subdued, I thought. Probably he would have preferred to keep the whole inspection on its original G.O.C. footing.

" Well, what about getting on, then? "

" *Aiua!* " he said again. There was evidently something on his mind.

" Have we left something undone we ought to do? "

Apparently we had.

" Over there," he pointed, sweating with embarrassment. " If so kind." He pointed to the camel stables. My heart sank. I realized we had so far inspected only one half of the establishment. If we were to inspect the other half on the same scale, we were going to be awkwardly late in Akaba. We still hadn't the ghost of an idea what we were going to do when we got to Akaba, whether we might creep into some sort of a hut somewhere, or whether we'd have to camp out on the beach. There was the problem of the commissariat to think of, too. Our supplies were getting uncomfortably low. Uncomfortably low for me, at least. Lucas would always have been ready to supplement the pot with a desert thorn soup and a fried lizard or two. We would have to think of getting some food from somewhere.

" I'd very much like to," I said. " But time's getting on, Mustapha."

The black colossus stood fiddling with his sash exactly like some small boy summoning up his courage to ask his teacher if he might leave the room.

" Officer! " he finally blurted. " Officer would like to talk! "

" *Officer?* " I repeated with horror. No one had breathed a word to us regarding the presence of an officer in the fortress. There had only been an *umbasha*, a corporal, in charge at Nekhl, and we had taken it for granted there would only be an *umbasha* here. Nor had anything that had happened in the car stables put the idea of an officer into our minds.

" How awful! " I said to the two others. " What a *gaffe!* We should have called on him the first moment we got here! Going about inspecting his troops as if we were Hindenburg! What will the fellow think of us? "

" We didn't know," said Lucas. " Anyhow he wants to see us! "

" He might get us that goat! " said Jim helpfully. There had been some talk during the last day or so about adding a goat to our stores. One or two of the books had said it was sometimes possible to buy a goat from a wandering herdsman when provisions ran low.

" We can't ask a man for a goat whom we've insulted so flagrantly! " I said severely. " Well, we'd better take what's coming to us! "

We left the car stables amid a great hand-shaking and back-slapping and tooth-gleaming, but our hearts were heavy. We crossed the intervening courtyard between the two stables, and kept our eyes averted from the flag of Egypt, feeling we had not treated it with due decorum. At the square archway Mustapha handed us over to another *umbasha*, and then did not advance an inch further. The *umbasha* led us in an awed manner to a small room in the left-hand corner, across the courtyard. A fawny-grey Seleuci lay curled round itself under the doorstep. We almost stumbled over it, its colour was so exactly the colour of the desert floor. The *umbasha* looked at us sharply and looked away again.

It all looked very portentous, and our confidence was not increased when we were ushered into the presence of the officer himself. He sat in a small windowless room before a table littered with maps. He was in full regimentals, which it was impossible to doubt he had put on in our honour. A large tabby cat was asleep, curled up at one end of the table.

The officer got up as we entered and proffered each of us his hand in turn coldly.

" What have we let ourselves in for? " I asked myself. " What sort of a report is he going to read to them in El Arish, or perhaps Cairo? It's lucky we're going down to Akaba to-day. That is, if he'll put no obstacles in our way! "

" Would you like coffee, gentlemen? " the officer asked. Yes, thank you, we would like coffee very much indeed. He was a handsome fellow, but I could isolate no expression at all on his face. He was as impassive as one of Pharaoh's officers in a tomb-painting. " And cigarettes? " Yes, thank you, we would like cigarettes very much indeed.

The cigarettes were there and we helped ourselves at once. The cat opened its eyes, yawned, and went to sleep again. The coffee was a long time in coming. Nothing happened for a long time. The conversation was not fluent. It is very hot in Kuntilla? Yes, it is very hot in Kuntilla. There is very little water about in these parts? Yes, there is very little water about in these parts. I began to feel the constraint stifling me. It was embarrassing enough following Lucas about inspecting rifles, as if I knew the difference between a rifle and a potato-peeler. But it was dreadful shuffling about in that room, making the most jejune small talk, waiting for coffee that never came, as the guests of a military gentleman whom we had unforgivably flouted and who was burning with resentment against us.

" I'm awfully sorry, sir," I burst out. " I really am awfully sorry. I assure you. It was quite unintentional."

The officer looked up, a bit startled. " I beg your pardon? " he said. " Intentional? Please, I do not understand." He seemed genuine enough.

" I mean . . . about not calling on you. If we had understood there was an officer in charge, naturally, as you can imagine . . ."

The officer wrinkled the smooth alabaster of his forehead. He clearly hadn't the least idea what I was talking about.

" But please, I am glad, the coffee will be here quite soon. I will ask them for quick."

The phrases tumbled rapidly out of his mouth. He clapped his hands. A servant came.

" Coffee! Quick! " he barked at him. That was what the words meant, I think. " Don't be all day about it! "

I was by now as puzzled as he was. Silence fell between us. Suddenly, simultaneously, we both started again.

" The fact is, I felt——"

" Please, please, I am glad——"

Then we both stopped at the identical moment. We could not have done it better had we rehearsed it.

Lucas resolved the impasse. " If we had known you were here, we would have called on you the moment we got here."

" Please, I thought you would be so tired." The man's tone was really quite pitiable now. " I did not like I should disturb you."

Lucas looked me straight in the eye.

" There seems to have been some sort of misunderstanding," he said.

" Yes," I admitted hurriedly. " I think there has." I turned to the officer. " We're very glad to have the chance of seeing you. Sooner late than never. Ha! Ha! " I tittered.

He tittered, too. He thought that must be a good joke in our country. My two friends retained a cold silence. The cat awoke, rose and stretched out its legs, and arched its back. Then it walked delicately over the maps, sprang on to the officer's shoulder, and perched there, staring straight at us with amber eyes. The silence continued.

Then suddenly Jim gave tongue. " What about that goat? " he said shamelessly. I tried to freeze him with a stare, but he was not looking my way.

" I suppose your work here is awfully interesting," I hurried, trying to direct our host's mind from Jim's crassness. " All those maps and things."

" Very interesting," he confirmed. " Very interesting indeed." But his voice did not sound as if he found it as interesting as all that. " I make weather-reports. I have instruments. Look, here are charts."

The cat lightly crawled round the back of his neck and perched on his other shoulder. We crowded round his table, and looked at his charts. He went on explaining about the weather in Sinai, and his charts, and his instruments, for a long time. He went on so long that he not only exceeded our interest in the subject, but his own. I had an uncomfortable feeling long before he finished that he had no interest in the subject at all. He merely wanted to hear himself talk.

No, that wasn't quite it. It was very puzzling. Coffee came in the middle of his recital. It was quite good, but we had other things to think about than coffee. Did I say that he finished talking about weather-reports? He did not finish. He tapered off. Then he stopped in the middle of a sentence. He was aware there was a certain listlessness in the atmosphere. The cat was sitting in his lap now. He had been stroking it rhythmically for many minutes. His hand paused midway along the beast's back.

" What? " he thrust over. " Did the young gentleman say a goat? "

You might have thought Jim had delivered himself of the ungracious thought not five seconds ago.

He had heard the word, after all. I had not succeeded in suffocating it. Why did he revive it at this moment? He seemed, so to speak, to be keeping it in cold storage. Why? Did he feel it might be useful when he had got all the goodness out of Sinai weather?

" Yes," said Jim clear as a bell. " I said a goat."

Once more I launched a gorgon stare which failed of its mission.

" You see," I explained, " we are not sure when we can pick up provisions again. We had an idea, if we could pick up a goat——"

" Oh a *goat*! " said the officer. " A goat will be here quite soon ! I will ask for a goat ! "

As before, he clapped his hands. His servant came in. " A

goat, quick! " he ordered. Or I suppose he did. You might have thought the plain of Kuntilla was black with goats.

The servant withdrew, and we got down to conversation again. He began to tell us about the time when Kuntilla had been quite a gay place, almost a metropolis. At all events, not only was the establishment of troops a lot bigger, but it was a market-place at which the Beduin from the plateau westward and from Akaba eastward got together and exchanged their goods. That had stopped in 1929, when a treaty with the Emir Abdullah made it unnecessary to hold the place strongly. Even Nekhl had been something of a place once. In fact, it used to be the provincial capital till the time the Turks took it in 1915. They didn't leave much of it; then El Arish became the capital in 1919. And it was all over.

He sighed. It was odd to think of Nekhl and Kuntilla in terms of metropolitan gaiety. He began to tell us about himself. He was an officer of the regular Egyptian army. He was stationed out here for a term of four years, with only two months leave per year.

The goat did not arrive.

Then he began to tell us about his grandfather. His grandfather had gone to the place every year since he was sixteen. A good Muslim is supposed to go to the place as often as he can manage it. His grandfather died on pilgrimage to the place. He told us a lot about his grandfather, and something about Mohammed and Mecca, though he managed to avoid referring to these two by their names.

Still the goat did not arrive.

He changed the conversation. He talked about his Seleuci, out in the yard there. He was very devoted to his Seleuci. To his cat also. The Seleuci was named Fiqs. He was very good at catching rabbits. Had we seen any rabbits on the way back from Ain Kadeis? There were plenty. There were gazelles about, too. But they were with young. They were not moving about much.

Slowly, devotedly, the hand moved along the cat's spine from the neck to the tail, then back to the neck again. It was

DESERT LEGION

as if that cat were his father and mother, his wife and children.

Then suddenly the truth flooded my mind like a switched-on lamp. That cat *was* his father and mother, his wife and children—that cat and Fiqs, the Seleuci hound. He was lonely, he was the loneliest man in all Sinai, in all Asia. He hugged his loneliness to himself like a hair-shirt. That was why he had not sent a message to us, suggesting we might meet and have coffee together. He was aching for our company, for any-body's company, except the company of these blackamoors that Fate had so foully thrust on him, for four long years, four whole years here in Kuntilla, the dewless burning nadir of the world. He was aching for our company, but he would do nothing about it. Nobody would do anything about it. The three westerners, who might have mitigated his appalling loneliness, with whom he might have held converse as gentle-men do with their social and intellectual equals, would come and go like a pool of mirage-water on the desert plain.

But he reckoned without Mustapha, whose exquisite tact rose to every occasion as infallibly as warm air rises. So he had got us after all. Well, there we were. He would not let us go without a struggle. He talked and talked, stroking the cat hypnotically, like a lama rotating a prayer-wheel. I now realized why his face was such a mask. If once he let his thoughts rise to the surface, it would crack like a bruised mirror.

There was nothing about his condition he did not resent. He resented the men in his charge because they were at once his inferiors, being Sudanese Negroes, and his equals, being Muslim like himself. He resented the British officers who held similar positions elsewhere. Being British, they were not troubled by any doubts of their own innate superiority, with the consequence that their men would do anything for them, they adored them. As for himself, he was only allowed to inflict punishment up to three days without pay, which he was always ready to do as an officer, but could not bring himself to do as a Muslim. After all, had they not wives and families? It was not the Prophet's will that innocent women and

Gc

children should suffer for the misdeeds of husbands and
fathers.

I was beginning to feel a little impatient, even a little
anxious. It was a long way to Akaba. We had serious problems to consider when we got there. The voice droned on and
on. It was like someone suddenly realizing he could play a
musical instrument a lot better than he had imagined.

He was telling us about a brother officer in the Egyptian
army. Even his brother officer let him down. The officer in
question had arranged to come and stay with him some time
this week. He had even got a chicken in for him. And then
the officer sent a message to say he was getting married.
Did we think that any English officer——

" If I might interrupt——" I quivered.

His manners were perfect. He stopped at once, and
gestured towards me with his free hand. " Please ! "

" Perhaps that goat . . . is it possible to find out——"

" The man will be here any moment now," he assured us.
Had we seen those women breaking up lumps of camel-dung
for the undigested seeds they contained? There were about a
dozen of them, all widows, or deserted women, with several
children apiece. They were the most wretched creatures
in Sinai. They were like lizards, sleeping in holes in the
ground, or under rocks. It was the reduction of the number
of troops in Kuntilla that had brought them to this pass.
His own soldiers fed them with what scraps they could
afford. But orders could easily be issued from Cairo or El
Arish——

It must have been the mention of El Arish. I remembered
that Mustapha and Hassan and Mohammed were not posted
to us indefinitely. They had to report themselves back in
El Arish by a certain date. I remembered this was Kuntilla,
not Mount Pisgah. There was still some ground to cover on
our journey.

I suddenly found myself on my feet. I put out my hand on
the table to steady myself.

" I'm sorry, sir," I said thickly. " I'm afraid we really

must set out for Akaba immediately. We'll have to drop that matter of the goat."

There was finality in my voice. He was silent for several seconds. The idea that we were going to leave him, and very soon, too, sank deeper and deeper. Then he sighed heavily.

"Very well, gentlemen, I am sorry that you should go. I will see still once more about that goat."

He lifted the cat from his lap and placed it on the weather-charts. Then he rose and went over to the doorway and clapped his hands. A man came. A brief conversation followed. Then he turned to us.

"I am sorry," he said, "it has not been possible to find a goat yet. But I insist. That chicken which I had bought for my friend—he shall not have it if he comes now. I have given orders. It is tied on the back of your car." He returned to his chair and stationed himself behind his table. The cat immediately clambered up again on to his left shoulder, and squatted there.

"Please, please!" we assured him. "We couldn't dream of robbing you! No! We would be very unhappy!"

He waved his hand. "I have given orders!"

"Good-bye!" I said. "It really has been most kind of you to entertain us! As for that chicken——"

"Good-bye!" said Jim.

"Good-bye!" said Lucas.

"Good-bye!" the officer said.

He sat down at his table almost before we were out of the room. We descended the two steps and stumbled over the Seleuci again. We hurried across the courtyard. We could see one of our cars drawn up outside the entrance, the men standing beside it. Then I stopped.

"One moment!" I said. I turned and retraced my steps across the courtyard. The others stared open-mouthed after me.

I climbed the two steps again. I was in the officer's room. He was sitting at the table, his chin on his breast, his two arms stretched before him.

" Excuse me ! " I whispered.

" Yes? " He did not raise his head.

" You did not send out for a goat? "

" No ! "

" There are no goats? "

" No ! "

" Forgive me. I think I understand." I waited for a moment or two, but he said nothing more, so I crept quietly out of the room and joined the others.

" Look ! " said Jim.

He took me round to the back of the car and showed me a peaked looking fowl tied by its legs to the tarpaulin lashings. I never saw a more hostile eye. Its hold on life seemed of the most precarious, yet there never was in any fowl's eye an expression of more intense hostility.

" I wonder if it will get so far as Akaba," I mused.

" Don't you think we ought to eat it now," asked Jim, " and take no chances? "

I thought it would be better to move on.

CHAPTER FIVE

"TO Akaba, Mustapha!" I said.

"*Aiua!*" he replied, smiling all over his face. I was, perhaps, just a trifle disappointed. I had expected his good humour to be tinged with a slight sadness. I was, after all, ordering him to the frontier, where we were to part company, he and his men to return to El Arish, ourselves to plunge forward into the unknown. We might, or might not, find a car waiting for us in Akaba; but whether we did, or did not, our escort had instructions to deposit us at the frontier and turn back. We had hoped they might take us some distance along the Arabah, but the Arabah belongs for half its length to Palestine, and the other half to Transjordan; the passage of two Egyptian armed cars up the wadi, we were informed, might lead to international complications. The idea of the gentle Mustapha provoking international complications became more grotesque from day to day as we got to know him better. However, there it was. This was our last journey with Mustapha, and Hassan, and Mohammed. They would be leaving us in a few hours now. It was all rather sad.

But Mustapha did not look a bit sad, there under the walls of the fortress of Kuntilla. He looked like a Boy Scout who has done his good deed for the day, and in the excitement has forgotten to tuck his shirt in. I got into the car between Hassan and Lucas. Mustapha gave one more look at the chicken tied up on the back of the car, and took the wheel. Jim and Mohammed got in beside him.

The mirages were more than usually impertinent that day. They came almost up to the wheels of the car, licking the ground like animals. We looked back to the twin hillocks of Kuntilla, and saw them floating in glassy waves. For many miles the track followed the shallow wadis of el Beidha and el Agheidara, where there may have been water once for wandering Israelites to drink of, and there still was, but it would have slaked no thirst. Range after range of small pointed hills came near to us, and closed in behind as we moved forward. At last we began to climb from the plateau level towards that final escarpment which buttresses Et Tih from collapse into the Arabah. Now, too, as we climbed, we rose from monochrome into colour. Ashen grey flushed into deep purple, and suddenly, as we came out upon the summit of Gebel Safra, we beheld high over the invisible Arabah, the far tops of the mountains of Moab misty blue in the sun haze. As if to leave our senses freer to enjoy that superb parade, we now came out upon a speed-track, over which we careered, for I did not register how many kilometres at how many to the hour. The surface of the track was some sort of bituminous material, so carefully, as it seemed, sprinkled over with sand, you might have thought the groundsmen of some Sinai Brooklands had been preparing the ground for an attempt on records.

" Holla! Holla! " the three Negroes in the car shouted at each other. The engines, too, sang happily. It was as if these were the golden minutes they had been waiting for during all the long tooth-rattling days between Suez and Akaba. No speed-limit, no pedestrians, no crossings, no car overtaking or to overtake—I am inclined to think that for the motorist who can show a completely stainless record at the end of his days, some such track as this must be laid up as his reward in Heaven.

At length the smooth dream petered out into a coarse awakening. The cars shivered to their back-axles, as they entered again into the old routine of jerk and bump and jolt. We came now to the head of the Southland, the Ras el Negeb, where a small Camel Corps station looks west to the broad plateau and east towards the imminent downrush into the Arabah. We dismounted to stretch our limbs while our men exchanged news with their colleagues. A pointed jar of water lay on its side near the doorway. Above the door someone had tacked up a handsome piece of white coral.

" *Thalassa!* " I cried. " We're almost at the sea's edge already ! "

Lucas made an unconscious gesture towards his coat. He cannot hear the word " sea " without wanting to strip then and there.

" The chicken is still with us? " I asked.

" Yes ! " replied Jim. He had already satisfied himself on the point. The bird had started out pale ginger. It was now pale dust-coloured. It had not stood the journey at all well, though the rancour in its eye was unabated.

" Couldn't we put it out of its misery? " I asked.

The others thought not. A dead bird would not wear very well in that great heat. Nor could we leave it behind, dead or alive. The men would think we were very ungrateful. Besides, we might need it before the day was over. The poor creature would have to jog on with us.

" Pretty ! " said Jim. He had walked over to the piece of coral above the door. " These fellows like to have their place looking nice, don't they? "

" I don't think that's the idea ! Coral's for luck ! They think bad luck will be splintered on the points ! "

" Luck? " said Jim hastily. " What ought I to do? "

" Don't do anything : it's just there ! "

" I'll touch it, to make sure ! "

We were quite pleased he touched it, before the drive was over.

A little distance beyond the Ras el Negeb, the road ricochets down a series of rocky ravines, then suddenly, as with a single explosion, the whole world cannonades into colossal beauty. Rearward the velvet-brown slopes of the Et Tih plateau are smothered in the folds of pinnacled red ranges of porphyry crag. Immediately below, the hills break desperately down into the gulf of Akaba, which is less like water than the blue steam of the boiling of the central places of the world. Beyond the gulf is flung in an enormous semicircle the great arc of the Transjordan hills. There is Mount Seir. Southward is Arabia. It is as if the Bible of the Hebrews and the Koran of

the Muslims had been expressed in rock, and the titan books
lay spread open side by side.

The descent began not many yards beyond the post. It is
not a gradual descent. The road plunges down in a series of
leaps like a waterfall. I would have liked the surface to have
been a little better tended, the hairpin bends to have been not
quite so violent, the precipices to have been slightly less
terrifying. I am not too confident a passenger even on Rich-
mond Hill. The whole time colour boomed and flashed like
a bombardment, far off the rose-pink and plum-blue of the
mountains of Arabia, deep down below the purple mist of
Akaba, on either hand the crimson and burnt ochre and golden
yellow of the upper and lower precipices.

It was not a simple situation. I wanted to savour the beauty
and splendour of it all, but I could not help anxiously studying
the surface of the road and peering down into the ravines.
It was when all of these were most disturbing that I perceived
something had gone wrong with the car. Hassan was bent
forward over the hand-brake, tugging away quite desperately.
Judging from the fact that the car was accelerating, and we
were at that moment negotiating a ferocious hairpin bend,
I concluded that the foot-brake, too, was not working
properly. Hassan was emitting a series of short sharp
grunts. The blood-vessels were standing out like cords under
the stretched skin of his gleaming face. Then we started
skidding.

Hassan's attention was so completely held by the jammed
hand-brake that he forgot about the steering-wheel. We cannot have been more than an inch or two from the crumbling
edge of the precipice, when Lucas overcame that correct
scruple which should almost always prevent a passenger from
butting in on the steering of a car during a moment of danger.
He flashed over his left hand, screwed the steering-wheel
round, then round again as we concluded the hairpin, and
we were careering in comparative safety down a straightish
stretch of road. A minute or so later we came to a halt in a
sort of saucer among the hills. The radiator was boiling like

a huge samovar. The front brake was giving off a smell like a hot garbage pail. We dismounted, Hassan by the left-hand door, we two by the right. Hassan stood looking the other way for a minute or two, having a word or two with his Maker. I turned to Lucas.

"That coral!" I said. "A jolly good thing Jim touched that coral!"

"I had something to do with it, too!" Lucas pointed out.

"Oh yes," I agreed. "You were helpful, too!"

Hassan came round from the other side of the car, and said "*Quais!*" rather sheepishly, showing all his teeth.

A minute later Mustapha's car swung round into view from the upper parts of the mountain. He coasted down to within thirty yards of us, then put his brake on. Mustapha and Mohammed tumbled out of the car and hurried over towards us. We were a very Hebraic spectacle, a pillar of fire and cloud. Hassan delivered his report. Mustapha beamed with pleasure.

"*Quais, quais,* Mistel Lucas!" he exclaimed.

Unfortunately, in his concern over all the fire and cloud we were emitting, Mustapha had neglected to put on his own hand-brake properly. A cry from Mohammed made us turn our heads. The second car was coming straight for the first car, with its bonnet down, like a bull for a matador. Between the car and ourselves Jim had been sauntering down. He, too, turned at Mohammed's cry, did a record sprint, vaulted into the driver's seat, switched round the wheel, and put on the hand-brake. The car stopped within an inch or two of the other.

"*Quais! Quais! Quais! Quais!*" roared the three Negroes. They clapped their hands and jumped with excitement. They were devoted to Jim. He could hardly tie his shoe-lace without evoking their enthusiasm. Jim blushed like the boy who gets all the medals at a school sports day. He murmured something about the piece of coral.

"Anyhow," I pointed out, "it means we can still boil that chicken whole. We won't need to eat it mashed."

During the next thirty minutes, everybody threw water at the sizzling brake-parts, wheel-linings and other inflamed sections of the mechanism. Then Mustapha gestured with the right hand towards the front car, the left hand towards the rear car, as if he were summoning us to our places in a Rolls Royce and Isotta Fraschini. The broad smile I had noted earlier once more enwreathed his face. I was disappointed. He seemed positively delighted he was about to dump us out on Akaba beach in not many minutes and turn his back on us. I sighed and took my place beside Hassan.

The descent continued with no mishap. The wild pageantry of shape and colour defiled again—the sulphur yellow, the rich orange, the poppy red, the cone, the dome, the tower, the pyramid. Here, in a Gothic niche, it seemed as if someone had draped a ruby-encrusted gold brocade before an altar. There, under a Muslim *mihrab*, the faithful had piled a memorial cairn. The wadi turned and twisted again, like a vast serpent with grey underside and painted flanks. Suddenly the serpent's flinty head hurled itself forward towards a blue dazzle. The wadi floor widened, as if the serpent, a cobra, had swelled out its hood on either side. We beheld mountains, but they were not near at hand, left and right; they were far off, not hard gold but soft lilac. They were the mountains of Arabia, with the twinkling waters of the Gulf of Akaba between. It looked almost as if the car once more were out of control, that it was bounding of its own will over the pebbles and shells to refresh its droughty tyres in the spray. Hassan braked at the water's edge. We got out.

We looked north and south, along the flank of the Sinai mountains. We looked east, across blue water to the mountains of Arabia. We looked down where we stood, on sea-things, lifeless or living. It was a lovely sight. " Glory! Glory! " we murmured. " Glory! "

The loveliness was not only in the sight, but in the sense of it all, the freshness, the wind-and-wateriness. It was like a deliverance. We had been constricted almost as tight as mummies in the car. The car had been constricted almost as tight as a sarcophagus within the painted walls of the long tomb of the wadi. We filled our lungs deep with the good air. We walked a few yards forward and stooped and flung the good water over our heads. Hassan followed and courteously imitated the rite. His turban prevented him from anointing his head. Instead, he moistened two fingers in the wave and then passed them over his lips. Once again I perceived how much more civilized his behaviour was than ours, on the hither side of an abrupt line. On the further side, he was as civilized as a puma or a forest fire.

I turned to Lucas. " ' And they journeyed from Abronah, and pitched in Ezion-geber.' Here we are in Ezion-geber. Do you remember? " Even as I spoke, the odd sense of the livingness and nearness of the host of Israel came upon me, as very rarely either before or later on the journey. He did not seem to have heard me. " Do you remember? " I asked again.

He turned. His eyes were quite urgent. " No! " he said. " I don't want to remember! " He stretched his arms out towards the mountains and the sea. " Not now! This is enough for me! "

He was right. I must not be so implacable. They were my people, not his. If I looked and listened hard, I would hear the women going out from the tents to collect drift-wood for the cooking-fires; I would see the lads spreading out north and south to find out how near there was fresh water. I shut my eyes hard to exclude them from my imagination; there were more immediate claims upon it.

Then I heard two words, the first low-pitched, the second higher, recurring in a sing-song refrain. " Arabah! Akaba! Arabah! Akaba! " It was Lucas humming to himself, as he stripped his garments. He had been slow about it, if anything. It usually took him fewer seconds to start undressing, when he came up against water.

Arabah, Akaba! On our left hand, a few kilometres away, the wall of mountain tumbled, like top-heavy masonry, into a plain. It was not a plain, but the mouth of a broad wadi, the wadi Arabah. The heat seemed to be sliding along the wadi-bed, like the ice of a glacier, and to thrust forward a blunt head on to the foreshore. Beyond the wadi, a shaggy arc of blackness thickened for a kilometre or two the white curve of the gulf-head. That was the oasis of Akaba. The small town of Akaba ran backwards for a little through a rift in the arc of palm-trees and spread out a few pale cubes of building left and right along the sea. Above Akaba the mountains sprang again, northward to flank the Arabah and southward to make the coast of Arabia. In between lay the lovely waters, like the supernal pavement seen on Mount Sinai, " a paved work of sapphire stone, and as it were the very heaven for clearness." Nearer the head of the gulf, where they were shallow, they were pale sapphire. Where we stood, where they were wider and deeper, a transverse wind was blowing, freshening the lazuline stuff with thin white veinings.

Lucas was ankle-deep out in the water, making a great splashing.

" Are you coming in? " he cried. " It's grand! "

Then suddenly a freshet of wind slapped the water and turned a vatful round upon itself, so that the underside of the wave gleamed white and fleshy.

" Sharks! " I cried at the top of my voice. My mind was aware in one moment with a shoal of sharks. I don't think anyone had mentioned the Gulf of Akaba to us without bringing up the subject of sharks quite quickly.

" Sharks! " cried Hassan in his own tongue. " *Qurush! Qurush!* "

At that moment, the second car drew up with its bonnet facing the waters, and Mustapha and Mohammed tumbled out precipitately and shouted " Sharks! Sharks! " Really, you would have thought they were packed belly to belly in the Gulf of Akaba, like sardines.

Lucas did not believe they were anything like so numerous, or, if they were, that they were as dangerous as they are generally made out to be. He had once dived from a transport outside Aden, he told me, and seen a couple of sharks approaching; so he did a specially fierce crab-crawl, and the poor creatures turned and slunk off with their tails between their fins. However, there in the Gulf of Akaba, after all that uproar, he did not think it would be courteous to go out any distance. He waded out another yard or two, splashed himself all over, and came out.

Mustapha drew a deep breath. He was immensely relieved. It would have been too tragic if, having looked after his three Englishmen so devotedly all the way to Transjordan, he had only two, or perhaps two and a half, to hand over at the frontier-post.

" *Mish quais, qurush!* " he observed, and shook his head.

" Have you got a handkerchief ? " asked Lucas.

" No," I said. " Let the sun dry you." Then I added with a sigh: " Take your time about it. They'll be leaving us soon enough, in any case."

Our faces were getting gloomier moment by moment.

" It's a pity," I said. " They've been grand."

" Well," said Lucas. " We can't do anything about it."

" We'll never see them again," said Jim brokenly.

" At all events," I observed, with a slight touch of asperity, " it doesn't seem to worry them very much. I hope the other car's arrived."

" Which one? " asked Jim.

" The one from Amman. The one we telephoned for from Suez."

" Oh of course," remembered Jim. Then, " I should doubt it," he added lugubriously, looking across the sweep of the beach to Akaba dim in the heat-haze. " It doesn't look as if there's been a car there since the time of Julius Caesar."

This was no time to point out the various historic improprieties of the remark.

" It looks very hot over there," I admitted. " I hope we don't have to hang about too long."

" We can bathe," said Lucas.

" I don't know." I did not share his contempt for sharks. " Are you ready? "

"I'm ready."

I went over to Mustapha. The smile was still all over his face. "Let's start!" I ordered a trifle curtly.

"*Quais!*" He climbed into his car with Jim and Hassan following. Jim's expression was a little like that of a corpse going into its hearse. Mustapha reversed a few yards then turned his bonnet, not northward toward Akaba and the heat-haze, toward the two frontier-posts, toward the car that might not be there, but southward, toward the unknown, toward the fresh wind blowing along the Sinai coast. He leaned out from under the hood and grinned at us mischievously.

"Where?" I cried. "Where?"

"Rest-house!" Mustapha said, and drove on.

I turned bewildered to Hassan.

"Rest-house?" I asked. "Rest-house?"

Hassan, too, was grinning happily. It was evident they were all in some little secret together.

"*Aiua!*" he confirmed. "Taba!"

"Taba?" I turned to Lucas. "Did anybody ever tell us of a rest-house at Taba on the shore of Akaba? Where's Taba?"

"It won't do anyone any harm," said Lucas, "if they keep a private rest-house all of their own at Taba, wherever that might be. We'll see if it's on the map."

It was on the map, some four or five kilometres away. The map named a wadi Taba, and a well, Bir Taba, at the mouth of it, on the sea. A wadi, and a well, and a rest-house.

"Rest-house at Taba!" I breathed delightedly. "That's what Mustapha's been grinning about all day long! Perhaps it isn't really there at all," I speculated. "He'll just shake a stick at the bare ground when he gets there, and abracadabra, there it is!"

"It's going to be very convenient," said Lucas, a more practical person. "It's good to know we've got a base of operations, till we know where we are at Akaba."

A shadow fell across my sky. Akaba was in Transjordan. There had been a police-officer who had advised against Mr.

Golding's entry into Transjordan. There had been a distinguished statesman—I shut my eyes hard and opened them again into bright blue sky. I would have no truck with shadows.

" —Unless those pernicious frontiers make things too awkward," Lucas was continuing. " Besides, we can bathe before we set out and bathe when we come back."

" And we'll be able to cook that poor chicken," I pointed out. I would be pleased to have it cooked, not because of the joy I expected from it, but because the thing would be much happier dead than alive . . . if it was still alive.

A pang of doubt assailed me. I walked round to the back of the car. It was still alive. I walked back again, and on the brief journey, a thought of another order struck me.

" A well! " I said. " There's bound to be palm-trees there! "

" That's not unlikely! " said Lucas. It was, after all, a natural association of ideas.

" Elath! " I cried. " Don't you see? Elath! "

The smell of the sea had muffled in his nostrils the scent of the Conqueror's tracks.

" What about Elath? "

" Don't you remember? ' So we passed by from our brethren the children of Esau, which dwell in Seir——' " I paused a moment and turned towards the wine-red hulk of the Transjordan range. " And that is Seir! " I said. I started again. "' So we passed by from our brethren, the children of Esau, which dwelt in Seir, from the way of the Arabah——' " I stopped once more. " And that is the Arabah! " I pointed out. It gave me a curious and deep pleasure to wed the sight of those places with the names written down for them long ago in the Book. "' —from the way of the Arabah,' " I concluded, "' from Elath and from Ezion-geber.' "

" Yes? "

" We know that both Elath and Ezion-geber were at the head of the Gulf of Akaba. The text makes it clear they were not one place, but two places."

"Meistermann suggests there could only have been one port at the head of a narrow gulf."

"It doesn't follow in the least. There are ports on each bank of the River Tyne; the Manchester Ship Canal, too. They're both narrower than the Gulf of Akaba."

"Go on."

"Elath is the same word as Elim . . . Strong trees, that is, trees that withstand the desert, palm-trees."

"Yes?"

"Elath is Taba!"

"Because there may be palm-trees there?" He did not look convinced.

"Prove that Elath is *not* Taba," I demanded truculently.

He made a gesture of surrender. I turned to Hassan.

"Come, Hassan!" I demanded. "Take us to Elath-Taba!"

So for five kilometres or more the cars trundled along the narrow space between cliff and sea, skirting the lean headlands. The mountains along this length of shore are of a reddish granite, criss-crossed with bold bands of deep red porphyry and black basalt. It gave them a curiously vertebrate appearance; (and it is exactly for that reason that the Hebrews called the port at the head of the gulf, *Ezion-geber*—Giant's Spine). The shore was powdered with miraculous shells. It was hard to refrain now and again from giving the wheel a twist so as to avoid crushing some shining beauty, though I was aware it would only mean the ruin of another twenty at least its equal. It is the same impulse which makes you walk zigzag through a glade of bluebells.

Then, turning round a headland steeper than the others, we came upon Taba. The rest-house was on our right hand, overhung by the sheltered side of the cliff, with its doorsteps almost in the cool water. But it was Taba we saw first. The line of hills was withdrawn a half-kilometre or so, where the wadi's waters had scooped them out, leaving a broad arena of stony beach. At the centre of the arena was a well, Bir Taba, parapeted by a few feet of stout masonry. Over the

Beach-Combers

well rose a bold clump of dom-palms; there was another clump some distance away, under the hills.

Beyond the palms and the well the southern hills were beginning to take on the crimson flush of sunset. The ledges of shadow turned from the sun were like planed shelves of ebony. The coloured waters were hissing close under our wheels.

" Elath! " I murmured blissfully. " Elath of the palm-trees! "

Lucas was looking round with something of the expression of an estate-agent.

" I don't see many traces of quays and breakwaters," he said.

" It's a long time ago," I pointed out. " Like Troy and Nineveh. And Kadesh-barnea. And what about those palm-trees? "

The palm-trees were certainly there.

Hassan had been waiting respectfully beside the right-hand door for the conclusion of the brief archaeological discussion. Then he untied the string from round the handle.

" Rest-house! " he exclaimed.

We turned our heads.

"Oh! " we exclaimed delightedly.

There it was, the green-painted magic box that Mustapha had summoned into existence, small and complete, with door-steps leading to a verandah, a central door, two windows on either side of the door, with shutters folded back against the wall. The first car was drawn up alongside. Mustapha and Jim were looking at brakes, Mohammed was unlashing the tarpaulin. We got down and approached the rest-house, our feet crunching over the pebbles. Mustapha straightened himself, and waved one hand towards the door. As if in direct response to that evocation, a creature took shape in the door-way. He emerged from the green gloom and slid towards the top of the steps, as if he moved by magic, not on human feet.

" *Farrash!* " said Mustapha, with a proprietary air, as one

Hc

might talk of a creature whom one could express into thin air again, by a reverse gesture of the hand. " Ali! "

Ali wore a knitted woollen skull-cap and a *djellabieh* a good many inches too long for him. He had a long greeny-khaki overcoat over his *djellabieh*, which trailed an inch or two on the ground. It looked as if he had not had time to get into his right clothes in the interval between the time Mustapha summoned him and the time he had to report on duty. His face was coal-black, his mouth was large, scarlet and slightly lop-sided, like two petals of poinsettia. His eyes had a greenish tinge and goggled from the sockets. He had some sort of pink sea-campion thrust over his left ear. He looked not unlike Petrushka, at the door of that enchanted rest-house. If Mustapha had been able to produce Petrushka, perhaps he was going to produce the Magician, too, to start Petrushka's arms and legs jigging to the orchestra. But Mustapha produced no Magician. There was no other orchestra than the sea fiddling among the rocks. The *farrash* bent low, crossing his arms over his chest. The excessive sleeves of his khaki coat dangled on either side.

Introductions followed. Ali bent lower, till his forehead almost touched the ground.

" One time in Camel Corps," explained Mustapha, but he had the air of giving a not too satisfactory explanation of a purely magical phenomenon. " Come! " commanded Mustapha.

Ali went off with him to help unload the cars. Lucas and I entered and examined the rest-house. The door opening off the verandah led into a small living-room, with a table and chairs, and a big cupboard with a wire-netting door. The cupboard contained teapots and crockery and cutlery and a shoe-horn, all so spick and span it looked like a music-hall conjurer's stock. From the living-room a bedroom, with real beds, opened on either side. The reality of the beds did not in the least mitigate the sense of magic that invested everything we did or touched while we were in Taba. The left-hand bedroom looked out towards the palm-trees of Elath.

" This is my bedroom," I said. The place was so close up against the sea, so full of the sound and scent of it, you could almost feel it was built out on piles over the water.

A minute or two later Jim entered. " It's good-bye, chicken ! " he informed us. He put his hands round his throat and emitted an expressive noise. " It won't take them long," he added. " The *farrash* asked for some petrol."

I did not like the thought of a chicken boiled in petrol, but I was assured that was to make the fire burn quicker. I was relieved to think the chicken was no more. It had had a long day. We put out our things, then stepped out to the water's edge. The golden lights on the Arabian hills were almost all extinguished now. The primrose-yellows and lilacs and shivering greens of the sunset were fading from the peaks southward. Sunset went completely. The gulf was without light or form, a swinging mass of soft sound.

" I'm getting hungry," Jim said.

The four Negroes were bent over a spindly fire in a sort of kitchen out-house. We could see them bending to and fro, making strange gesticulations, as if they felt it necessary to propitiate the ghost of that outraged chicken.

The cliff hung black and immediate over us. The stars momently stoked up their pulsing fires. Venus moved mellowly along the sky sending out five clear radiations, like the tinsel star of a Christmas card. Then the dark silhouette of a mountain engulfed it, as a tarn engulfs a dropped stone.

" I'm hungry, too," I said. I had been hungry a long time. " That chicken's very slow about it."

We watched the progress of another planet. It may have been Jupiter. The planet moved very slowly across a great tract of sky.

" I'm very hungry indeed," I said.

I went over to the group in the mystic hut. The *farrash* was turned away from me. He was stirring a basin of rather scuddy water with a piece of driftwood. A gnarled object lay half-submerged in the water, with strange protrusions that looked like more driftwood. The chicken was certainly putting up a good fight. I touched the *farrash* on the shoulder. " When? " I asked gently.

He turned round with such a start he very nearly upended the basin on to the already uncertain fire. His eyes swivelled in the sockets like yellow marbles.

" Soon, soon! " promised Mustapha. He uttered a syllable or two to console Ali. It was clear he would like me to leave them to it. I went back and joined the others in the contemplation of the skies. The supply of planets had given out, so we watched the stars, wheeling in their more unhasty movements. After a time, Ali brought a lamp over from the out-house and hung it above the verandah. We sat down and waited. But the chicken still held out, so we crawled about on all fours within the half-circle of the lamp's beams, having turned our attention from stars to shells. Even in that limited area we could find shells strange enough in form and lovely enough in colour to enchant us. Each of us made a small collection for himself, piling it up at a jealous interval from his neighbour's. The lamp cozened into its orbit a number of creatures, some of which one could anticipate, others not. There came moths first, blundering heavy and fatal against the metal circlets round the lamp. Then a dog came, more silent than the moths, a sort of Seleuci, if he was earthly dog at all. He sniffed at each one of us in turn, but not audibly, then went back into the night again. Then came another ghost, this time with a mortal appearance. He was, in fact, mortal, for we saw him again next day, though next day again he was as silent as the moths and the dog. He was deaf and dumb, and very old, wrinkled like a scorched leaf and brown as a betel-nut. He wore a white rag for a head-cloth, and a piece of sacking over his shoulders. It looked as if Mustapha had done another bit of magic for us, rather casually, to entertain us while the chicken entered the last stage. The old man advanced out of the darkness towards us, holding a large mother-of-pearl shell on the outstretched palm of each hand. He had evidently noted we were interested in such litter, and hoped to touch our strange taste to the tune of a millieme or two. We removed the shells from his outstretched palms and placed a piastre or two on each. At once he recoiled into the darkness again, as a dog does with a meaty bone, of which he fears he can only have been given it by accident. Only the moths remained with us, and the stars, and the sound of the water.

Then at last Mustapha came over to us. " Chicken ready ! " he announced, still a shade anxiously, I thought. We ate the chicken, and I could not help feeling it was less a victory than an armistice. We also had some tinned young potatoes and tinned peas, and in a glass of brandy and warm water drank the health of the kind officer of the fortress at Kuntilla, who had provided the main item of our supper. There was not much meat on the bones really, and the bones tasted like drift-wood, but we were hungry, and enjoyed it a good deal.

We went to bed. The others slept, I think, but I did not. I did not want to cease being conscious. I was conscious of the sea so close that my heart-beats seemed to direct the rhythm it was moving to. I was conscious of the stars hardly any further away. The earth itself, its mountains and deserts, seemed a small round thing suspended between two substances of an order different from itself, stars above and seas below. I was conscious of the Host of Israel, a thin line of animalculae, as it were, stretched out upon a minute arc of this small round globe. I heard a voice, not distinguishable from the voice of the waters swinging in the void below, telling again the tale of the wanderings of the Host of Israel.

" So we passed by from our brethren the children of Esau, which dwell in Seir, from the way of the Arabah from Elath and from Ezion-geber."

Elath of the palm-trees. I raised myself on my pillow and looked through the window towards the palm-trees in the midst of the wide wadi, standing over Bir Taba, the well

Taba. The shutters had not been brought to. The palm-trees stood out sharply, their leaves nailed like swords on the black stuff of the night.

We got up in intense blue daylight and bathed. Lucas looked round and said it was not good weather for sharks, as one might say it is, or is not, good weather for trout. The episode at Aden seemed to have endowed Lucas with some authority on sharks, their habits and customs. I asked if he meant that weather which was not good for sharks was good for bathers. He said that was so, so I, too, bathed. Lucas went out of his depth, Jim went in up to his waist, I went in up to my knees. Then we came out and basked in the sun, and piled up more shells. We received the generous assistance of Mustapha, Mohammed and Hassan, and the more expert collaboration of Ali and the aged deaf and dumb beach-comber with whom we had established a transitory and somewhat bat-like contact the night before.

We should have moved on to Akaba immediately after breakfast, but were in no mood to do so. We knew we should have been there yesterday, in fact, for Mustapha and the two cars were expected back in El Arish and the car from Amman might be awaiting us. That could wait, a few days if necessary. But could El Arish wait, at all events without grave displeasure?

We stretched our limbs out happily to the sun. If El Arish chose to enlist wizards and warlocks in the personnel of the Camel Corps, it was their own look-out.

We stretched out the maps and books on the pebbles, and studied again this matter of Elath and Ezion-geber. The scholars were agreed, on the whole, to place the site of Ezion-geber on this side of the gulf and have the site of Elath on the other, nearer to the existing village of Akaba. It is true there are scattered ruins found to this day in the sand of the wadi Arabah, north and slightly west of the gulf-head; it is true also that brings them a little nearer to the "Giant's Spine" which extends between the gulf-head and Taba. But there are ruins also on the other side of the gulf-head, north and slightly east of the present Akaba.[1] The Giant's Spine would have impressed itself even more on the imaginations of those living opposite than those living under it. It seemed to me quite logical to reverse the scholars' order, to place Ezion-geber north and east of Akaba and Elath opposite, at the mouth of the Arabah . . . perhaps even a few kilometres further down, as far as the palm-trees of Taba.

For this reason, too. They point out that in early Muslim records the two names are linked together. For a time we read of Akaba-Eyleh, the name of a station on the *haj* route. The name means quite simply Mount Eyleh. Then the name " Eyleh " drops out. We read of Akaba alone, henceforth, the Mountain.[2] The Mountain may have been the one by which the pilgrims went up into Transjordan out of the Arabah. In that case Eyleh, or Elath, was on the eastern side of the gulf, near the present village of Akaba. But it may also have been that other Mountain, the one by which they descended from Et Tih into the Arabah. In that case, Eyleh was on the western side, perhaps our own Taba.

It is in Deuteronomy we meet the name Elath first. It is in the way of the Arabah, and belongs to the kinsmen of the host of Israel, " the children of Esau, which dwell in Seir." We learn in Samuel that David conquered the land of Edom; that was some time in the eleventh century B.C. But the place is not named again till Kings, where we read that Solomon " made a navy of ships in Ezion-geber, which is beside Eloth, on the shore of the Red Sea, in the land of Edom." It is Ezion-geber where the shipyards are. It may be that Eloth, or Elath, was the place for the leisured folk, the rich farmers and

---

[1] Since the time of writing, Dr. Nelson Glueck has definitely established the site of Ezion-geber at Tel el Kheleifeh, some half-mile north of the shore. He has found, not only a great number of copper spear-heads and fish-hooks, but even the very ropes used to tether King Solomon's ships to the bollards.

[2] From Professor Yahuda I derive the following meanings of "Akaba": In classical Arabic, " a difficult way in the mountains "; in Palestinian Arabic, " a bridge over a wadi "; in modern Egyptian Arabic, " a ship decorated with flags, used in a Nile festival."

the overseers. Certainly the air in Taba, protected by the Giant's Spine from the oven-heats of the Arabah, is fresher than the air in Akaba. Thereafter, the place has a troubled history. It doubtless played its part in the revolt of Edom against Joram, when " Edom revolted from under the hand of Judah, and made a king over themselves." It was recaptured by Azariah in the ninth century, only to be lost again half a century later to Rezin, King of Syria, who " recovered Elath, and drove the Jews out from Elath, and the Syrians came to Elath and dwelt there to this day." Nothing is known of the Syrian history of Elath. We do not hear of it till the time of the Romans. Josephus calls it Ailane, the pagan writers Aelana, whence they call these waters the Elanitic Gulf. It attains some importance as a frontier town and the seat of a bishopric, then nothing more is heard of it. In the Arab writers, it is nothing more than a name, Eyleh. Then the name goes, too. It is a ghost. It is Akaba. It is Taba. No man knows. In 1906 the Turks occupy the beach of Taba, the well, the palm-trees, though the place is clearly within the frontier of Egypt. The English object. The Turks go. So they bickered among themselves two thousand years ago, the Edomites and the Jews and the Syrians.

But only Ali is left of them all now, Mustapha's Ali, with the woollen cap and the greeny-khaki overcoat several inches too long for him. Only Ali's overcoat is left of all their panoply, the standards of their armies and the pennons of their ships.

CHAPTER SIX

§ 1

HAVING bathed, we collected shells, bathed again, and then had lunch. We were very hungry and cleared out most of our larder. Then we got the men to collect our things and pile up the car. We dared not delay any longer the transfer to Akaba.

Mustapha looked as if he would have preferred to keep our things at Taba, till he was quite sure we were satisfactorily placed elsewhere. I also like to think he wished to prolong our association till the last possible moment. But we had not done badly. He had magicked an extra day for us, and a sea-enchanted rest-house to spend it in. He and his men must hie them to El Arish. We must ourselves go forward in the steps of the Conqueror.

We said good-bye to Petrushka, standing in the centre of the verandah where we had first seen him, his huge overcoat trailing on the planks. Then we set out for Akaba, between rust-red cliffs and cornflower sea, this time in reverse tracing the huge articulations of the Giant's Spine. We passed the mouth of the wadi by which we had descended from the Et Tih plateau, and would not have distinguished it from the other wadi-mouths if Hassan had not pointed up towards the pass and made some dramatic play with his hand-brake. Some kilometre or two further the cliffs began to withdraw from the shore, and the Arabah became palpable, the walls of mountain on each side of the sterile plain protracting themselves northwards in huge knots and humps. The pebbly beach which had been our track till now dithered down into a region of gravel and rumpled earth, streaked here and there with a sort of coarse twitch-grass. Then, as we came out further from under the shadow of the hills towards the centre of the Arabah, the gravelly region smoothed down despite eddies and back-thrusts into a plain of yellow sand, almost as silky as the waters that flanked it. For the waters, too, had undergone a like sequence of modifications since we left Taba, like the earth, like the very air. The air had been fresh at Taba, we had entered into great heat on the fringe of the wadi, but there was still some movement in it. Here, in the centre of the wadi, the air was like hot glass. So at Taba the water had been quite choppy, a bright Prussian blue, very masculine, with the wind bringing it out in white weals. Then, when the shelter began to fail, it broke up into a hundred criss-crossing tracts of blue, like a vast blue nursery-garden where the seedsman had got out of hand. Here, finally, on our right hand, the water was a Madonna blue, fragile as egg-shells. Some distance away a fishing-boat floated in that pale blueness; it seemed literally floating like a cloud, rather than held by its own weight in substantial water. It was a fishing-boat, but the sort of fishing that was going on from it added to the dreamlikeness of its whole setting. Four or five men were at the oars, naked so far as we could see. A mast was up, but no sail. There was no wind to fill it. In the bow another man kneeled, curved like a bow. He seemed to be looking along the barrel of a gun, though it was probably no gun at all. For many seconds, for a minute or two at a stretch, the men remained immobile, bronze against blue, like a fresco of Puvis de Chavannes. Then we sighted a small cloud beyond the prow, hardly above water-level. The sound of the explosion reached our ears several seconds after the tranced stillness was shaken into a quicksilver flurry of movement. One of the men had jumped into the water, he was struggling quite fiercely with something, a huge fish, we saw a second or two later. The other men leaned over, hauled in the man and fish, there was a quick downward thrust with an oar or a bar to abate the fish's struggles. A few seconds later, the breathless dream prevailed again, the painted men at the oars, the painted man in the bow. Leftward, across that hyaline stretch of water, the arc of the black palm-trees of Akaba fringed its meed of shore. At right-angles from the line of palm-trees a

line of white cubes thrust inward. It was the one street of
Akaba, height and width without substance, a sequence of
theatre properties to make a South Sea setting, wheeled in by
supers, shortly to be wheeled out again.

That was Akaba. Akaba was Transjordan. It looked sleepy,
too tired to yawn, exhausted with its tremendous history.
Akaba looked safe enough. "It would be inadvisable for the
Jewish member of your party to enter Transjordan." So the
important police-officer had written to Lucas. Inadvisable?
Inadvisable to eat Turkish delight, or take a Turkish bath?

But we had not reached Transjordan yet.

"Al Qoods!" the voice of Hassan broke in on my reverie.
He made a comprehensive gesture with his right hand, which
included the men in the boat, a lonely palm or two in the
foreshore, the deep recession of the wadi Arabah. Then it
came to rest in the direction of a small white-painted
house.

"Al Qoods!" He meant, as I knew, the Holy Land. It
was true. We were in Palestine, a political entity called
Palestine. But in the Holy Land, the Land of Promise? Not
yet, I thought, we had a long way to go.

We had, in fact, soon after leaving Taba, passed the frontier
of the political Palestine as drawn up after the War. It had
been the frontier of an earlier Palestine, too, the Palestine
which David had aggrandized by the conquest of Edom. But
we were not moving and dreaming in terms of M. Clemenceau,
not even in terms of King David. This was not the land
promised to Moses and the dwellers in the House of Bondage.
We were in Edom.

It is as "Al Qoods" the Arabs speak of Palestine, and more
especially, of Jerusalem. The word is the same word as
"Kadesh," Holy, (a word we had much pondered over in the
remote wadi-head of Ain Kadeis). It is said that the Arab
use of the word to describe the Holy Land, and the Holy City,
is due to the fact that Hebrew coins of the Hashmonaean time
bore the inscription in Samaritan writing, of "Yerushalayim
ha-Gedochah," Jerusalem the Holy.

" Al Qoods! " said Hassan once again, as if he were turning over a Hashmonaean coin in the palm of his hand.

" *La!* " I said. I threw my head back in negation. " It's a long time before we reach the Holy Land, however they plot out their frontiers in maps."

" *Aiua!* " insisted Hassan respectfully, following Mustapha's car in the direction of the white-painted hut. He pointed to the fishermen in their boat.

" Balestina Camel Corps! " he exclaimed.

" That's fine! " I said. They were evidently the frontier-post. It seemed highly unlikely they were going to create any difficulties for us in the matter of our transit from Egypt to Palestine, and Palestine to Transjordan.

The cars stopped. At the same moment a gentleman issued from the hut, very bronzed, but blonde. We assumed he was the officer in charge of the frontier-post, and expected no difficulty from him, either. He was wearing a minute pair of slips, which would have put him at a disadvantage, if we were trying to rush the two frontiers with a load of contraband, all the more as his men were a considerable distance away, at least as lightly clad.

But we were not trying to get through with a lot of contraband. And he was not the frontier official. He was in charge of the wireless station here, which goes by the name of Um Rasras, the Mother of Water-holes. He was a pleasant fellow, a Palestine Arab. He had no idea who we were, and expressed no curiosity, though the bathing-slips may have done something to make him less curious than he might have been. At all events, we gathered that at least the tract of ether which lies above Palestine had not been tick-tacking with excitement about us. We were disposed to believe that the Transjordanian ether had been fairly quiet, too.

We said good-bye to the wireless official, who fiddled about with a salute, then gave it up, feeling he was not quite dressed up to saluting standard. It was galling to Lucas to see somebody else about to bathe, and himself unlikely to, for a whole hour, perhaps; but we kept on. Not many yards later, I suppose, we crossed the frontier-line between Palestine and Transjordan. The yellow sand of the middle wadi roughened into gravel and humpy earth. The gravel became shells and pebbles again, pebbles of quartz, and greenstone, and porphyry. But the air did not change from hot to less hot. The sea remained blue, romantic backcloth blue, de Vere Stacpoole blue.

The car lumbered onward to avoid a scooped-out water-bed. The soil became darker, became, in fact, soil. We came to a rough garden, planted with vegetables and walled in by a shabby mud wall; then one mud hovel and another were the suburbs of Akaba. There was evidently water here, if anyone were strenuous enough to go down for it. Then we came to the sole street of Akaba, sloping to the sea, with the palm-trees of the oasis struggling in tufts among the mud-huts. You felt there should be juicier growths than these, if a little digging and channelling were done. There was an approach to decoration in the carving of spear and crescent on the wooden doors of certain houses; and some even had glass on their windows. Someone, then, had actually lifted a hand to do something in Akaba, since the Allied warships came and violated the Sabbath peace early in the War and bombarded the Turkish positions.

There were, moreover, two or three caverny shops in the main street, though we had been made to feel that we were as likely to find a skating-rink in Akaba as a shop. Further down, on the left hand, was the derelict fort of Akaba, a grim-looking building still, though it had suffered badly in that same bombardment. A painted plaster escutcheon of the Sherif of Mecca above the massive gateway gave it a superficial freshening-up. Beyond the fort, the street took a sharp dip towards the sea. There was a stone drinking-well on the right, and a trough for beasts, with a small group of men and boys gathered round, who looked up surlily as we approached, then turned their backs on us. Opposite the well was a white-washed, flat-topped building which made the angle of the street and the sea-front. We turned, and found ourselves on an open space from which a small jetty ran down to the cobalt-blue sea. The space looked very open and empty. We drew up along the front wall of the white-washed building, and got out.

" It's not here," I said.

" What? "

" The car from Amman."

" No," Lucas admitted. " Did you expect to find it waiting here, with the engine running? "

I realized that that was exactly what I had expected, and that it was a little unreasonable.

" It might be in some courtyard somewhere. Anyhow, there's a camel." On the edge of the open space a camel, with its legs drawn in and its neck thrust forward, lay panting with its back towards the sea. The sea lay panting along the yellow curve of sands, with the moppy line of palms giving no shade. The camel did not make the empty space look more crowded.

We turned to the white-washed building again. It was divided into two sections by a great arched gateway and the courtyard to which it gave admission. A small but unfriendly field-gun stared at us from a low concrete emplacement.

" Bolice-Bost Akaba! " said Hassan tonelessly, a strangely different Hassan. He was no longer the smiling one, the debonair Hollywood Sudanese. We were not in Egypt any more, Hassan's land. We were in Edom, among the brethren of the children of Esau, which dwell in Seir.

" Yes," I said. " I had already gathered it was the Police-Post." It was a much more recent building than the fort, but it looked as uninviting. There was not a soul about, excepting a mangy dog hugging a lip of shadow, and that panting camel nearer the sea.

" I don't see any flags anywhere," I pointed out. " And no band."

" It may have been gayer in the time of King Solomon," Lucas admitted.

We took a few steps towards the gateway. Then, " No," I

said. " Let's wait for Mustapha." I did not like to tackle the place without him. We turned once more to the sea. At the end of the jetty stood a small arbour roofed and walled with sheets of petrol-can tin and palm-tree branches. Two or three fishing-boats were drawn up on the beach, against the stone embankment of the jetty. Two or three others were riding at anchor a few yards out. It looked almost cool in that arbour. At that moment a queer little craft shot out of the sun-dazzle and came up against the jetty. We went up closer to it. It was a coracle, painted blue without, white within, carved out of a single tree, but no tree that grows in these parts. A very old man, wrinkled as a tortoise, stepped from the coracle on to the jetty. He held up by its tail a large greeny-blue fish and stood sniffing the air for some moments. He was blind in one eye, we observed, and there was precious little sight in the other. He got the wind of us, the smell of petrol and foreigners, and walked over in our direction. Then he stopped and held the fish high before us.

It did not look at all as if he merely wanted to sell the fish, though that must have been what it was. It was a curiously hieratic gesture, as though he were elevating a god; and indeed the fish had a quite bronze-like patina, the greeny-blue of the objects excavated from the lava of Herculaneum. We remembered the moment of the greeny-blue fish-god, Dagon, or Atargatis, or whatever its name might have been, a good many times subsequently during that journey through Trans-jordan where he got a certain amount of attention in ancient times. He kept on rising up at us out of the cobalt-blue sea of Akaba.

Mustapha arrived at that moment and got out of the car and came over to us. He had been making inquiries. He threw his head back. " No car! " He looked worried.

" All right! " I assured him. " Camel *quais*! " He was taking it even more seriously than I.

I looked round. There was almost an air of animation about the place, in the sense that certain other living creatures than that panting camel and half-dead dog had come on view. The group had come down from the drinking-well, with their head-cloths drawn low over their eyes. How strange, I mused; how strangely like my own people they are, standing here outlined against the sea, with the head-cloth drawn down like the *tallith*. It is as if they had come down to utter the prayer of *Tashlich*, which they say by some river or tract of water, in the hope that the Lord might take from them the burden of their sins and cast them into the wave. But my own people would sway forward and backward, and from side to side, and beat their fists upon their bosoms, and tears would be in their eyes. But these people are very motionless, and their eyes are hard and dark and empty, with the darkness of the desert at noonday.

These folk were shoddy and bare-foot. A more impressive spectacle outlined itself against the white wall where, during the last half-minute, a group of four soldiers had ranged themselves with the speed and silence of which only desert-dwellers are capable. They stood erect, like a carved frieze.

We recognized them to be men of the Desert Corps of Peake's Arab Legion, concerning whom, and the British officer who commands them, Major Glubb, we had heard much. Their eyes were ringed round with the kohl which protects them from the desert glare. They wore muffled round their chins a copious white fringed headcloth, profusely sprigged with red spots, and bound by a double black rope. The head-badge was a crossed sword and crown of brass set in a laurel wreath. They wore a long khaki shirt-coat that swept down almost to their heels. The highly ornamental cartridge belt was suspended by two straps from the shoulders and fastened round a red waist-band. In each belt was thrust a short dagger in a jewel-studded haft, such as craftsmen make in Mecca. From the sleeves of the shirt-coat the loose white sleeve of an inner garment hung down to the ground.

We approached. Three of the four men remained impassive against the wall. One, a corporal doubtless, stepped forward

BIR TABA

and produced from the depths of his sleeve, as by an act of legerdemain, a long-lipped brass coffee-pot and a tiny coffee-cup. He filled the cup and handed it over to me. There was no other form of salutation. The long faces remained grave and aloof, the deep-set eyes quite expressionless. The coffee was bitter, with a spice called *behar*, cardamom, which has something of the taste of liquorice. Though on first tasting, the stuff was unpalatable, I drained the cup, fearful lest to leave anything might be a discourtesy; then I handed it back to the pourer. A moment later the filled cup was in my hand again. I drained it again and handed it back, and when I saw the pourer fill it a third time, I said " *La!* " feebly, afraid to say it with more emphasis, but a third time I found the cup full in my hand.

It was Mustapha, as might have been expected, who came to my rescue, and I rank it high among his benefactions. He uttered a few words, by which doubtless, my uncouthness was explained. The cup was handed to Lucas. He drained it twice, then Mustapha relieved him of it, and tapped it sharply against the coffee-pot. In that way, we realized, the pourer is made aware the guest has had his fill. The man turned and poured out a cup for Jim.

I do not suppose this ceremony of the coffee took a long time, but to me it seemed interminable, for I found the silence and impersonality of it all most oppressive. I can remember in the middle of it my mind clicking, like a joint, in a wild dislocation. It was early morning. It was New York, Sixth Avenue. I was in an Automat, alone, quite alone. There was no visible attendant, even. I placed a nickel in a machine. I removed from it a mug of steaming coffee. I put the empty mug down. Exactly so silent and impersonal was that coffee-drinking in Akaba. From a distance the few waking inhabitants looked on, hoping (one gathered from their hostile faces) the stuff would choke us.

It seemed interminable, I say, though it doubtless took only a few minutes altogether. But by the time the last cup was drunk, a good deal had happened. In the first place, the little

Ic

blue policeman had appeared and disappeared. That took place during Lucas's first cup, I think. The policeman was small and fat. He was wearing a ridiculous travesty of a London policeman's uniform. His helmet, a size or two too large for him, was topped by a large spike, and had a cloth neck-protector tacked on below. He had a pencil in his mouth and a file of papers resting on his fore-arm. He shot out of the archway, trundled up to each of us in turn, gave each a quick scrutiny, then shot back into the archway.

I was still wondering if I had, or had not, seen him. Jim was still sipping his first cup of coffee, trying hard not to make faces, when I became aware of a noise coming up out of the desert. There was a movement among the rags of the onlookers. Mustapha stepped three sharp paces toward the sound. The soldiers remained lined up against the wall. Mustapha turned.

" Automobbil ! " he announced.

" Amman ! " I whispered. " Amman ! I knew they wouldn't let us down ! "

" They must have made out what you said," said Lucas, " that time you telephoned in Suez ! "

" It's almost supernatural ! They couldn't have timed it better ! "

" Must I finish this coffee ? " asked Jim.

In two minutes the car had drawn up alongside us. It was a five-seater Buick and contained one passenger.

A young man, an Englishman, stepped out of the car. He wore a pair of flannel trousers, an open-necked shirt, and no hat. He carried a small attaché-case. He was an attractive-looking fellow, about twenty-six. He looked rather like the young man loaned by one week-end party to another to make up the four at tennis. He spotted us.

" Hello, you chaps," he said, " what are you doing here ? "

My heart sank.

" Aren't you from Maan ? " I asked.

" Maan ? "

" We telephoned Amman from Suez asking them to send on a car from Maan."

" Oh yes," he said, " I think I heard something about it, this morning, in Amman."

" From the British Resident? " I asked.

" No. From the hotel-porter."

I kept my eyes turned carefully away from Lucas. In a sense it was all very unflattering. In another sense, it was all very comforting. *It would be better if the Jewish member of the party did not enter Transjordan.* Really, really, it was above all very funny.

" What did you hear? " I asked.

" I'd forgotten all about it," he smiled frankly. " I'm so sorry. He said there might be some Englishmen at Akaba wanting a lift. That's all. How long are you staying? Perhaps we can come to some arrangement about the car. My name's Rolfe. What's yours? "

We told him. He knew mine. He had just been reading one of my books. He was excited and schoolboyish about it, for Akaba is not the sort of place where you would expect to come on the author of a book you have just been reading. I experienced some pleasure, too. I told him about the journey we were on, in the steps of Moses. I became aware that another person had attached himself to us. I felt the rub of thick cloth against my sleeve. The little policeman had come up out of his burrow again.

" I'm from Jerusalem," the newcomer said. " But I know a bit about the country between here and Amman. Anything I can do, you know——" He looked round, and saw that our cars were not yet unloaded. " You've only just got here yourselves, eh? "

But before I had time to reply, I was asked another question, in Arabic, not English.

" *Inta Yehud?* " asked the little blue policeman. " Are you a Jew? "

In that same moment Rolfe bent as if to tie a shoelace, and kicked me hard on the shin. It was clear he wished me not to answer that question, at least not then and there.

" *When* did you say you got here? " he asked loudly, as he rose.

" I really don't see——" I started.

" You'll see in a minute," He turned to the policeman, the three Sudanese, the four Arab soldiers. His demeanour had changed completely. He had become in one moment the white man among natives, the pukka English sahib. " Come on, all of you! " he exclaimed in Arabic. " Don't hang about! Get this stuff unloaded, will you? Where's that *farrash* ?"

I felt rather resentful to have Mustapha and his companions spoken to in that way. I felt a little piqued that the fellow had switched off that Jew topic so brusquely. I would not deny being a Jew to the Grand Lama of Thibet or the Reichspräsident or any scruffy little blue policeman from Akaba.

" I don't know where we're going," I objected. " We haven't seen anyone in charge yet."

" That's all right, he'll be along soon," said Rolfe. " I've been here before. They've a big guest-room, inside there, on the left. There'll be beds for all of us—that is "—he paused— " if you don't mind? "

" But, of course," I said.

" Of course," added Lucas.

Jim was half-way through his second cup of coffee. " Do you think," he asked piteously, " you could make them take it away? " He saw that a Strong Man had appeared on the scene.

" Certainly," said Rolfe. He barked a word or two at the Arab corporal. He had no time for the fussy little native punctilio. The corporal silently relieved Jim of the cup. The three soldiers filed off after him into the courtyard. Mustapha and the two others got to work on our kit.

" Hello! " said Rolfe. " Here's the *farrash!* Where have you been all this time? Get some hot water plenty quick! " He turned to us. " Well, what about looking at our beds, eh? And taking a bit of this stuff off our hands? " Then he lowered his voice. " If you don't mind, I want a word with you."

" I should think you do." My head was going round, but I
was conscious of a growing anger. I was conscious, too, of a
growing shame.

" *Inta yehud?* "   " Yes! " I should have shouted. " Yes! "
Even if all the ex-public school boys in the Near East made
a flying rugby tackle at me.

We passed under the archway into a long courtyard. I was
in no mood to note details at the moment. I was aware there
was some sort of an office immediately on the left, and the
soldiers' quarters beyond, then a fenced-off enclosure with a
gate, and the guest-room on the left. We entered the guest-
room. There were two washstands, two chairs and four narrow
bedsteads separated from each other at enormous intervals.
Two long narrow rugs ran along the floor, rather coarse
both in texture and colour. The room was long and high and
cool. Hassan and Mohammed came in after us, carrying the
first pieces of our kit.

" What's it all about? " I said.

" You mustn't say you're a Jew! " said Rolfe, looking at me
very seriously. He kept his voice quite low. " Not in Transjordan! "

" You remember," added Lucas quietly, " what the police-
officer wrote while we were in England."

" What did the police-officer write? " Rolfe put in. " Which
police-officer? "

Lucas told him.

" I think it disgraceful! " Rolfe said. " What's the good of
being English? "

" Well then. What did you want me to lie for? "

" I didn't ask you to lie. I said you mustn't say you're a
Jew, that's all. Say you're English! "

" I don't think you can understand, any of you." I brought
the words out slowly. " I can't be disloyal." It was neither
the time nor the place to go into the matter. I meant that the
tenacity of Jews holding out in the fortress of Masada, not
many miles northward from here, imposed certain obligations
upon me; and the Jews who had not forsworn Israel, at the

stake in Toledo, or during the pogroms of Kishinev. The whole history of Jewry imposed those obligations upon me, all the way back to this same Moses in whose steps I was wandering now.

Lucas rallied to my side. "We knew what it was about, and made up our minds to come. That's all there is to it."

"That isn't all there is to it," insisted Rolfe. "Look here, I don't want you fellows to think I'm poking my nose in, but it's really very serious. It's not safe for a Jew to go travelling through Transjordan. It's far worse than Palestine. A Jew's got official protection over there, at least he's supposed to have. He's often got his own people, within a mile or two. It's not like that in Transjordan. I don't suppose there's a single Jew in all Transjordan. The people are armed to the teeth. The place is blazing with Jew-hatred."

"It wasn't like that in twenty-seven," I said sulkily. "I crossed the Jordan and travelled about quite a bit with some friends from the colonies. They used to tell me that they all had their favourite villages and favourite sheikhs. They used to load each other up with presents."

"Now, old chap," said Rolfe a shade impatiently. "That was twenty-seven. A lot has happened since then."

"But I'm not coming in on a Jewish political job. I'm an Englishman doing a book for an English firm."

"That's the point. You can't let them down. And there's your two pals here."

"That's all right," they both said gruffly.

"Do you mean to say that if they knew I was a Jew——"

"You'd not get very far," said Rolfe, "the whole lot of you. Once you're out in the desert—what is there to stop them?" He pointed a finger dramatically at his forehead. "Bang!"

"After all," Lucas pointed out. "It was just the same with Burckhardt. He had to pretend he was an Arab. If they'd known he was a Christian, he'd never have got anywhere."

"I won't pretend anything," I said. "I'm bad at it."

" You don't have to pretend," insisted Rolfe. " When these fellows ask you are you a Jew, these chaps must come bustling in. ' English! ' they say. ' English! ' That'll see you through! "

" I see." I was not happy about it.

" I think he's right," said Lucas.

" I shouldn't mind a scrap now and again," mused Jim. " But when it comes to rifles——"

" It probably wouldn't be rifles."

" What then? "

" You've seen those daggers." He made another expressive gesture, coupled with a choking noise. " That's what those daggers are for! "

Jim raised his hands in surrender. " English! " he exclaimed. " English! "

§ 2

We washed and put our things away. Rolfe had made inquiries and discovered that we were, in fact, expected. We had been expected yesterday. Amman had done something about our existence after all. It had known that Rolfe was on his way to Akaba, and obviously decided that that was good enough; we would be able to make arrangements with the car that brought him down.

" You'll like Salim Bey," said Rolfe. Salim Bey was the officer of police in charge here at Akaba.

" What's he like? "

" You'll see for yourself," said Rolfe. He seemed to know more about Salim Bey than he wanted to talk about for the time being. " He's been out on business. He ought to be along any minute now." There was a pause. " He's got very nice manners," he added.

The pause was resumed. A slight sense of constraint possessed the air. The awareness was growing upon us that Rolfe knew a great deal about us, really a great deal, while we knew nothing whatever about him. It was true he wore an open shirt, and his hair waved a little. But that did not explain the mystery of his appearance in this wild backwater; if anything, it deepened it. He, too, was conscious of this flapping of a dark wing.

" You'll be surprised," he said, breaking the silence.

" What at? "

" What nice manners I've got, too."

" Not at all," I murmured awkwardly. " You've been pretty decent to us already."

" Oh I don't mean that." He flushed slightly. " I mean Salim Bey."

" Yes? "

" I've got to get on the right side of him." He paused again. " He'll have to get on the right side of me, too, when I've fixed it all up."

We waited. He would tell us if he wanted to. He did at once.

" Fish," he whispered. " That's what I'm after. The fishing rights of the Gulf of Akaba. There's a fortune in it. We'll clear up a packet."

" Really? " We were thrilled. It sounded at once very romantic and very good business. " We saw an old man land with a fish the moment we got here."

" A fish! " he exclaimed. " A fish! The whole place is teeming with fish! We're going to live on it while we're out here. It's first-rate fish, too, much better than the stuff you get off the Palestine coast. I'm going to make the whole country live on Akaba fish; Jews "—he dropped his voice— " and Arabs alike. The Jews think it's good for the brain. The Arabs think it's good for love-making. You'll come out with me, won't you, as soon as we've seen Salim Bey? I'm going to be out on the water night and day, all the time I'm here. The fact is "—again he lowered his voice—" my backers will want to see specimens. Of course, we're interested in the Transjordan market. But it's the Palestine market that counts, the Jewish market."

I looked round involuntarily to see if there were eavesdroppers. I had an exhilarating feeling in that same moment that I was going to like Transjordan, after all. It seemed to me it was a good country, a Phillips Oppenheim country, in which even such bone-witted creatures as fish were things you could only talk about in dark corners, with a finger at your lips.

Rolfe turned to me impulsively. " You can be any amount of help to me," he exclaimed.

" I? " I was genuinely astonished.

" Following in the steps of Moses, aren't you? "

" I am! "

" There you are! "

But where was I? What had Moses, what had I, to do with this piscine imbroglio?

" I don't quite see! " I stammered.

" It's chiefly for the—for *that* market we'd work the concession," Rolfe whispered. He meant the Jewish market. " You see? " It was all getting more Phillips Oppenheim from moment to moment. " And they only eat certain sorts of fish, don't they? I mean they must have fins and scales and things. Isn't that so? "

Yes, that was so. I saw now how Moses the Lawgiver rubbed shoulders with Edgar Wallace.

" That's where you could be so useful," pleaded Rolfe.

The thought gave me an odd and melancholy pleasure. At last, at last, a long way away in Akaba, I should be fulfilling the rabbinic function to which my father in Doomington had vainly devoted me. I should sit in the seat of judgment, deciding between *Kosher* and not *Kosher*. I should go out fishing upon the deep waters with, as it were, the Pentateuch in one hand, and a fishing-rod in the other. It seemed to me a picture that would have given Izaak Walton rare pleasure.

" But it's all very simple," I was forced to point out. " You know all there is to it. No scales, no fins, no good."

" Is that all? "

" That's all."

Rolfe looked very relieved.

" The sooner I get out on that water the happier I'll feel. But I'd like you——"

The conversation was interrupted by the glooming shadow of a large figure in the doorway. It was Mustapha, who had come to say good-bye. Hassan and Mohammed stood in file behind him. The thought of the sea, the wind filling the sail, the water-drops glistening from the flanks of the raised fish, were obliterated. We had had, even so soon, a sharp sense of how much more difficult life was going to be without them. But it was painful for another reason. It is very rarely in a lifetime you come across men with so much grandeur and so much simplicity. Perhaps you are likelier to find it among women than men. They asked us for a *shehada*, a document which would state whether we had been pleased with them or not. That is probably an Egyptian habit which goes back as far as Menes. We composed documents for each, each signed by all three of us. The triplication of signatures impressed them immensely. The moment would have been a great deal harder to bear if not for the air of ritual formality thus introduced into it. So they left us, marching down the courtyard into the arch of intense sunlight framed by the gateway, disappearing appropriately into the element which had nurtured them. We heard with great melancholy the diminishing roar of their engines; Jim kept his face turned from us for a good ten minutes.

" You'd better get your passports fixed up," said Rolfe after a time. " I really don't know what Salim Bey can be up to." He strode over to the door.

" *Farrash!* " he shouted, rather like a sergeant in a chain-gang film.

The *farrash* emerged from a smoky little hole in the end wall, evidently the kitchen.

" Salim Bey, where? "

Apparently Salim Bey had arrived some time ago, and was in his office near the gate beyond the men's quarters.

" Why the roaring devils you not tell me before? " He was

a different person when he addressed his inferiors, with whom he usually used a splenetic pidgin-English, though he spoke Arabic excellently.

"Let's go along, shall we?" he said, turning again. "There's a lot to fix up."

"You have the letters?" asked Lucas.

Yes, I had the letters. We went out into the courtyard. Down at the bottom, an Arab sentry posted at the office noted our emergence and passed out of view, doubtless to announce the Englishmen were on their way. We paused a moment at the gate which led out of the enclosure, where two capitals were ranged on either side, flanked by pairs of broken columns. They looked very interesting, but Rolfe was getting restless, and we walked on. Salim Bey was waiting for us at the foot of the steps which led up into his office. He was a small slim man, rather round-shouldered, wearing a khaki uniform like a British officer's, excepting for the headgear, which was a white headcloth, with a double black headrope bound round it, and further secured by a silver badge. He was fair and had a fairish moustache. The nose was slightly aquiline. The most extraordinary feature was his eyes, which were intensely blue, and set rather close together. There was a small cast in one eye. He was a Druse from Lebanon. Such features are not uncommon in that region.

He saluted, as a soldier to civilians, then shook our hands cordially. He already knew Rolfe; they had met elsewhere. His hand was a little cold and damp, but his manners, as Rolfe had apprised us, were charming. They could not have been more charming.

I passed over to him two or three of the letters we had with us to explain who we were, and what we were doing, and to commend us to the kindness of certain notables in Transjordan. They included letters to Colonel Cox, the British Resident at Amman, and Peake Pasha, Colonel in charge of the Arab Legion. We had one, too, for His Highness, the Emir Abdullah, bearing the signature of Sir Ronald Storrs, but I did not happen to have that with me.

Salim Bey hardly looked at the letters. They were a pure formality. He spoke English, with very little accent. He sent out for coffee at once, and handed round cigarettes. He had been expecting us yesterday, he informed us, and had been most disappointed we had not arrived in time to take lunch with him. But, he insisted, we must eat with him as soon as we were free. As often as we cared to, so long as we honoured Akaba with our presence. He begged to relieve us of our passports, and sent an orderly off with them to get them franked. There was not the faintest suggestion of curiosity as to our racial origins. Yes, Amman had advised him of our impending arrival, and had recommended us to his good offices.

He would be delighted to give us every assistance in his power. The Nebi Musa was undoubtedly one of the greatest of the Prophets, and a journey in his steps was a *haj* supremely worth making. He had his library with him, he would be enchanted to put it at our disposal.

We were very flattered. We had not come across such polish since we left London, where, too, it is not plentiful. It made it all the more heart-shaking to come across it in Akaba. But, as he himself explained, he was in Akaba only for the benefit of his health. He had been overdoing it rather badly during his periods of service in Jerusalem and Amman. Not that there wasn't enough to do here in Akaba. Indeed there was, indeed. He was Civil Governor, Military Governor, Head of Police, all in one. In addition, he was in charge of Customs, Fishing——

The word was just more than Rolfe could stand. He had been getting very restive during the last few minutes.

" That's what I want to talk about, Salim Bey ! " he burst out. Then immediately, as if he realized that that was no way for a diplomat to talk, he took himself in hand. " Any time will do, of course. But we were thinking of taking a boat out——"

" We want to look at those capitals," I said hastily. " And then we'll go down to the jetty. It looks awfully pleasant in that little loggia there."

" I will see some coffee is sent out to you," Salim Bey assured us courteously. He liked us to call the petrol-tin palm-leaf shanty, a loggia.

" That will be lovely," I murmured. It seemed we were going to get through a lot of fish in Akaba and a lot of coffee in Transjordan. A pity the coffee was so bitter, but I remembered that I had in time got used to the resinated wine of Greece, too. We left Salim Bey and Rolfe in the office and walked back up the courtyard to examine the capitals at leisure. A moment or two later, Rolfe and Salim Bey followed us and began walking up and down the courtyard, their heads close together, talking in low tones. When we went out on to the water-front they were still murmuring in a corner within an inch or two of each other, too preoccupied to notice us. Throughout the rest of the time we spent in Akaba, I noticed they got into a huddle as soon as they were left together for even half a minute. It impressed itself on our memory, for it was our introduction to the great national pastime of Transjordan, whispering, murmuring, scheming, whispering, murmuring. It was really quite fantastic to see the broad-shouldered young Englishman, the open-shirted one, converted in the twinkling of an eye into a Near Eastern intriguer. But we were to get used to the phenomenon. It does not matter what race they spring from, what their professions are; when two Transjordanians get together they put their heads close and start murmuring, Arabs of the villages, Beduin of the desert, British soldiers, Italian missionaries. Transjordan is one vast whispering-gallery.

The two capitals by the enclosure were midway in time between Edom and Transjordan. One may have come from some very early church, of the fifth or sixth century, perhaps, the time when Elath-Aila was the seat of a bishopric. It had an angel carved in full relief, entirely Roman in feeling and execution, though it carried Christian symbols. The angel, garbed in a toga like a senator, stood with outspread wings, holding in his right hand a staff, in the left an orb crowned

with a cross patée. The remnants of a halo were visible behind
flowing ringlets. The second capital dated from a later and
doughtier age, when men debated with lances rather than
words. It had a knight in armour carved in it, resting on a
shield, with a smaller shield guarding his heart. He may have
been one of the warriors of Baldwin, king of Jerusalem, who
came to reclaim Aila for Christ early in the twelfth century.
We were informed some days later by the oldest of the fishermen of Akaba that the two figures were Jewish warriors of the
Nebi Musa who fled this way a hundred years ago when
Pharaon was pursuing them. We thought that unlikely, but
noted with excitement the persistence of the Nebi Musa
tradition across so many and such tortuous histories.

We passed out of the courtyard, leaving Rolfe and Salim
Bey murmuring in their corner. It was cooler now, and Akaba
was bestirring itself. Very desultorily, the men and boys
emerged from their mud houses; they did not seem to care
much whether they were dead or alive. The females remained
within doors, as if the open air were at no time their element.
A few merchants gathered round us as we walked down to the
jetty, with red and green circled reed baskets, and jewelled
daggers, and one or two lengths of rug. These things had not
been made in Akaba. No one makes anything in Akaba.
They are an idle and exhausted people.

Two old men placed shells at our feet, spiny as hedgehogs
or smooth and luminous as patches of oil; but they were not
more beautiful than those we had gathered for ourselves at
Taba. Another offered lumps of coral, not merely red coral,
but greeny-blue, sulphur-yellow, white, deep purple, pale lilac.
Though the sea glistened in its hollows, and the soft weed still
clung to it, the stuff looked against Nature, as if the old men
had been playing tricks with it, as flower-sellers at home do
with teazle and carnations. We bought neither shells nor
coral, because we thought merchants should have more
amiable faces. That made them angry, for they had gone to
all the trouble to bend down and pick the things up. One lad

sought to sell us four moribund crabs. He had a dead-white, much-freckled face and a towy mop of blood-red hair. Lucas thought it was clear the Crusaders had been this way. I thought the child went further back. This land was once called Edom, which means " red," with the redness of blood, *ed dumm*. It is usually thought the redness was of these mountains, the great sandstone range between the limestone crusts. It may well have meant rather the redness of the people, most of it overlaid long since with layers of Arabian darkness. Esau himself might have been the sire of this tough young man of Akaba, with the sullen underlip. The young man was muttering fiercely, for we had not liked his crabs. On the whole, the people of Akaba were below the standard set by their hills and sea.

Three or four owners of fishing boats were busy with nets and tackle. They were the aristocrats of the place and had no truck with us. After we had spent some half-hour or so in the loggia, sipping the coffee Salim Bey had sent out to us, we saw Rolfe issue from the guard-house, and engage one of these in conversation. A great deal of chattering went on, till things were at last fixed up and Rolfe shouted to us to come and join him.

" Dirty old robber ! " said Rolfe. " But he knows the best fishing-beds. Step in ! Let's get going ! "

A small boy who had been hovering round, stepped in, too. He was the brother of the old robber. The man's name was Abdullah, the boy's Ali. They were the sons, we learned later of the one-eyed greybeard in the coracle. He had lost his eye in an accident with a stick of dynamite.

We rowed away from the small jetty on to a sea still and transparent as glass. Below us the coloured coral branched, the colours that had seemed unreal with artifice had now the unreality of dream, those blue violet grottoes and primrose arches, those mazes of azure and scarlet. Through waters darkening from depth to depth, shoals of ghostly fish swept in the wind of a sudden panic. Like leaves, they seemed, leaves before an enchanter fleeing, gold and bronze leaves in a flurry along the submarine hedgerows. Or before the surge of some terror guessed but not seen, they rose, punctured the water, and sank again, to a doom there was no escaping.

So began our career as fishermen in Transjordan. It was only in the waters of Akaba we threw our bait, but we kept on catching fish all the way to the waters of Jordan. After a minute or two, Abdullah ran the sail up, but that did not help much, as there was hardly a breath of wind. Both brothers tugged away at the oars for ten minutes or more, then stopped, for we had arrived at one of the fishing-beds. The anchor, which was a large stone smooth as a seal, was let down. Then Abdullah handed each of us a line weighted with lead, with two hooks attached. Then, from a still heaving octopus in the thwarts, he cut six cubes of milky white flesh which we impaled on our hooks. Then at last we let the line run between our fingers into the depths below.

I should say at once that the fish was more exciting than the fishing, which for me attained its immediate climax. I had no sooner let my line down than I felt a most disturbing tremor run along my fore-arm. I closed my eyes and pulled, and found some seconds later I had landed a huge red sea-bream that glowed like a polished copper brazier. Rolfe somewhat abated my pleasure by declaring, after a cursory examination, they would not look at it in Tel Aviv. But the fact remained, the least expert fisherman had landed the first fish.

The fish, I say, was more exciting than the fishing, and we landed some very lurid specimens, fish Tyrian-purple, daffodil-yellow, rose-pink, fish cross-gartered, fish armour-plated, fish with faces like blue masks, fish with bodies like leather purses, fish from deep down with enormous buttony eyes, whose sides burst when they were dragged up from the heavy pressures they were accustomed to, so that their intestines came gushing through. Despite its appearance, it was for the most part very edible, all the more as we did not feel in Akaba so constrained as they are in Tel Aviv by the Mosaic punctilio with regard to scales and fins.

MAAN

After a time we moved on to another and another fishing-bed, for Rolfe was very anxious to study as many specimens as possible. In one place we dragged the fish up as fast as we could bait the hooks. In another, for all the phantom jerkings on the line, hours, it seemed, went by without a catch.

"Bite?" asked Abdullah, seeing a wrist stiffen. His voice was rough as a bream.

"Nibble?" asked Ali. His voice was smooth as a herring. There was no nibble, no bite.

"More bait?" asked Abdullah.

"More hook?" asked Ali.

"But they talk English," I whispered to Rolfe. "For heaven's sake, be careful what you're saying." He was saying enough to set the Gulf of Akaba on fire.

"They're showing off," said Rolfe. "Look!" He turned to the two brothers and told them what he thought of them, their faces, their habits, their mother and father, their ancestors back to the Stone Age. The two brothers sat grave and silent. It might have been a sea-gull yammering.

Rolfe turned to us again. "I'll go on with what I was saying, shall I?"

It was not till the third or fourth excursion that Rolfe perceived how completely the success or failure of these fishing-excursions depended on Abdullah. If Abdullah wanted to take us to a good bed, we caught much. If he wanted to take us to a bad bed, we caught little or nothing. By that time Rolfe had found out that it was all bound up with quotations on a Jew market. At one moment the village inclined to the belief that Jewish finance was at the back of it all. At once our fish dwindled in numbers and size to vanishing-point. At another moment it got about that the strangers bore letters to no less a Muslim than the Emir himself, son of the late Sherif of Mecca. At once the boat was almost swamped with fish. What the quotation would have been if the conclave of fishermen had found out the boat contained a Jewish passenger was not speculated on.

Rolfe regretted that they would not let him use a gun, as

Kc

these people sometimes do when they go out fishing. That was sport, but if it was results you were after, nothing came up to a few sticks of dynamite. The natives of Akaba did a lot of dynamiting, which was illegal, of course. But who could stop them? The fishermen ruled the roost here. They had enough dynamite stowed away in Akaba to blow the place to bits—all stolen, said Rolfe, from the back of Colonel Lawrence's supply-camels. When he got the concession, he would be tempted to do a bit of dynamiting himself whenever a rush order came through from Jerusalem. With all this dynamiting, the Gulf would be cleared of fish in five years, perhaps, ten years, at most. But he would have made a packet by that time, anyway.

He was full of ideas. He was not going to make the mistakes of the people who got the concession in 1927. It was true there was a great variety of fish in the Gulf, which was carried in by the currents from the Red Sea. But the biggest fish did not come within twenty miles of the gulf-head. So he would do his fishing out there, and bring the stuff up to Akaba in a motor launch. The other people used to unload their stuff into sacks and have it carried up on camels along the Hedjaz coast. Of course it wasn't fit for anything by the time it got to Akaba, and then it had the journey to face to Maan and Amman. He would see to it he would have not only a motor launch here, but an ice factory so that he could run a fleet of ice-trucks between Akaba and Amman. You can't get far in the fish industry without an ample supply of ice. The ice-factory was ready to his hand. He meant that dingy old fortress, of course. He would toff it up a bit, get rid of all those hornets' nests and clean out the old cisterns. The massive beams of the gate might come in useful for his boats.

But the ice-factory was not all. His imagination soared as the crescent moon soared above the mountain-peaks; both tossed lightly on the wave of their own radiance.

" Then there's the matter of steam-trawlers," he murmured dreamily. " I'll assemble a fleet of steam-trawlers at Jaffa. I'm already in touch with Yarmouth, and if Yarmouth falls

through, there's always Oslo." He had a mind equally indifferent to distances in space and time. " There's a chance
the Hedjaz people will make difficulties about letting the
trawlers come up the gulf. Well, I'm prepared for that. I'll
have the things dismantled in Jaffa and carried over piecemeal
in motor-lorries. Oh yes, it can be done. Well, what do you
think of that? " he asked with a note of triumph in his voice,
as if it were done already.

And in fact, it *had* been done already, although I did not
think it necessary to point it out. It had been done so long ago
as 1182, when the crusader, Reynaud de Châtillon, had had
five galleys dismantled in Askalon, a little further up the
Syrian coast, and carried on camel-back all the way here to
Akaba—or Aila, as it was called then. The fleet harried the
Red Sea coast for a whole year. The Faithful quaked in their
boots in Aden and Mecca. Then a storm came up and harried
the fleet. Then Saladin came up and completed the ruin.

All this was long ago. But riding there on those mackerel-
dappled waters, it was easy to play with the idea that a drop
of the blood of Reynaud de Châtillon still sported in the veins
of this burly-chested Englishman, who had come back to the
shores of Araby six and a half centuries later, no less a blunt
practical man, no less a preposterous dreamer.

There was a brief silence.

" No nibble! " croaked Abdullah, athwart the moon and
water washed air.

" No bite! " fluted Ali.

We weighed anchor and moved to another fishing-bed. But
Rolfe was hardly aware we had shifted. He had by now sent
out a branch line of the Hedjaz Railway to Akaba. He had
imported a dance-band or two, and a couple of floor-shows.
The phosphorescent water-drops cascaded like pearls and
moonstones from the lifted oars. The words of the dreamer
cascaded more and more bright and meaningless. Overhead
a comet rushed like a rocket on to the peaks of Transjordan.

No, not Transjordan. Mount Seir. The two thousand years,

too, fell like water-drops from Time's lifted oars. That was Mount Seir, where the men of Edom and Moab dwelt.

The comet was a rocket to announce news:

" They, the host of Israel, that have fled from Egypt, and have in the desert become mighty, they are come to Elath and Ezion-geber. They have sent messengers demanding that they might pass through our land, saying they would not go through field or vineyard, but would go along the King's high way, turning neither to the right hand nor the left.

" Remember how Israel mistreated Esau, our father.

" Beware. Their way is northward. They must not pass."

§ 3

There was a mighty mound of fish for dinner that night, fried in green oil, and banked by spring onions and green tomatoes. Jim caused some harsh laughter by setting down on the table a tin of salmon and a tin of sardines, which he dug up from the bottom of his kit-bag. He had been keeping them for an emergency, he said. It was felt a more acute emergency might arise. The bread, on being cut into, looked like a mince-pie, it was so thick with ants, and Rolfe saw to it we got back the two piastres we had paid for it, though it meant awaking half Akaba. He was not going to be done, he said, by any thieving Arab. He liked the tables, however, in the dining-room, with their metal feet and marble tops. They reminded him of Lyons' Corner House. A dimness came upon his eyes.

Then suddenly, " I wish they would stop that noise," he exclaimed. He meant the music coming from the guard-room, a man singing at an instrument, and the other men singing in the chorus. I looked up. I was surprised he was not used to it. He must have heard a good deal of that sort of music by now; moreover, they give music, do they not, with your food at Lyons' Corner House? I recalled he shared his dislike of the Arab viol with Doughty, and could the more readily forgive him. " So they make to themselves

music like David," wrote that not less sturdy Englishman,
" drawing out the voice in the nose, to a demensurate length,
which must move our yawning or laughter."

" Come on, Jim," said Rolfe, though he neither yawned nor
laughed. He was thinking of fish again. Jim needed no persuading. They went out through the gateway and we stood
for several minutes looking after them, and listening to the
strange music. It was like a scene from an exotic opera, the
voice and the instrument, the solid bars of light and shadow
on the courtyard, the motionless guard at the gateway with
his great cloak hanging from his shoulders, beyond the gateway the still water, with a felucca moving slowly out into the
gulf, a single bright light in its bow.

After some minutes, one of the men noticed us standing
there, and with a sweep of the hanging sleeve summoned us
into the guardroom. The guards with their red cloaks spread
round them were seated round the room, on mattresses
covered over with red, black and white striped rugs. They
rose as we entered, all but the singer singing to the instrument.
His eyes were closed. He seemed as if he would go on singing
and playing if the walls tottered about his ears. The corporal
motioned us to take our seats on two high-arched camel
saddles, very gay and ornate; he then lifted a coffee-pot out
of a charcoal brazier and poured out coffee for us. We drank,
the men seated themselves, no one said a word, the man went
on playing and singing, the others joined in the choruses.
The man had made the instrument himself, *rhibab*, they called
it. It was very primitive. There was a broom-handle let
into an oblong wooden box, one side of which consisted of a
stretched piece of gazelle skin. The bow, of wood and horse-
tail hairs, was drawn over a single string. A series of holes
carved in one side of the box gave the small range of notes.

The song went on for hours. It did not seem to have
had a beginning and seemed unlikely to have an ending. No
one had any thought of us again, after we had each clicked
our coffee-cups against the pot to show we wanted no
more.

Salim Bey translated the song for us later, though even he found some difficulty in understanding the desert dialect. He was not quite sure, he said, if it was the same song as we heard that first night. But that did not matter. They were all the same song. They related largely to the exploits of Major Glubb.

" They call Major Glubb Abu el Heneik," said Salim Bey, " the Man with the Jaw," because of a wound he had in the Iraki fighting. He was at first an engineer, and built bridges over the Tigris, but when peace came, there was little peace in Irak, and he stayed on, for he understands the tribesmen as no other man from the West at this day does, and they think him a prince and hero. He lives as they live, and thinks with their thoughts. Peake Pasha is loved, too, but that is more in the sown places. Major Glubb is the man of the desert, and the sheikh's sons burn to be his men, and the singers sing songs about him. Now before he came to Transjordan, a certain Sultan ed Dewish revolted against his overlord, Ibn Saud, later to become Lord of Saudi Arabia. In single battle the British soldier overthrew the Sultan and handed him over to Ibn Saud. Whereon Ibn Saud assembled presents and loaded them on a fine camel. And in the moment the messenger was ready to go forth, a love-sick warrior came and sang this song to the messenger, which now they sing to the *rhibab* in the four deserts, and we heard that night in the guardroom by the water's edge at Akaba:

> *Oh thou rider of a noble camel,*
> *Whereof the saddle-bag is gay with embroideries,*
> *Woe is me,*
> *I come from a far country,*
> *I clap my hands because of my sorrows,*
> *Such sorrows as none other knows the like of,*
> *The sorrows of the sidelocks of the brave tresses*
> *Which are death to lovers.*
> *Oh thou rider of a noble camel,*
> *Swift as an ostrich,*

That came westward to el Chaib from eastward of Thenia,
O thou rider of a noble camel,
Act as my envoy to the brave stranger,
To bear him my greetings.
He has the eyes of a hunting falcon,
That is so fearless hunting the sky.
His own land is a rich land,
Where he flaps his wings.
But lo! he flies over
To the land of fear.
There he comes with formidable soldiers
And without fear wholly.
O thou rider of a noble camel,
Act as my envoy to the brave stranger
To bear him my greetings.
I will forget the sorrows of the sidelocks
Which are death to lovers.
Let him but behold me,
He who has fixed up with the far-seeing eye
The machine-guns ever loaded in readiness.
Oh what fine men they are, with what fine belts on,
How many fine men have been enlisted by him!
Oh thou rider of a noble camel,
Act as my envoy to the brave stranger,
To bear him my greetings.

We had no notion that night of the meaning of the words the singer sang. The song loped on without change, without pause. It was as if we were riding out into the desert on those camel-saddles we sat on.

An hour or two later, it may have been less or more, we rose silently from our places and stole out into the courtyard. No one marked our going. We did a turn or two along the water-front, and saw, far out in the gulf, the lamp beaming like a planet in the bow of Abdullah's felucca.

There was a time, I thought, when all that dark water was like a heaven starred with the lights of ships, the ships of the navy of King Solomon. They were stout ships, built for King Solomon by shipmen " that had knowledge of the sea," the servants of Hiram, King of Tyre, who had earlier built for Solomon a temple in Jerusalem before building a navy for him here in Ezion-geber. Here too, from the southern reaches of Arabia, the laden ships of the Queen of Sheba came to disbark their " spices and very much gold and precious stones," so that these things might be loaded again on camels and borne northward to Solomon, in the " very great train " of the dark queen.

But there were earlier Hebrews in Elath and Ezion-geber than the custom officials and the dock-labourers and the mariners of Solomon. And these were the men in the host of Moses who had come down from the parched desert of Paran, having wandered for many days, and made their encampments among cirques of stones where no water was, saving you could scoop it with the edge of a pail from the damp gravel of a water-hole.

So they had come upon this brief remission of the desert doom, here in Elath and in Ezion-geber, by the edge of the unbelievable water. And they had come from a land of a great river with many arms to it, and canals connecting the arms of the river, and the overflow of the canals filling countless backwaters. And all these waters were so thick stocked with fish, that there was no traffic in it, it was the fish that they did eat for naught, as they cried out in the desert when there was no diet for them but " this manna."

And there was an abandoned boat lying keel upward on the beach, and a certain Hebrew and his son put it to rights again, and pushed it out into deep water. And there, with a single light burning in the bow, there they were fishing out in the still water, so that there might be fish again for the folk in their company, even though there were no melons in that harsh land, and no garlic and no leeks nor cucumbers.

It had been a long day and we turned in soon from walking along the water-front. I fell asleep at once, but not so soundly

that I did not hear Jim, some hours later, creep into his bed
on his return from the fishing expedition.

But there was a fourth bed in that room. Someone should
have got into that fourth bed. Who was it? Where was he?

Then I heard two pairs of feet walking steadily, relentlessly,
up the courtyard and down again. I heard two voices whispering together, murmuring, intriguing. It was the two
Transjordanians, Rolfe in his tennis-shirt, Salim Bey in his
headcloth.

" That bodes ill," I murmured, " for the poor fish in the
Gulf of Akaba." I pulled the blanket over my ears, but I still
heard, till dawn came, the feet going up and down and the
voices whispering.

§ 4

In between the next fishing expedition and the one that
followed it, we had a brush with the young Edomite, the red-
haired lad with the dead-white freckled face. When we first
met him he had tried, unsuccessfully, to unload upon us four
dying crabs. Since then we had evinced a great interest in
fish, and it apparently occurred to him we might now be
more interested in his crabs than before. At all events, he
had them waiting for us on the waterside. There was no
doubt it was the same boy. We were as sure they were the
same crabs.

" Crabs! " said the boy. " Good! Cheap! "

" No! "

" No! " said Lucas and Jim. Rolfe was a few yards away,
making arrangements with Abdullah.

" Crabs! " the boy repeated. catching hold of my shirt.
" Good! Cheap! " His surly lower lip protruded unpleas-
antly.

" No! " I said firmly, tearing my shirt from his fingers.
" No crabs! "

There was silence for three seconds more, then the lad dis-
charged a stream of black language into the air, like a squid
discharging ink; the voice became extraordinarily adult and

gruff. There was only one word I recognized, but it occurred several times, *imack*, your mother.

We walked on. Our backs were turned on the young man. We were several yards away. Then suddenly we heard a hoarse cry. It was not a voice we recognized at all. We turned and saw Rolfe towering over the boy, with both fists lifted. The boy crouched shrinking with his arm over his forehead. Rolfe's face was deathly pale, his eyes staring black and dreadful. He would have done the child serious damage if we had not cried out to him.

" Rolfe ! "

The cry snapped a spell. The fists dithered a moment in mid-air, then he brought them down to his sides, turned away from the boy, and shambled over towards us.

" Sorry ! " he muttered. " Shouldn't . . . shouldn't talk about mothers . . . like that." He had considerable difficulty in bringing the words out.

He did not look a bit, at that moment, like the open-shirted Englishman that one week-end party lends another to make up a set of tennis.

It was not Akaba, however, nor Transjordan that was at the bottom of all this. It explained itself slowly, and in mono-syllables. Some few years ago, Rolfe's mother lay dying in England. She bade her son come over to be with her, but he was dilatory, and when he came to her at length, it was too late. He had not spoken a friendly word to any woman since.

That boy, so blaspheming, was in greater danger than any of us knew, we three, the boy, or Rolfe himself possessed of an avenging shade.

We had one more bottle of *arrak* left. It was broached forthwith.

§ 5

We were not quite finished with that red-headed boy. We were to find him a sort of epitome of Akaba, a distillation of its history. He went back three and a half thousand years to

Edom. Time paused while a Crusader added a ruddy potion to the alembic of his blood. He came up through nameless centuries and swept forward into modern war, Lawrence's and Feisal's war, pistols barking from plunging camels, aeroplanes zooming over white-hot ravines.

We pointed him out that afternoon to Salim Bey.

" What's wrong with that lad? The other youths will have nothing to do with him, and he has no love for his own company. What's wrong with him? "

" Yes, he is not good. He will come to a bad end, I think. He should go back where he belongs. He is not from here."

" Where then? "

" His father was of the Howeitat over towards Ain Sadaqua. He fought against the Turks."

" Against the Turks? " I cried, my heart contracting. " And who was his leader? "

" I do not know," he said. " I think it was Nesir. And sometimes, your Lawrence. It was like that. They would fight. They would rob. They would go back to their tents. Then they would fight again."

" Lawrence! He fought with Lawrence! Up on those mountains there! "

Salim Bey looked curiously at me.

" Why not? " he asked.

It was impossible to stand and explain to him what a thrilling thing it was to meet a living link with Lawrence, a son of one of his soldiers if not the soldier himself, here on the doorstep of Lawrence's Arabia.

" The father died some years ago," Salim Bey continued, " and the mother came to Akaba to be with someone of her family. She brought the boy with her. He has heard tales of the fine times his father had, charging on camels and shooting and stripping the dead of clothes and money. And there are tales told of great banquets in the evening after the battles, and there were women, and carpets, and chickens. It is much nonsense," Salim Bey deprecated, " but women will talk and boys will listen. Sometimes his father was with Lawrence, when it was bridges in Hedjaz railway shall be blown up. Perhaps true, perhaps not true." Salim Bey shrugged his shoulders. " But the boy is excited. That is a fine thing to do with dynamite—blow up men, not fish.

" That is why he is not happy," Salim Bey summed up. " He could be happy if it was a war and he was with his father, and both of them with Auda or Lawrence or Nesir. Perhaps it will be a war again soon, if it is will of Allah . . . but his father, no, Lawrence, no. So he is unhappy. He is angry with life."

Not he alone, I said to myself, was thus unhappy and thus angry with life. So, too, this Lawrence was. A year or two earlier, hunting for flints in Ain Kadeis, no man was happier, I think, nor found life so pleasant. Then the huge planet swung up that wrenched him into an alien orbit; it was a dislocation not only in direction but in tempo. For the intellectual's ordered gait almost overnight was substituted the hero's whirlwind hurtling. No racing camel was swift enough to outstrip his torment. The planet at length removed its immediate compulsion. He tried to resume the ordered gait, vainly. In nightmare he was strapped on to the racing camel. In waking daydreams he sought again, faster and still faster, to outstrip with petrol the racing camel to which nightmare fastened him more and more inexorably.

With petrol he attained from day to day at least an illusion of escape, he touched the fringe of at least an illusion of ecstasy.

Certain pencil scribblings were found among his papers after his death. " Confession of Faith " their heading is. These words follow :

" Not the conquest of the air, but our entry thither
   We COME.
   Our soiled overalls were the livery of that sunrise.
   The soiling of our bodies in its Service was prismatic
      with its light. (Three illegible words, then :) From
      ground to air. First we are not earthbound.

These lines follow in ink:

" In speed we hurl ourselves beyond the body
    Our bodies cannot scale the heavens except in a fume of
        petrol.
    The concentration of our bodies in entering a loop.
    Bones, blood flesh all pressed inward together."

The scribbling, still on that same page, goes back into pencil again. The lines cross each other:

" In speed we hurl ourselves beyond the body.
    Not the conquest of the air. Be plain, guts
        we entrust. We come."

Then the repeated line sums the whole tale up. All is consummated.

" Our bodies cannot scale heaven except in a fume of
    petrol."

§ 6

It was on July the ninth, nineteen hundred and seventeen, that Lawrence the Conqueror, having captured the important spring of Abu el Lissan midway between Maan and Akaba, raced during a driving sand-storm down the last four miles of that bitter journey and splashed into the sea. It was to be a critical date for the Revolt in the Desert. " Our capture of Akaba," he wrote, " closed the Hejaz war, and gave us the task of helping the British invade Syria. The Arabs working from Akaba became the virtual right wing of Allenby's army in Sinai."

But he had already been to Akaba, under quieter auspices. That was during that archaeological excursion to which reference has already been made, when he found his way to the brackish spring at Ain Kadeis. He was not much impressed, it will be remembered, with the identification between Ain Kadeis and Kadesh-barnea, for he felt that in the desert country, subjected to the fluctuating waves of nomad invasions, old names are little likely to survive. Moreover, he pointed out, places are usually called after some temporary and recent inhabitant, or after some prominent but not always permanent natural feature.

With Akaba he found no such difficulty. The natural feature which gave it its ancient name, Ezion-geber, the Giant's Spine, is permanent as well as prominent. He had a sense, confirmed by the very scarcity of ancient ruin, that the aspects of modern Akaba and old Ezion-geber were very similar.

" Here there are no great harbour works, no ruins of thriving towns, but on the sandy beach and rocky islet doubtful traces at most of a little trading station where the troops of the convoy drowsed between the rare visits of the Eastern fleet."

There can be no doubt that themes no more bellicose than that were all that preoccupied him on the occasion of his first visit to Akaba, though Mr. Graves, in his book on Lawrence, speaks of his journey with Mr. Woolley as " a surveying party in the desert of Sinai which was ordered by Lord Kitchener for military reasons, though put under an archaeological disguise." Mr. Graves does not make it clear whether he believes that Lawrence himself was conscious of putting on some " archaeological disguise " in order to serve Lord Kitchener's " military reasons." In any case it seems regrettable that a cloud of doubt should be allowed to blur the outline of the obscure and happy life Lawrence was leading before the extraordinary adventure in Arabia sent him dazzling into world-fame. He was to endure enough and too much of it later, when he sought so grimly to return to the obscure life again, and was so tragically thwarted.

The facts, it appears, were these. At that time (1913) about five thousand miles of territory between Egypt and Palestine remained unmapped. Kitchener being then G.O.C. in Egypt, it fell to him to arrange with the Turkish authorities that the Royal Engineers be allowed to conclude the unfinished survey. It was a venture that Kitchener had at heart, for he was no mean archaeologist, and had himself landed in Akaba to embark on it in December 1883. But three weeks or so after his arrival, when his party had made some progress up the Arabah, Kitchener was recalled to Egypt by letters announcing the defeat and death of Hicks Pasha. Far different duties now lay ahead of Major Kitchener.

The long-interrupted survey was in 1913 put under the direction of Major (now Colonel) Newcombe. Colonel Sir Charles Waters, at that time Chairman of the Palestine Exploration Fund, then made representations that the opening for archaeological study which the survey offered should not be neglected, and two scholars working in Carchemish on the Euphrates, Mr. Leonard Woolley, as he was then, and T. E. Lawrence, were detailed to the task. They had both spent some years excavating in the neighbouring countries, where they had acquired an extensive knowledge of the remains in stone and pottery of bygone civilizations. Both spoke Arabic well. Their work was done brilliantly, though they could only spend six weeks on it, as they tell us, through pressure of work elsewhere in Syria.

Those six weeks were among the happiest in Lawrence's life. Perhaps the happiest moment in them was that in which he embarked on the craft he improvised to sail the narrow strait between the mainland and the island of Gaziret Faraun where he wished to examine the ruins of a Crusader's castle. The Turkish soldiers had refused to let him use their boat and had drawn it up on the beach where single-handed he had no hope of moving it. He waited till the post took its siesta, then strung together three of his camel water-tanks and propelled himself over with a favouring wind. The return journey across the shark-infested strait may not have been so blissful. But he may well have entertained himself with the thought that not Hiram's most cunning artificer fitted out for King Solomon's use on these same waters a more cunning craft.

Two and a half years go by before Lawrence, a how different Lawrence, is in Akaba again. He had just fought the wild battle of Abu el Lissan, and taken the three Turkish posts that still maintained resistance between him and the sea. With Khadra, the last of the three, yielding, he came down on Akaba, a how different Akaba. " Through the whirling dust we perceived that Akaba was all a ruin. Repeated bombardments by French and English warships had degraded the place to its original rubbish. The poor houses stood about in a litter, dirty and contemptible, lacking entirely that dignity which the durability of their time-challenging bones conferred on ancient remains.

" In the blank light of victory we could scarcely identify ourselves. We spoke with surprise, sat emptily, fingered upon our white shirts; doubtful if we could understand or learn whom we were. Others' noise was a dreamlike unreality, a singing in ears drowned deep in water. Against the astonishment of this unasked-for continued life we did not know how to turn our gift to account. Especially for me was it hard, because though my sight was sharp, I never saw men's features: always I peered beyond, imagining for myself a spirit-reality of this or that: and to-day each man owned his desire so utterly that he was fulfilled in it, and became meaningless."

Lawrence left Akaba the very next day for Suez and Cairo to give the authorities an account of what had happened and request that supplies and money be sent forthwith to finance this dagger-thrust into the desperately long-drawn Turkish communications between Damascus and Medina. He was back again in Akaba in the middle of the following month and thereafter he was perpetually there and away and back again, with the incalculability and speed of summer lightning. He records over a score of descents upon Akaba between that first appearance on July the sixth and his farewell on August the fifth, a year later. There was, in point of fact, a flying visit two days after that, but that final mustering on the beach was his true farewell; beyond lay the encirclement of Deraa, the capture of Damascus, the triumph that had for him the wormwood flavour of failure and dishonour.

CARVED STAIRWAY IN PETRA

" So for the last time we mustered on the windy beach by the sea's edge, the sun on its brilliant waves glinting in rivalry with my flashing and changing men. They were sixty. Seldom had the Zaagi brought so many of his troop together, and as we rode into the brown hills for Guweira he was busy sorting them in Ageyl fashion, centre and wings, with poets and singers on the right and left. So our ride was musical. It hurt him I would not have a banner, like a prince."

He has his banner, none the less, and like a prince.

§ 7

We were making a journey in the steps of Moses the Conqueror, a journey that led from the foot of Sinai to the top of Pisgah. We had attained a narrow gulf-head where at one time stood two sea-cities, by name Ezion-geber and Elath. Though that gulf-head is so narrow, the text seems to insist they were two cities rather than one city, however close to each other they must have been. It is Ezion-geber we read of first, in the detailed account given of the host's journeys, in the thirty-third chapter of Numbers. " And they journeyed from Abronah," we read, " and they pitched in Ezion-geber," making that the twenty-first station after the encampment in the wilderness of Sinai. In this enumeration no mention is made of an encampment at Kadesh until after the encampment at Ezion-geber is listed. It is only then we read how " they journeyed from Ezion-geber, and pitched in the wilderness of Zin (the same is Kadesh)." Yet other texts make it quite clear the host had already encamped once at Kadesh. It is stated, for instance, that when the spies returned from spying out the land, it was to " the wilderness of Paran, to Kadesh," they returned, to make their reports to Moses.

At all events, it is clear the ground between Kadesh and Ezion-geber was covered once at least. The actual route between the two places cannot be decided. If Kadesh is Ain Kadeis it may have been, as indicated earlier, by one of certain wadis that led directly eastward into the Arabah and so

Lc

straight down the Arabah, " by the way of the Red Sea," to Ezion-geber. The host may, on the other hand, have turned on their tracks westward and come down, as we had done later, by way of Kuntilla and the Ras el Negeb.

Here they were, then, at Ezion-geber, as the thirty-third chapter of Numbers tells us. The place called Elath is not coupled with it till we come to the second chapter of Deuteronomy, where Moses, " speaking unto all Israel beyond Jordan in the wilderness " reminds them: " So we passed by from our brethren the children of Esau, which dwell in Seir, from the way of the Arabah from Elath and from Ezion-geber." But Moses is talking of a time long subsequent to that first encampment at Ezion-geber. All the decades of the penal wanderings have come between. After that first sojourn on the gulf-head, the host turned northward again; no stations are enumerated on the bitter return journey, but at last they reach the wilderness of Zin again, and the place called Kadesh. Much happens, as was before described, during that same encampment at Kadesh. And then at last, Miriam having died at Kadesh, and Aaron being about to die on Mount Hor, the host sets forth again on the final stage of the wanderings. The narrative in Numbers jumps directly from Mount Hor to the encampment in the direction of the land of Moab, Zalmonah and Punon and Oboth. The journey from Oboth is to Iye-abarim, which is quite definitely stated to be " in the border of Moab." The account in Deuteronomy fills in the picture. It states clearly, as has just been said, that the host a second time goes the whole way to Ezion-geber, with which this time is coupled the twin city of Elath.

We, too, had arrived at Ezion-geber, we later travellers. And once more, as at Kadesh, we could do no more than arrive a first time, shut our eyes, allow well-nigh forty years to go by between the shutting and the opening again, and then arrive a second time.

Well, then, which way did the host go then? Which way must we go now? The list of stations in Numbers has already made that plain. So does now the account of Moses in

Deuteronomy. "We turned and passed by the way of the wilderness of Moab." A little later he is more specific. He recalls the Lord's command. "Now rise up, and get you over the brook Zered." We, too, must make our way to the brook Zered, wherever that may be, and our road must take us by way of the encampments Zalmonah and Punon and Oboth and Iye-abarim, if we can find them.

First, then, the brook Zered. The word translated "brook" means more properly "wadi" or "torrent-valley." From the emphasis laid upon it as a frontier, it is clear it must have been one of the deepest and broadest torrent-valleys in all that region. Equal emphasis is laid on another "brook" or "torrent-valley" the host encountered on the northward journey to the plains of Moab over against Jericho. This is the "brook Arnon," concerning which again the injunction is uttered: "Rise ye up, take your journey, and pass over the valley of Arnon."

What is the present name, then, of these two torrent-valleys? Again controversy is acute, as in all, or almost all, these attempted identifications between exodic and contemporary place-names. But the fact that two "brooks" are so clearly insisted on in the narrative, and the fact that the great plateau of Transjordan between Amman and Akaba is in fact cloven by two colossal "torrent-valleys" vastly deeper and broader than any of the parallel wadis north or south of them, makes the traditional identification between the brooks Zered and Arnon, on the one hand, and the wadis el Hasa and el Mojib, on the other, almost irresistible; I should say to us quite irresistible, exactly because it is the dominant tradition.

From Akaba, then, we must find our way to the wadi Hasa, which runs ninety-five miles east to west and slightly north, cleaving the Transjordanian massif, and withering away into the salt flats on the south-eastern extremity of the Dead Sea. If we could establish the route taken by the host to Zered-Hasa, our route, too, would lead by way of the encampments at Zalmonah and Punon and Oboth. With the great wadi behind us, we, too, should be "in the border of Moab," en route for the station of Iye-abarim.

Now the traveller from Akaba may take either of two ways in order to get to the wadi el Hasa. He may make due north along the Arabah towards the broad mouth of the wadi. Or he may thrust north-eastward by way of the wadi Ithm directly upward on to the main Transjordan range and make for the narrow upper reaches of the wadi. Do the scholars help him to choose one route or the other by identifying for him Zalmonah or Punon or Oboth? Alas, they do not help him far. There is a vague suggestion that Zalmonah may have lain in this same wadi Ithm, just north-east of Akaba; for when the host journeyed it by the way to the Red Sea, to compass the land of Edom, the narrator points out that " the soul of the people was much discouraged because of the way." Certain scholars have fastened on that phrase. Why was the way so specially discouraging? Was it not because the road out of Ezion-geber which would compose the land of Edom, led up a steep mountain, that same mountain which has given the place its modern name, assuming that the mountain meant was the one east of the Arabah, not the one west? If it was the eastern mountain, it was one which, whether or not it discouraged those ancient Israelitic pilgrims, discouraged year by year for centuries the later Muslim pilgrims pushing up north-eastward to join the caravan coming southward from Damascus.

But that seemed to us a flimsy reason for placing Zalmonah in the wadi Ithm beyond the Akaba mountain, for in those countries it does not need a mountain to make a way hard. A desert can be quite as discouraging, as the whole tenor of the exodic tale indicates. Yet, of course, Zalmonah may well have been a site in the wadi Ithm. It may also have been the same as the modern Maan, as others have thought, some sixty miles north-eastward along the high plateau. Who can prove that it was not?

So much then for Zalmonah, a finger pointing, but very spectrally, to the mountain road. What then of Punon?

Punon is in a different case; so different, that it exercised a preponderating influence on the whole nature and scope of this Mosaic adventure. The word is now so full of association for me, that I cannot say it to myself, or see it printed in its inconspicuous place among the stations listed in Numbers, without feeling my nostrils smart with that hot sand-storm on the Arabah, without feeling myself drenched to the skin during the titanic downpour at the head of the wadi Dana.

Yet, of course, the word had no slightest significance for me when I first let my mind dwell on it, in its place there among the other stations. I think I can say, too, that the word means just as little for all but the most devoted students of the Bible, and little enough for most of them. It was not one of the places where my father's capricious imagination lingered. It might well have been, but it was not. He had an oddly clear picture in his mind of many of these encampments, which he managed to convey to the rest of us by the accumulation of a series of touches regarding which I still cannot make up my mind whether they were artful or artless. Perhaps they were both, as the Talmud so often is. He was clear enough about Zalmonah. The Talmud informed him that only thorns and thistles grew there, but I can still see, as he saw them, those very thorns, those very thistles. The same authority placed for him there the episode of the brazen serpents, which Catholic writers (I was to learn later) ascribed to Punon. If I correctly throw my mind so far back, Punon to him was a mere name, like certain others of these names. It remained for a short time a mere name for me, too, during my first general consideration of the route to be followed between Sinai and Pisgah.

And then suddenly, in a matter of moments, it became charged with emotion for me, though I had not gone any further than the maps and the books. It would have remained so charged, if my friends and I, having emerged by now from the stage of maps and books, had never made our three-fold assault upon the place called in modern speech Khirbet Feinân.

This is what happened. I learned first that a little more was
known of this Punon than of many other stations, Zalmonah,
for instance, or Oboth. Certain of the early doctors of the
Church identify it with Pinon, the seat of an Edomite tribe.
Later, St. Jerome identifies it with Phaenon, a place situated
between Petra and Zoar, somewhere south of the Dead Sea.
We learn there are copper mines there, in that sultry region,
and that the Christian victims of the persecutions of Diocletian
were banished there. We learn from St. Athanasius that
even the hardened criminals who are condemned to the mines
of Phaenon, do not survive there many more than a few days.

Not more than a few days? Not more than a few days?
I repeated the phrase stupidly half a dozen times, and then the
horror took possession of me. I saw the wretches passing from
the outer to the inner hell, from the airless oven of the Arabah
in high midsummer, to the furnace heats of the mine-galleries.
I saw the yellow faces, and the leathery lips, and the green
copper-dust in the sunken hollows of their eyes. It was a
mercy, after all, was it not, they did not survive here more
than a few days?

And then (I read further) the Austrian scholar and traveller,
Musil, came upon the very name and the very place, fourteen
hundred years later. Accompanied by a young Arab from the
northward plateau, he came upon a vast tract of ruins called
Khirbet Feinân, where the wadi Dana opens out into the
Arabah, some ten kilometres north-west of the wild hill-
fortress of Shobek. There was no doubt this place was the
Phaenon of the Christian fathers. The place had once been
the seat of a bishopric and the ruins of ancient aqueducts and
cisterns are found there still. So, too, are the scoriae of the
copper-smeltings, and the tumbled entrances of the atrocious
mine-galleries. Here, then, was Phaenon, which to those
ancients was the Punon of the Biblican tale. Here was Punon,
wherever the dim place Zalmonah might be.

We had settled the matter of transport very simply, having
arranged to take over the car that had brought Rolfe down

from Amman. The car would cover the greater part of the journey, but at certain points we would have to find other modes of transport. The car was a medium-sized Lincoln, which was something of an anti-climax after our two Ford trucks and escort of three armed Sudanese soldiers, but it would do. The chauffeur's name was Jemil. He was more impressive at the head, where he wore a flowing white head-cloth, than at the feet, where he wore a pair of brown canvas gymnasium shoes. But he would do, too.

We were still in the guest-room, about to set off to the home of Salim Bey, when it occurred to me to show Rolfe the letter I had from Sir Ronald Storrs to present to the Emir Abdullah.

" I don't think you've seen this one," I said. " Do you think there'd be any point in letting Salim Bey see it? "

" Could I see the others, too? "

I handed them over to him. He looked through them swiftly, then spread them over his palm in a sort of fan, like a pack of cards.

" You're a lot of fools," he said bluntly. " What are you wasting your time for, down here in Akaba? Why on earth don't you go straight up to Amman and present your letters? "

" What for? "

" ' What for '? " he repeated. " Don't you see it would make all the difference in the world? Instead of creeping in through the back-door like you're doing here in Akaba, they'd send out bands for you wherever you went! I wish I had letters like these! "

" We've had it all out before," said Lucas.

" We're not going to Amman," I said. I tried to explain why. Rolfe sighed. He still thought us very foolish people.

" You haven't answered my question," I pointed out. " Ought I to show Salim Bey Storrs's letter to the Emir Abdullah? Would it make him double up a bit? "

" One minute," said Rolfe. He took it up and read it more carefully. He had only glanced at it before. Then he looked up.

" No! " he said, with great firmness. " No! " He folded it
and handed it back to me. " For the Lord's sake, put it in
an envelope and don't take it out till you get to Amman!
You'll be almost out of the country by that time! "

" That's rather a bore," I said. " I thought it a useful
letter."

I ought at this stage to quote a few sentences from that
letter, or rather from a translation that had been made of it.
The original was, of course, in Arabic. I quote it here not
because it was addressed by one distinguished Near Easterner
to another, but because it played from this point so integral
a part in our journey, that I am tempted to say we now
became a company of four rather than three.

" Your Highness " (the letter went), " It is some months
since I had the honour of your Highness's news and I write
first to present to you my compliments and good wishes for
our New Year and to enquire with respect after your health,
which from news I have received I learn to be excellent.
I also learn with deep satisfaction (and no surprise) of the
continued close and friendly relations of Your Highness with
the Palestine Government." Then followed an account of who
the bearer of the letter and his friends were, and what their
purpose was in visiting His Highness's country. It continued:
" Mr. Golding has been chosen as a descendant of a long line
of illustrious Jewish scholars for the composition of a work
which will be entitled ' In the Steps of Nebi Musa, al Kalim,'
and it is for this reason that any assistance Your Highness
may be able to afford him to visit hills and valleys trodden
by the Prophet will be especially valuable."

I replaced the letter in my wallet.

" You mean," I said, " this letter will tell Salim Bey I'm a
Jew. There seems to be no harm in telling the Emir Abdullah."

" It's a long way between Akaba and Amman."

" All right," I said. We had had that out, too. " Let's go
now."

We drove some little distance along the beach, on the side
towards Arabia, and in a few minutes reached Salim Bey's

house. The house consisted of a mud-hut put to rights recently, and daubed over with whitewash, with a mud kitchen at one side, and a brown marquee in front, which served as a dining-room. We were ushered first into the main room of the mud-hut, where there were carpets on the floor, some plush-upholstered chairs, and some large photographs of relatives on the wall, of the type that are called " Enlargements to the Trade." There were books, too, in a bookshelf. But despite the books, and the striped rugs, the room looked uncannily like one of the " parlours " of my childhood in Doomington.

We had heard a great deal from Salim Bey about his library, which was going to make plain all the dark places of our journey; but actually the only work which dealt with our problems at all was an early edition of the *Encyclopaedia Britannica*, which we consulted gratefully. We had also heard a certain amount about Salim Bey's education in a Christian University in Syria, enough to make us feel that he was likely to be as " western " or " modern " an official as any we were likely to meet in Transjordan, an official of the type that is being encouraged by Ataturk's regime in Turkey. Indeed, not only did he talk of " Mohammed " and " Mecca " by their own names, rather than by a periphrasis, but he embarked upon an illuminating exposition of the greatness of the Prophet, so that we could appreciate the grounds on which the informed Muslim holds Mohammed to be so incomparably the greatest man who has ever lived on this planet. I thought he maintained the thesis with great tact, despite the intense fire of his conviction.

I do not recall that he actually said we should have the honour of meeting Madame, but we certainly got the impression that the idea of keeping her in purdah would be distasteful to this emancipated graduate of a Christian University. She was not there to receive us in the drawing-room, and, in fact, she did not sit down to lunch with us in the marquee dining-room. On our way between the two rooms we did see, at the door of the kitchen, a woman who can hardly have been other than Salim Bey's wife, but she disappeared again into the kitchen the moment she saw us. It seemed there had been an error in timing.

After lunch had started, I went so far as to ask, though with great diffidence, if we might hope for Madame's attendance. For though that was awkward, it seemed just a little more awkward to make no acknowledgment at all of the existence of a lady who, whether or not we had seen her with our own eyes, had gone to a great deal of trouble to prepare for us so noble a repast.

"She's busy," said Salim Bey tonelessly. "You will have some of this sauce? It is special."

I gathered that perhaps Salim Bey was not so emancipated in the matter of women as, perhaps, he thought himself. Or perhaps he felt we were not the right sort of masculine influence for an untried Muslim lady to be subjected to.

The food was princely, and the service ample, being provided by two henchmen and a whole horde of children. They were all our host's children. He was clearly a devoted husband and father. Enormous platters of fish were set before us, many varieties of fish cooked in a variety of ways. There were radishes, chipped potatoes, several sorts of olives, spring onions, fried aubergines, a tomato and onion salad, a pea and potato salad soaked in a luscious brown sauce, a rice couscous in a tomato and egg sauce, and a sweet rice pudding with subtle Eastern flavours. There was coffee, a syrupy sweetening of the bitter stuff we had been drinking. It was good, though strange.

After luncheon we discussed this question of Punon and Feinân. We got out maps, for Salim Bey had not heard of the place, which was many miles beyond his jurisdiction, being about three quarters of the way up to the Dead Sea. We had two ways of getting there open to us. We could leave Akaba by the wadi Ithm and make for Shobek, by way of Maan and Petra. At Shobek we would have to find horses to take us down the steep gullies to the eastern ledges of the Arabah where Feinân is. Or we could make directly northward along the Arabah and attempt to get as near as possible to Feinân that way. The road, apparently, was extremely bad; in fact there was no road. But you could doubtless get a certain distance, anyhow, on pneumatic tyres. Salim Bey was not averse from finding out how far, a piece of knowledge which he might want to have for official purposes some time.

We decided on the second alternative. As we had worked out the route, we would be going the same way as Moses and the host had gone before us. It was true we would not be able to go on from Punon to Iye-abarim, assuming, as is possible, that Iye-abarim was a station at the upland end of one of the terrific west-to-east wadis that climb up to the high plateau. Whichever wadi it was, it must have been a very tough job for the host, with all the women and children and baggage and flocks and herds. For a car it would be quite impossible.

We would sooner or later have to turn back again to Ezion-geber, that is to say, Akaba, and take the wadi Ithm route to the plateau top. But that would be thoroughly in the spirit of the original adventure.

The Israelites spent a good many days, the Bible tells us, compassing Mount Seir. What was more important, we would get some idea of what those journeys were like up the atrocious wadi. If the car could not get all the way to Feinân, which seemed extremely likely, we might even find camels to take us the rest of the way, said Salim Bey vaguely. We did not think that that was likely, either, for he had just said the place was " entirely null." He used that phrase. Sometimes there was a little meagre grazing on the edges of the Arabah and the Beduin would come down from the Transjordan wadis for a few days and nights, and then make off again like ghosts, or as if they were afraid of ghosts.

" If it's been such a bad year," said Lucas, " we'll find no camels. In that case, we might walk."

" Walk? " said Salim Bey. He, too, looked for a moment as if there were goblins round him.

We arranged to leave for the Arabah early next morning.

Rolfe and Jim did not come with us. They went fishing.

"You will be careful," muttered Rolfe, as he went off to the water-front swinging his empty packing-case. He took a case with him now each time he went on the water to hold specimens of the fish he was going to show the secret backers, wherever their den was.

"Careful?" I asked, opening my eyes wide. "Careful?"

Rolfe strode off. He preferred not to explain.

"He means about that other thing," Lucas said quietly. "Being a Jew."

"Oh yes. I'd forgotten." I bit my lip. "Anyhow, he's our host."

"Yes," said Lucas. "He's charming."

A few minutes later Salim Bey joined us. He had his rifle with him. He and I sat at the back of the car. We had food with us, and rugs, in case we could not get back that night. We lurched off and were out of the village a few minutes later. A few minutes after that, we were bumping along the mid wadi. It seemed already, so long as we kept our eye northward, we had been in the wadi for hours. If we turned round, the sea swung and chopped the wadi clean, as an axe might a stick.

The wadi was, as Salim Bey had said the day before, "entirely null." There were a few long graves of humped sand some three miles away, but they did no more than confirm the nullity. Or they may not have been graves at all, but blown sand heaped by the wind. There was a little thorny scrub here and there, gangrened over with a dry lichen and blistered with empty snail-shells. There were a few stunted acacias, so coated over with sand, they seemed static, not growths at all. There was some tamarisk, too, drooped in abject surrender.

It was a morose journey, unsusceptible to division either in time or space. The earth below was always the same, sapless and lightless. The air was yellow and hot and stagnant, already charged with apprehensions of the storm coming out towards us from the Dead Sea. There was no mirage. Air and sky were too sullen for that; so, too, were the mountains on either hand. They contracted, they drew further apart, but beyond that they were opaque matter, without dignity.

Some ten or twelve miles out, Lucas spotted a flower. We got out to pay tribute to its hardihood. It was a bulbous yellow flower with a red centre, that grew in a clumpy mass on a furred stalk with no leaves. We saw nothing else to mitigate the desert, no other plant, no bird, nor beast, nor even the track of any.

" If that is Punon, all those miles northward," I said disconsolately, " we have not even arrived at Zalmonah yet."

It was not more fresh outside the car than in it. There was a smell here of hot soot we had not noticed within.

" Something's burning," I said.

" Sodom and Gomorrah," observed Lucas. " The fire's not gone out yet."

We got back into the car and drove on for some time. Our throats were so dry that we sucked orange after orange without interval. We were glad we had brought a great many. The air ahead of us was getting thicker and browner. There was a metallic sheen on the slopes of the further mountains. The car was bucking and rearing on the broken ground.

Jemil turned.

" Further? " he asked.

" Further! " said Lucas. The sulphurous glare, the sense of doom, exhilarated him. " All the way to Punon! "

" Further! " repeated Salim Bey. His face was without expression.

The host must have come up against these Dead Sea storms frequently, I said to myself. It can't have been easy to urge them into them. There is no shelter here. There is no shelter anywhere. Half an hour later it was impossible to see more than five yards ahead of us. The engine stalled and spluttered.

" Turn again? " asked Jemil. I felt I was going to like him. He was the sort of driver who will keep moving in the direction demanded of him, so long as there are still four wheels to the chassis.

Salim Bey was peering hard through the window.

" Did you see it? " he asked.

" No, what? "

" There was a hyena."

" No! I didn't see it. Jemil seems very worried. Will you ask him to turn again."

" Turn! " commanded Salim Bey. " When I was small, I had a baby hyena for a pet. I loved him greatly. I am sorry you could not get to Khirbet Feinân. You will have to go the other way, by Shobek. I am sorry I shall not be with you. I should like to be with you."

He was very talkative on the return journey and good company. I could not decide whether that was because he had seen the hyena, or because he was so relieved we had not pressed any further into that sulphurous storm. He was as charming as he had ever been. He insisted we should go back to his home. There were one or two maps he had found among his papers, and some letters he would like to write for us, for some of the police-officers up country. Besides, we were very dry. We had got through all our oranges. He must make us some tea with special flavours.

We were delighted about the maps and letters. They would be useful. We liked the idea of the tea, too. We emerged from the hem of that smoky pall into the broadening of the wadi. The wind had arrived before us, making the sea a dark rich purple, splashed with bold white commas. We drove straight up to Salim Bey's house and drew up alongside one of the blind walls, then walked several yards in the direction of the marquee. He came with us, joking and laughing. I forget what the joke was about. Then he said: " Excuse me a moment, I will get some cigarettes, too." He turned away from us towards his front door. At that same instant, the woman we had seen before stepped a foot or two over the threshold and on seeing us at once withdrew again. It was the same woman, evidently his wife, and yet not the same.

Something had happened. Her face was dead white. Her coal-black hair lay lankly over her face.

Lucas and I walked on to the marquee and sat down. The big table had been cleared out of the way. There was only a small round table there.

" Did you see her? " I said. " Something's happened while we've been out. Something rather dreadful."

" I saw she'd lost her hairpins."

" All right. Anyhow, it doesn't concern us."

" If one of the kids stuck a pin into another kid's neck ? No, it doesn't."

" You liked that storm, eh? "

" I liked the idea of Salim Bey and his pet hyena. Now I come to think of it——"

" Quiet ! " I said. Salim Bey was approaching. He entered.

" There will be tea at once ! " he said. " The kettle was boiling already. Look, I have found the map."

His face, too, was deadly-white. His hands shook as he spread out the map on the table. But his voice was as smooth and soft, his manners were as courtly, as we had ever known them. He took out a pencil and followed the route he proposed we should take. Up the wadi Ithm to Maan, from Maan to El Dji and Petra. Then back up the wadi Musa again by the Ain Nejel road to Shobek. We would not have to go back to Maan again.

" I will let you have a letter for the officer at El Dji. He is a great friend of mine. He will see they will meet you properly down in Petra."

The tea came, brought in by one of the old Bedu henchmen. He poured it out for us and hoped we liked the flavour. He was not the same man at all as had stepped out of the car with us. What had happened? What? There was no suggestion on his part that he would not like us to stay one hour, two hours, all the rest of the day if it pleased us. But his lips were trembling. All the blood had gone out of them.

" Excuse me," he said. " I will go and fetch pen and ink and paper. Then you will have the letters for certain. You think you may go the day after to-morrow? What a pity. I wish I could go with you."

He rose and went off into the house.

Lucas bent over towards me. " You're right. Something's happened. Something dreadful."

" What can it be? Anything to do with us? My head's thumping! Let's get out of this! "

" Nothing to do with us. He can't be such a hypocrite. His wife. Somebody must have attacked her." We saw Salim Bey approaching. Lucas straightened swiftly. " It ought to be much easier by Shobek," he said in a normal voice.

" A pity about Shobek," said Salim Bey. " I do not know the officer there. I shall write some letters now, shall I? "

He wrote them. He gave us advice of one sort or another. He put his hands round the tea-pot, and said it was cold, he would order more tea for us.

" No! " I got up suddenly. " It is so kind of you! We are a little anxious about our friends! We have many notes to write, too. You have been so kind, Salim Bey! "

" Please! Only if you must! " he begged us. " As for your friends, you need not worry. Abdullah is sure to have come in when he saw the storm blowing up. I am sorry we could get no more close to Khirbet Feinân. Another time, perhaps, another expedition. Good-bye! Good-bye! "

" What can it *be*? What can have *happened*? " I asked, as we drove back into the village. " Something was eating him up all the time and yet he kept us! It was uncanny."

" The hospitality of the man! " exclaimed Lucas. " That's what gets me! Just because we were guests . . . You'll admit no Westerner could behave like that! His wife, I'm sure that was it! Rolfe will know. He probably knows all about it already! "

" If they're back! " I said anxiously.

They were only just back when we arrived. The water had become very choppy, but the fish were biting well. The sky

LADY OF PETRA

was untidy with torn clouds. There was a lurid green and yellow sunset over the copper mountains of Sinai.

We let Rolfe settle down a little before we told him of this matter of Salim Bey. We let him sort out his fish, some to fry, some to go on the journey northward. He was keeping them fresh with palm-leaves in a cistern behind the kitchen. He told us that he had come across the traces of the Prophet Moses out in the water. They had hooked a fish, a sort of big sole, and on being asked what its name was: "*Samakh Musa!*" Abdullah had said at once. "And why *samakh Musa*?" Rolfe had asked, loyally. Because the Nebi Musa had once caught a certain fish, and it was so big, the half of it was quite enough for him. So he threw the other half into the sea, and that half became the father of the grandfather of that fish.

"So the Nebi Musa, too, was a fisherman?" asked Rolfe.

"And the Nebi Harun, too!" said Abdullah. "But the Nebi Harun swallowed a large bone, and choked, and died. They carried his body up to the Jebel Harun!" said Abdullah. "The bone is still in his neck, they say."

"Do you think that is a good story?" asked Rolfe. "What are you fellows looking so blue about?"

"It is a good story. We have one to tell you." I told him about Salim Bey.

"Good God!" said Rolfe. "Good God!" He slumped down into his chair, the palms of his hands over his bare knees.

"What's happened? Do you think you could find out?"

"I know," he said gloomily. "I'm almost sure I know."

"What?"

"Oh nothing!"

"Don't be absurd, Rolfe! What's in your mind?"

"Won't you ever understand?" said Lucas impatiently. "He thinks Salim Bey's found out you're a Jew." He turned to Rolfe. "Isn't that so?"

Rolfe nodded.

The idea was like a dentist's prod touching a nerve.

Mα

" It couldn't be that! " I said.

" Who'd tell him? " asked Lucas.

" I don't know! I suppose it came out in some wireless message. That's the sort of country it is! You can't blow your nose up in Ajlun without somebody in Kerak informing the Intelligence Service——"

" I don't believe it! " I said flatly. " He was so kind, so helpful! Are you trying to tell me that if he knew I was a Jew——"

" I'm not trying to tell you anything. Let's have a drink. Have you any of that *arrak* left? "

I looked helplessly from one to the other.

" It's preposterous! "

" That's all right! " said Lucas. " It's exactly the same sort of thing as Moses was up against. You said you'd like it, didn't you! "

" What do you mean? " asked Rolfe, puzzled.

" Well, when Moses was somewhere round here, he sent messengers to the king of Edom—old name for Transjordan, you know."

" Yes? "

" He wanted to go straight through his country. But old man Edom wasn't having any. ' Thou shalt not pass through me,' he said, ' lest I come out with the sword against thee.' Friendly, wasn't it? "

" Ah well! " Rolfe sighed heavily. " It won't be as bad as all that. There wasn't any Peake Pasha, then. That *is* the fish frying, isn't it? Thank the Lord for that! "

" Do you mean, Rolfe," I insisted, " that it's going to upset things for you? "

" No, no! " objected Rolfe, too hastily.

" You're wrong," I said. " It wasn't that. You'll see."

" All right. I'm wrong," said Rolfe. He refused to discuss the matter any more. We went into the dining-room and drank some *arrak* and waited for the fish to be brought in. It was brought in at last, and we ate it and went to bed. We had made up our minds to leave for Maan next day. The soldiers in the guard-room were whining to the *rhibab*, but we were used to them by now. They did not keep us awake.

Next morning Salim Bey was in early. He was as courteous and helpful as ever. Nothing was too much for him. I looked at Rolfe triumphantly. Rolfe grimaced. I did not know these people, the look meant.

No, I did not. It turned out that he did not, either. He was wrong about Salim Bey. Lucas was not so wide off the mark. When we had settled our affairs, Salim Bey told us what had happened yesterday, while his back was turned. He could not talk about it to us then, because we were his guests, and a man must not make his guests feel unhappy. A *fellah* who lived in a small hovel not far from Salim Bey's home was in the habit of calling to his small daughter and asking her to play with him. When he saw the father going off up the Arabah, he called her as usual, and then attacked her.

" If they let him go," said Salim Bey, " I will strangle him with these hands. It is a bad country. Yes, it is a very bad country. You must go now? I am sorry you must go. You must come again. Will you come again? But perhaps I shall not be here then."

" Good-bye, Salim Bey. We have much to thank you for."

" It is nothing, nothing," said Salim Bey, and turned to the little blue policeman with the spiked helmet, who stood beside him, with a great sheaf of papers over his arm, like a napkin. " You must come again," he repeated, as if Akaba were Kensington.

§ 8

I was sitting at the back of the car between Rolfe and Lucas.

" Well, you see, Rolfe, you were wrong," I said.

" How do you mean wrong? "

" About why Salim Bey was in such a state yesterday."

" Yes, I suppose I was. But I'm glad we've got away just the same."

" So am I," added Lucas.

" Why? " I asked.

" I just happened to overhear Salim Bey one day, when he and Rolfe were whispering in that courtyard."

" What did you hear? "

" Nothing much. It was just the way he said it. ' Dirty Jews! ' I never in all my life heard so much poison concentrated into two words."

" He didn't mean you," Rolfe assured me hastily. " He was talking about business interests."

" I don't think he meant us," I said. " I have a feeling he knew one of us was a Jew."

" Absolute rot! " Rolfe exploded. " The fellow's a fire-brand. They're the sort of people who've caused the whole trouble—the effendis and small officials. It's they who've set the desert ablaze. That's why he's here, in exile in Akaba. He's an absolute fire-brand. When he was in Amman——"

" That may be," I said stubbornly. " I still think he knew. He's a great host."

The others turned away impatiently and glued their faces at the windows.

CHAPTER SEVEN

§ 1

GREY limestone fringes the wadi Arabah west and east,
and, beneath a covering of blown sand and gravel, forms
its bed, out-cropping here and there in a toothy snarl.
Grey air, grey gravel, grey limestone, make the wadi a mournful place to be in. " To Edom ! " the traveller says to himself
with pleasure. " To the red country ! "

But the way is long before the limestone breaks off sharp
against the granite and porphyry, and the sandstone, a great
tawny blanket, muffles these. First come the rubbly foot-
slopes of Jebel Neseileh, scattered with the bleached bones of
camels, dead on the last lap of their journey. A dead sheik
lies in a pressed-sand grave, surrounded by his worthies. Not
far off is a sacred tree. " He had a stick," said Jemil, " carved
from a bough of that tree. His enemies fell even before he
smote them with it."

At a distance of some four miles the track turns due eastward
into the wadi Ithm, the main high-road up into the highlands
of Edom, where once the caravans of balm and spices from
southern Arabia went tottering northward. It is all still grey
and broken and waterless, with little green stuff or none for
the two or three herds of camels and black goats you may see
plodding disconsolately upward from the still more niggardly
comfort of the Arabah. Some miles further are the remains of
a dam, as it would seem, thrown at some time across the wadi,
(though Colonel Peake, in his *History of Trans-Jordan and its
Tribes*, declares it was probably a Nabataean defence work or
customs barrier). Jemil had another idea about it. He said
that the sheikh whose grave we had recently seen had built it
in order to practise jumps with his horse, for he had been the
greatest horseman in all the country. Colonel Peake recounts
a similar legend, with one or two important differences. The

sheikh was not a Muslim, but a Christian, by name Hadid. This Hadid " occupied the wadi Ithm and the country east of it, and as he was at war with the Arabs of the wadi Arabah, erected the wall to shut out his enemies. Hadid had a famous horse on which he descended upon his enemies from the wadi Ithm. After loading himself with booty, he returned to safety by leaping over the wall, his horse being the only one in exist- ence which could make this jump." The Crusaders did not come down the wadi Ithm, it would seem, without leaving one doughty ghost behind them.

Jemil was not stimulating company. His face never changed expression ; his mouth hardly moved as he spoke. Even Rolfe found him difficult to understand, and it took us some time to recognize on his tongue the few Arabic words we knew. Gebel, for instance, was now Jebel. But evidently he had a well- stocked mind, worth digging into, and he was a good mechanic.

Now the wadi issued from its limestone banks and thrust steeply between cliffs of black granite veined perpendicularly with basalt and porphyry. The sheer hopelessness of the lime- stone country, which sinks to its nadir in the Arabah, lifted. But there was no ease yet, no whisper of greenness. The sense of strain hung heavily over the landscape, the buckled crusts, the riven strata. The wadi still thrust fiercely upward, then the pace slackened. We attained a stony shelf, which they call *el Mezradh*, the sown place. Nothing of that sowing remains now. But Rome was here once, and Rome remains. We are in the track of the road built by Trajan to connect Gerasa, now called Jerasch, with the vast storehouses of Petra and the dockside sheds of Aila. Of the road itself nothing more is to be seen than a few scattered milestones poking up out of the sand, and a few squared stones where Trajan's block-houses were.

Now, too, we have emerged from dark granite into ruddy sandstone. There are thin patches of grass here, and even flowers, tiny dandelions, and golden celandine. A large rank wormwood becomes frequent. It is a deep green. It can be as rank as it pleases, so long as there be a lot of it, and so green. We rub our eyes incredulously, half afraid we will rub away that appearance of feathery tuft and golden star. But it is true. It is there. We have come out upon the great plain of el Hismeh, the Red Valley. Here live the Atauneh, and they have wells and they grow wheat, not much or good wheat, but it is grown most years, for there is often rain here.

Here and there along the route are the bases of old forts. In one of them the tribesmen bury their dead, in the rooms where once the Roman soldiers caroused, seeking to forget the loneliness and bitterness of their exile. On a cairn beside the doorway, Jemil perfunctorily drops a stone, as an Italian peasant might drop a bead in his rosary. A great last rampart, the Jebel esh Sherat, extends between us and the high tops of Edom. (Perhaps Sherat is none other than Seir, in the Book we have been reading?) We reach it at last and climb from the middle levels to the final pass, the Nagb Shtar. The track zigzags rather fearfully up the pass. It is cold and misty. The wheels fail of their grip, the car sets out on a return journey to the plain, stern foremost. Jim, always admirable with engines and animals in distress, leaps out and wedges a spar of rock under the back wheel. We reach the summit without mishap and dismount to look down upon the titan landscape. The view here is a complement to the view described earlier, from the Ras el Negeb on the knife-edge of Et Tih, across the sunken Arabah to these very mountains we stand on now. It is a complement and at the same time quite unbelievably different from it. It is, of course, partly a matter of the air and sky, but it is not only that. Then we looked across air as pellucid as crystal under a sky shrill-blue in its purity, so that the colours of rock and sea blazed like forest fires. You could see their smoke spiralling upward in the intense heat. Here the air is misted and muted. We are going to have cold and rain in Transjordan, but for that we shall have flowers and greenness. The sea's blue is almost not blue at all. It is dun and northern. The colour of all the hills is a damped-down red. The landscape there from the top of Sinai was romantic, arrogant in the variety of its forms and the unbridled license of its colour. Here it is abstract, restrained. There are hills like cones and obelisks, like cubes and cylinders, like the junk-room of some cosmic drawing-class. There is a banked-up square platform exactly like a vast tennis-court, in proportion and composition. Two walls chiselled square out of the side of a mountain form a monstrous *fronton*, where the Edomite gods played pelota a long time before the Basques knew about it in Guipuzcoa.

We turn our faces northward; we have some distance to go up hill and down dale before we attain the high steppes. There are remains of old forts, old enclosures, old terracings. The conviction grows upon the traveller that once this country harboured fine flocks and grew goodly crops and harboured clans that lived, if not settled, then at least, comfortable lives. It is a conviction that is from day to day bound up with a growing melancholy, that the dwellers in this land now are so few, so racked, so improvident.

Somewhere on our left hand, Jemil tells us, is a land of three hundred wells. He gives the number with complete sang-froid, as if he spoke of three hundred blades of grass. He means, doubtless, there are many wells, that is to say certain wells. He is using number poetically rather than arithmetic-ally, exactly as his remote kinsmen did, in both Bible and Koran. It may well be there are certain wells in that trackless country of which there is hearsay among the natives, but they are not marked down in maps. His imagination wanders deeper into those mysterious depths. He tells us of secret gardens, where there are figs and grapes. He is not of the sort that tells wild travellers' tales. He means what he says—gardens with figs and grapes.

And in a moment a flash leads from those spoken to certain written words, words that had seemed mere poetry and polite-ness until then, the words sent by Moses to the king of Edom. "Let us pass, I pray thee, through thy land: we will not pass through field or vineyard, neither will we drink of the water of the wells; we will go along the king's high way, we will not turn aside to the right hand nor to the left, until we have passed thy border."

Are these the vineyards of Edom, that Jemil the Edomite points out to us, where Moses vowed he would not pass, where we do not pass? Are we here on the king's high way, where later the Roman generals built their roads and set down their fortresses?

We come to a narrow valley and a patch of green-yellow grass, and a spring seeping out of it in a bed of bright pebbles. The waters flow into a basin of prepared stone. We dismount to stretch our limbs. Water is too scarce in these parts to pass it by without paying due respect to it.

" This spring," I ask. " What is its name? "

" Abu el Lissan! " responds Jemil casually.

I pause and listen hard, straining into the silence. Abu el Lissan! Almost before my mind consciously registers the import of the name, I hear the roaring of the plunging camels, the whine of bullets through the air, the smart crack of bullets against the rocks, the screaming of the tribesmen red-eyed with blood-lust as they go hurtling after the fleeing Turks.

This is Abu el Lissan, where such fighting was, such anguish and ecstasy, now in the heat as hushed and virginal as cold is on untrodden mountain-tops blank with snow. Only a few years ago Lawrence, this later Conqueror, was fighting here, and already his tale seems as remote as the Hebrew's tale, or the Roman's, or the Crusader's. It is as if the cliffs had come together and ground it into dust, and the winter torrents have swept the dust away.

I recalled that in Akaba our minds had been full of Abu el Lissan, the springs under the pass, " the crux of our plan," as Lawrence had called it, which he must needs capture before he could march down on the sea. We had rehearsed the names of the three outposts between Abu el Lissan and Akaba— Ghuweira and Kethira and Khadra—which we would come upon in the reverse order from his capture of them, as often as we had rehearsed any three stations in the Israelite Wandering. We had gone by or through them all, but they had no more thrust themselves up into our notice out of the silence and the heat-dazzle than Zalmonah had, or Oboth, if Zalmonah or Oboth had lain along this road.

This was Abu el Lissan, then, captured after a long wild battle in hell's heat. So we sat down there, as he and his men did when it was all over, on that " delightful turf, green and soft, on which we lay, wrapped in our cloaks, wondering if something to eat were preparing: for we were subject at the moment to the physical shame of success, a reaction of victory, when it became clear that nothing was worth doing, and that nothing worthy had been done."

So the day drew to its close, and night came, bringing calm to the living and beauty to the dead. " The dead men looked wonderfully beautiful. The night was shining gently down, softening them into new ivory. Close round them lapped the dark wormwood, now heavy with dew, in which the ends of the moonbeams sparkled like sun-spray. The corpses seemed flung so pitifully on the ground, huddled anyhow in low heaps. Surely if straightened they would be comfortable at least. So I put them all in order, one by one, very wearied myself, and longing to be of these quiet ones." It was a longing that was never again to desert him. Instinct said " Die! " then, and on a later occasion he tells us of; " but reason said that was only to cut the mind's tether, and loose it into freedom: better to seek some mental death, some slow wasting of the brain to sink it below these puzzlements."

So, duly, some five years later, he sought his mental death, his great book written, a settlement having been achieved which, as he wrote, " has honourably fulfilled our war-obligations and my hopes." He sought to submerge his Arthurian legend in the day-to-day ennui and ardour of a nameless airman. But he could as effectively will his mental death as he could command his heart to pump no more blood. Another book must needs be written, in glamour to be compared with the earlier one as an aeroplane careering mortally through sleet-grey heavens is to be compared with a *fantasia* of desert horsemen thundering across golden sands. Not that way lay death. In speed only, in speed, he might hurl himself beyond the body, the body that could not scale the heavens except in a fume of petrol.

We rose from beside the green-yellow grass, and the spring of Abu el Lissan seeping out of it in a bed of bright pebbles. The place was newly littered with dead, which had not been there when we sate down, and amongst them one living shade, longing to be of those quiet ones. We would come up with him again on this journey, we thought; and so went further, climbing for a time, and came out at last on the high steppe, the top of the land of Edom, the fringe of the vast desert of Arabia.

There are some twenty miles to go between Abu el Lissan and Maan. It is getting dark now, a cold and melancholy darkness. The landscape is featureless, here and there a hump which may once have been a fortress, or may be nothing more than a bare swirl of earth. We arrive at length at Maan, a few mud houses, and then a few more and then at last a street. There are few folk about in the driving wind, and those few hug the wall with faces averted. They are enough to make you know that strangers are not loved in this town.

There is no hotel here. There was until a few years ago, but it withered and died in the cold wind and the sour looks of the townspeople. Jemil makes straight for the police-post. If there is a police-post anywhere on your route in Transjordan, you are well-advised to make for it. An iron post like a skinny arm thrusts a guttering lamp forward over the portal of the police-station. Three policemen in blue with spiked helmets are waiting round a bare table, crowded importantly with documents. We enter. The question comes before even our passports are handed over.

" *Inta jehud?* "

My heart turns over sickeningly and infuriatingly. I feel I should like to do a little damage among those helmets and documents.

" English! English! " proclaims Lucas, proclaims Jim.

Rolfe merely swears a little in their own tongue. The police-men shuffle among their papers. They pretend they can understand the entries on the passports, but it is clear they do not. A lot of transcribing goes on. Perhaps they are merely writing down suras from the Koran.

I have time to recall that my folk entering this land a long time ago seemed a little disposed to rash action. " Take ye good heed unto yourselves therefore," Moses requested them. " Contend not with them." He continues : " Ye shall purchase food of them for money, that ye may eat ; and ye shall also buy water of them for money, that ye may drink."

But there is no hotel in Maan. The shops are as tight-sealed as tombs.

" And now, Jemil," Rolfe commands, " go Camp ! Air Force ! "

" Thank God for the Empire ! " cries Jim. There are no more fervent imperialists than all four of us that night any-where east of Suez.

§ 2

In terms of the Mosaic journey our objective was Punon-Feinân. We had been frustrated in the effort to get there by the direct northward route up the Arabah and proposed to get there by Shobek, which lies above it, over towards the western edge of the mountains. It was not a likely route for Moses and the host to have taken. They were hardly likely to have descended the steep wadi to Punon, merely for the pleasure of coming up again. They had had enough of the Arabah and of compassing Mount Seir, and once up on the tops, it seems likely they would have tried to keep there. On the other hand, news might have come to them that some tribe of Edomites was massing against them to dispute the passage. They had been given strict injunctions not to contend with them. The Lord had announced he would not give them of the Edomite land, no, not so much as for the sole of the foot to tread on, because he had given Mount Seir unto Esau for a possession. It may have seemed wise to get down to the plain again, perhaps by the wadi Shobek to Punon, and then march northward again for a time. The encampment named after Punon is Oboth. Oboth, too, may have been in the plain. We read of a wadi Oueibeh a few hours north of Punon, and the name has been thought to preserve a phantom reminiscence of Oboth. After Oboth, they pitched at Iye-abarim, " in the wilderness which is before Moab, toward the sunrising." The word *abarim* means " the regions on the other side," that is to say, on the other side of the Dead Sea, seen from the standpoint of the dweller in Palestine. In other words, in Iye-abarim we are definitely on the tops, wherever the preceding stations may have been. Where in those " regions on the other side " Iye-abarim might be, we would consider later. We were now making for Shobek and Feinân by way of Maan. We could even give ourselves the satisfaction of remembering that Zalmonah, the next station after Eziongeber, had been placed at Maan. It was in the encampment of a later host, here at Zalmonah-Maan, we hoped to pitch our tents.

And, in fact, we did.

Rolfe was well in with the Air Force, we gathered, as well as with the Residencies at Jerusalem and Amman. He had not stopped at Maan on his way down from Amman, but he believed there was a Flight stationed at the camp at Maan doing special training. If there were, he was sure they would put us up. If not, we could always have a drink and a doss in the men's mess. There was a permanent guard to look after the hangars.

The camp was several miles away from the town. The hangars, the canteens, the lines of huts looked uncanny looming up out of the dark and morose desert. We drove in and an airman came up from behind a hut, a nameless airman, such as Lawrence was to be, and had now been. The airman's blue breeches and puttees, his grey shirt, his standing-up hair, looked at once familiar and quite incredible. We had seen something like them before but could not believe we were seeing them now. The corporal scratched the back of his skull with a pencil.

He, too, was not sure if he was seeing things. He went off to put the issue up to the officers. We gathered there were a few about the place. We had not drawn blank.

A couple of minutes later we were in the officers' mess, sitting on upholstered leather chairs before a roaring wood-fire, with a gramophone going, with whiskeys-and-soda going, with a vague feeling that it was the Last Week of Term, and what would the Old Man say if he saw the bottles, but we were leaving anyway, so let's have a jolly good time.

It was all dream-like, the hot bath, the excellent meal, the sheets in the beds. Was it Merchiston, was it Radley, and these swells looking after us were the Prefects, and the rather inferior creatures on the edges of things, batmen and waiters, they were fags, no-account juniors in Shell A and Lower Remove? And the conversation, was it not exactly Cheltenham: girls and games and—now and again, but a little furtively—books? The games were somewhat more complicated than they are at Uppingham, and were played with aeroplanes, not with balls, but they were taken neither more nor less seriously. They piloted aeroplanes and took photographs from them and practised how to spot people massing together below when they had no business to. They had come to Maan to practise shooting at a flying target, a long red balloon slung out from behind another aeroplane. And the marksman is high up in the heavens and swoops down and past the drogue, as he calls it, and fires a hundred rounds into it. And next morning one among their number went up and scored eighty hits, and the other chaps talked about it, respectfully but not fulsomely, exactly as if he had scored eighty not out in a Trial Match at Repton.

It was enchanting, being at Repton, on the edge of the Arabian desert. I wondered if the young Roman gentlemen who once were planted in forlorn outposts in these same marches of empire, sang so gaily and drank so lustily, hoping they might thus forget how far Rome was?

They could not have been more hospitable.

§ 3

There was a basin with running water in my bedroom, and a standard lamp beside my bed, and in my bed sheets and a pillow-slip. I had drunk and eaten well in my encampment at Zalmonah; a good deal better (I told myself) than my people, concerning whom it is written: " And the people spake against God, and against Moses, Wherefore have ye brought us up out of Egypt to die in the wilderness? for there is no bread, and there is no water; and our soul loatheth this light bread."

I switched out the light on the table beside me, and lit the candles in the kitchen in Doomington. " For you must know," my father said, " the merchants would come in of an evening to the edge of the camp at Zalmonah, and tempt our fathers with the produce of their fields and vineyards, with loaves and with the meat of their flocks. And our fathers would lust after these things, despite the manna in their wallets and their chafing-dishes. And in the moment they stretched forth their hands, the food wasted and withered, like an abandoned shoe in the sun. And for that reason, as the passage saith, ' the Lord sent fiery serpents among the people, and they bit the people, and much people of Israel died.' And why should it be serpents that the Lord sent among the people? This was the reason. In the beginning of things the Lord had cursed the serpent, saying, ' Dust shall thou eat,' and whatsoever else the serpent might eat other than dust, still tasted of dust, yet the serpent did not complain. Not so the people he had blessed so abundantly, and given ample store of manna to eat, which had all flavours of all air-food and earth-food and sea-food. The people complained bitterly. And the Lord sent fiery serpents among them, and many among them died, and some did not die. 'And the people came to Moses,' as it is written, ' and said, We have sinned, because we have spoken against the Lord, and against thee; pray unto the Lord, that he take away the serpents from us. And Moses prayed for the people.' "

My father paused and sighed. " So great the love of Moses was. There has been no man like to him unto this day." He shook his head and resumed. " ' And the Lord said unto Moses, Make thee a fiery serpent, and set it upon a standard : and it shall come to pass that every one that is bitten, when he seeth it, shall live.' And Moses did this thing, and made a serpent of brass, and he held the standard on high, and hurled the serpent high above the top of the standard, and by his magic art held the serpent suspended in mid-air for half a day, high above the standard. In that way there was none so small but that he might get a clear view of the serpent, and so be cured, and live. And why a serpent? And why of brass? Because in the Holy Tongue *nachash* means ' snake ' and ' *nechoshet* ' brass. And there is much magic in the mingling of thing and sound, and there was no magician so potent as Moses who wrought magic in the Lord's name.

" And so the people lifted their eyes, and looked up not only to the brass serpent but the Lord in his glory. And they were cured of all the ills that afflicted them in that place, in Zalmonah, of the venom of serpents, of dogs' bites, of all agues and fevers. And they took up their tents, and went further on that long road."

§ 4

Rolfe had gone off very early that morning, having found that an army lorry was returning to Amman. He left his box of fish specimens strapped on to the back of Jemil's car, which seemed curious, because he had travelled a long way, and spent a long time, in getting them. I had imagined once or twice the day before that I smelled them, but thought it better to say nothing, for perhaps it was the brakes burning, after all.

I did not think the secret backer would really need to see the fish with his own eyes, for it is well known the fish of Akaba are better than the fish of Palestine. It is also known that while some have no scales and fins, others have. The abandoned fish accompanied us for a few hours on our journey

Façade in Petra

the next day, and then we flung the putrescent corpses out on to the loam and gravel of the desert, wondering as we did so whether we were not ensuring dark confusion in the minds of geologists aeons later, who might find the petrified skeletons of fish at this great altitude and deduce that the waters of the Red Sea once flowed over the high plateau of Arabia Petraea.

Before setting off on the next stage of our journey, we thought it wise to spend a little time in Maan; we found that neither the place itself nor its inhabitants encourage you to spend there more than a little. It is an old town, yet it has little known history, or none. Was it Zalmonah? That is a rash thing to believe. It is hardly more likely that it is the same place as that Maon named among the cities of Judah. There are no Roman remains among its fragments of old walls and stones. The Roman road from Akaba ran some miles westward. Doughty saw there " two chapters of ancient marble pillars, and upon them some sculptured barbaric ornament of basket or network." They seemed queer things to be in that niggard city, and we made an attempt to find if they were still to be seen anywhere. Our questioning was received with such suspicion, whether or not it was understood at all, we thought it best to desist forthwith.

If Maan was no station on the road to Zion, it attained some importance as a stage on the *haj* to Mecca. To the Beduin by whose aid Lawrence had captured the spring at Abu el Lissan, it was a place that lured them by a dream of unmeasured loot; but to less Spartan livers it seems a pusillanimous place.

We were followed up and down the main street by companies of fly-bitten boys, of whom one in particular was as distressing a creature as I have seen. He had a pear-shaped head, swollen and red-rimmed eyes, and legs which were like sacks of skin to hold the two leg-bones. He carried about with him a chicken whose eyes were identical with his own. He thrust the chicken in our faces as insistently as a fly buzzes about one's head. What his motive was it was impossible to fathom, whether he wished to sell us the chicken, whether

Nc

he wished to show off the chicken, or whether somehow he expected to move our pity by letting us see he had no friend in the whole world saving only his chicken. The townsmen of Maan loved him, or perhaps they feared him, as a zany possessed with powers.

Apart from that young man, they did not seem to have much in common. They have a reputation as a cantankerous people, and the air was full of gritty wind and sudden spurts of dispute. There was some unpleasantness in one of the stores on the main street, and the townsmen were beginning to gather round ominously. The townsmen hold their merchants to be alien, for their fathers came from Hebron over the border. The merchants have gold teeth, they themselves have few or none. When the unpleasantness began, one old man threw himself on to the floor of the shop and began to recite a prayer, banging his forehead on the ground repeatedly. That method of keeping out of trouble was denied to us, so we moved away, all the more as we remembered most vividly that incomparable account in *Arabia Deserta* of a quarrel among the townsfolk of Maan.

" It is a proverb here," says Doughty, " that a man will slay the son of his mother for an old shoe-leather. The breach was this: some children disputed for an apple, the strife increased, men rose from the clay branches, men came forth from the thresholds, and drawing to their partialities, every hot head cried down, despised and threatened his contraries. Men armed themselves, and the elders' reverence was weak to appease this strong sedition. Barbarous shoutings are answered with bloody words; they ran apart from both sides to their quarters, and as every man entered his cottage there he shut himself in and fortified the door; then he mounted upon his clay roof to shoot against the next hostile houses. None of them durst come forth more in all that year, for their adversaries would let shots fly at him from their house terraces. Upon both sides they saw the harvest ripen and stand out so long, without reapers, that all their bread was lost; at length also their pleasant autumn fruits, hanging ruddy in the orchards, rotted before their eyes. There fell eight beleaguered champions in eight months, beside some it was said who perished with hunger. In this time many, not partisans, had abandoned Maan; the most went to settle themselves in the Hauran: all but the small traders removed to Shemmîa.— These Eve's sons were lost for the apple at Maan! even the peasant soldiery had taken part with their seditious fellow-villagers, but the end was near. The Pasha, at the returning of the Haj, enclosed their place with the caravan guard, drew out the hunger-starved rioters and binding the ringleaders and the sheyks, carried them, about twenty persons, to Damascus."

For our part, not thinking the time was ripe for a journey to Damascus, we turned back hastily to Jemil, who, being himself a townsman, had thought it prudent to keep on the edge of things. The town was already wearing a brisker air. The fellaheen coming in on their donkeys from the desert with loads of scrub, *hamiz*, were trotting up to the place of the gold-toothed merchant. Only the camel that lay dying under a yellowing mulberry tree remained indifferent.

" To Petra, Jemil! " I said. In an experience so full of strangeness and wonder, I could say " To Petra, Jemil! " as one might say, " Leicester, third week-end."

§ 5

It was, of course, unthinkable, not to go to Petra, even if it were in no wise caught up in the skein of the Mosaic journey. It is taken for granted by any traveller in the near East that not to make a great effort to get to Petra is folly. Having seen Petra, I should pronounce it worse than folly. It is a place regarding which, the world having heard so much of it by now, it is impossible not to anticipate one will be, at least at first, disappointed; as one certainly is on first going to Venice or Rome or Athens. But it seems to me a place where one's experience transcends any possible anticipation of it, for the reason that its quality is unamenable to words, like music itself, in a degree which I do not believe true of any other place.

Excepting one only, and I speak with the last intention in the world of being paradoxical. I mean New York. In these two places you are absolved from the possibility of preliminary betrayal by any squalor or banality of approach. You approach New York—at least the European does—by the waste sea, over which it springs towering. You approach Petra by the waste desert, from which it hides itself beyond unsurmisable crevices.

But it is a matter by no means of the approach only. In a way that music, most of the arts, produces at its highest the sensation that it is something more than human that has devised it, so New York and Petra. The spectator feels that if human agents achieved the skyey thrust of Radio City, the mountain-subduing façade of the Tomb of Um Zakekeh, they were endowed with superhuman, or at least, inhuman, powers. In New York form conspires with sky, in Petra colour with mountain, to promote a sibylline argument, beyond comprehension, beyond good and evil; or, if they incline towards either opposite, it is towards evil the balance tilts.

It was for Petra's own sake we moved towards Petra from Maan. Further, it was en route for Shobek, whither we intended to descend to Punon-Feinân, the present focus of our Mosaic wanderings. Finally, the Muslims have so tied up all that region with the tale of the Nebi Musa, that on those grounds, too, it could hardly be omitted.

The Muslims do not very busily play the game of indentification, as, indeed, the Jews do not, either. It is principally a diversion of the Christians. The Muslims are content to let a legend grow and grow about a town, a tomb, a tree, a fountain, without examining whether there is any inherent probability of any association between that legend and that town, or whatsoever else it might be. Then a point is reached at which it would be dangerous heresy to deny the imputed sanctity, even though the same holy tale may be told with regard to two shrines at a great distance from each other.

I could not gather that they definitely said of Petra it was Kadesh-barnea, that crucial centre of the Israelitic wanderings, and so made a shrine of it. Fortunately, the wanderings do not interest them to that extent. But it is recorded in their legends that Pharaoh of Egypt set up his godhead here, to do battle with Moses and Aaron, and they call some of the greatest of the Petra temples by his name. Further, they call the springs which water the Petra valley, the Ayun Musa (though they are by no means the only springs so-called) and the valley itself they call the wadi Musa. The Muslim hallows of Petra are, however, concentrated upon Jebel Harun, which stands at a couple of hours distance westward from the narrow defiles of Petra, commanding both the sunken city and a long reach of the Arabah. There, on the top of Jebel Harun, is a small white *weli*, or saint's tomb, which throughout Islam is held for the tomb of Aaron, the High Priest. They take it, in fact, to be that Mount Hor concerning which it is written: " And Moses did as the Lord commanded: and they went up into Mount Hor in the sight of all the congregation. And Moses stripped Aaron of his garments, and put them upon Eleazar his son; and Aaron died there in the top of the mount."

The Christians go elsewhere for their Mount Hor. Some seek to place it at Gebel Madra, an isolated hill some twenty-five miles north-east of Ain Kadeis. They point to the similarity of name between Madra and Moseroth, one of the stations listed in the Numbers' itinerary. Others incline to place it at Gebel Moweilleh, some twelve and a half miles west and a little north of Ain Kadeis.

Not so the Muslims. To them Jebel Harun is one of the most sacred of their shrines and they make it one of the most difficult for the infidel to gain access to. None the less, we were determined to make strenuous efforts to get there. We did not believe there was any chance at all that Petra and Kadesh-barnea were the same place, and did not feel it very probable that Jebel Harun and Mount Hor were the same place, either. In terms of actual climbing it would have presented to Aaron about to die similar difficulties to those experienced by Moses, if it was actually Gebel Musa he had to ascend in order to receive the Ten Commandments. But Jebel Harun and Gebel Musa have a similar moral and aesthetic validity, though it is the Muslims who have so invested Jebel Harun and the Christians Gebel Musa. The Jews, whose saints Moses and Aaron are, have taken little interest in the matter.

We must get to Jebel Harun, we told ourselves. It means going back a good many stages on our journey. But we are making for Punon-Feinân in any case, so we might as well go back a few stages further and make for Mount Hor. We have had no chance to get there before. We must be grateful for whatever chance presents itself now. No one can tell us that Aaron is not actually buried in that little shrine on the mountain-top. All we know is that a great many people have believed he is, for a good many centuries now, chiefly Muslims, of course. But a Jew so long ago as Josephus believed it, and a Christian so recently as Dean Stanley.

We will make for Jebel Harun, then, and the way lies through Petra. And the way to Petra lies through the village of El Dji.

"To El Dji, Jemil!" I said.

Although Maan was his own town, he seemed as glad to get away from it as we were. His association with us was not doing him any good in the eyes of his townsmen. He seemed, alone of them all, to have no use for that red-eyed cretin with the red-eyed chicken. He was a chauffeur, of course. His horizons were wider than theirs. We went on our way, not mourned by the townsmen of Maan.

§ 6

The road swings out northward across the bare plateau. Neither shape nor colour is there, in that sea of gravel tugging and rolling like the grey waters of a northern sea. This is that "sorry landscape," as Doughty speaks of it, " the beginning upon this side of the Flint Ground, strewed from an eternity in the sun and wind," the most desolate we had seen on all our journey. The wind whistled as in a chimney through the car, and strove, it seemed, to tear the roof from over our heads. The discouraged eye did not seek to distinguish man's ruin where all was ruin, though Jemil, it seemed, would not let us easily pass by. " Bridge for water," he pointed out. " Tahuneh," he said later, " Windmill," meaning certain black stones on a hill, where once some fortress was.

The dun desert heaves for several leagues more, then the flint and gravel begin to fail, the limestone breaks before the soft insistence of the sandstone, as cliffs do when water thrusts at them. There are traces of ancient terracings, worked a long time before the Turks became masters here, and unlikely to be worked again soon, under the not more strenuous new masters. A town was here, Basta by name. A few tumbled stones lie on the slopes of a hill. A spring rises brightly, flows a little distance, then expires into ungrateful sand. It is very cold. Snow lies in hill-crevices and under rocks. The track crosses the Roman road that runs southward to Akaba. There are fields of barley now. The descent from the high tops sharpens. We have seen no creatures but camels till now, and few of them. Now there are herdsmen with herds of sheep and goats. Donkeys with ears almost as large as their heads stare at us indifferently. A foal is skittish, lifts its heels and scampers after us, descending now into the wadi Fara. The red earth is everywhere coarsened with great clumps of scrub. But in places sheltered by the sides of hills, and on terraces smoothed long ago, there is spring grass and broad tracts of barley.

At length the Prophet again, we come upon the traces of the Nebi Musa. We are at a well, Ain Musa, Jemil describes it, using the singular. There are other wells, then, making the Ayun Musa which flow down the channels of his wadi. We are never to feel in this region that it is Moses or Aaron who came this way before us. They were two holy men, dervishes, Nebi Musa and Nebi Harun by name, who had come up, not from Sinai and Egypt but from Medina, perhaps, in the great Arabian desert.

The water of Musa springs full and clear from within a cool well-built chamber tufted with maiden-hair. We had not come across such sweet water since we drank from the fern-swept fountains of Gebel Musa. Having drunk deep, we fared further down that astonishing wadi, our faces towards the red mountains which hold in their bosom the prodigy of Petra. Above and beyond them, Jebel Harun soared into the bright air, holding up its casket of Harun's bones. On either flank the wadi was terraced with such skill and beauty as made it at once evident that the terraces dated from centuries before the coming of the present dwellers in this land. In a country where the destructive forces of desert and torrent have for so long been given their head, the first sight of these terraces is quite astonishing. They have a Roman air. You might imagine yourself among the Alban hills. But you are ready to believe it was the Nabataeans themselves, the artificers of Petra, who first squared the hillsides and levelled the plat-forms. The city contained so vast a population, they must have needed to go outside the protection of their gorges to grow wheat and olives and fruit and vegetables enough to feed them.

And there they still grow, but for a meaner citizenry.

" El Dji! " Jemil pointed out. " *Mush tahib!* Arabi not good! " Himself an alien, coming from Maan, he agreed in that pronouncement with the general verdict of travellers, who speak of them as " churls " as " perilous fellows," who, " in their habits of life are at once submissive and tyrannical."

We moved forward to find out for ourselves what sort of folk they were. Before you come to the village itself, you come upon the police and telephone post, built below road-level on a small plateau. A handful of horses, waiting to take the chance traveller down into Petra, stand scrabbling their hooves in the rock road. The car goes no farther than this point, and would not be allowed to if it could. There was trouble enough to carry it so far. When it was first proposed, early in 1926, there was a full-scale rebellion in the wadi Musa, during which four soldiers in the garrison were killed and the governor thrown out. It was not till Peake Pasha sent three hundred and fifty members of his Arab Legion down, that the trouble subsided.

We got out of the car and Jemil went down to the post to announce us and see what could be done about a night's lodging. We did not feel that first seeing Petra was the sort of experience we wanted to push into the back end of a day. I think we were a little afraid of it, in turn fearing it might let us down, or it might be too vast for us to come to terms with it. We were to find the second true, not the first.

On the other hand, Petra seemed likelier to give us some sort of lodging than El Dji. We had heard that a tourist agency from Amman had a tent or two pitched down there, but no one knew whether they had gone again. Few people were visiting Petra these days; the place was dropping back into its secular isolation. The parties organized in Palestine had ceased since the troubles, and the government fee of one pound per person had seriously discouraged the caravans of Egyptian students for whom Petra had begun to be an object of pilgrimage. Someone had told us of a party of four hundred Egyptians which had got no further than El Dji, because, not knowing anything about the fee, they did not have the money with them, and could not have afforded it if they had.

If there were no tents from Amman in Petra, there would be caves enough to house us. We might spend a night in Pharaoh's Treasury, even though that might be a little perverse and belated. Or was it still felt in the wadi Musa that it was gold treasure the infidel came to seek in Petra, and they would rather have you sleep where they had their eye on you?

Whatever happened, we must present ourselves at the police-post. We followed Jemil on to the shelf below. On the left, close against a brimming conduit of the water of Moses, was an isolated room. Some yards away, beyond a vine-pergola and a fountain, was a courtyard, with soldiers' rooms built on one side of it, and stabling for their horses on the other. After some moments, a corporal, as we took him to be, and three or four men, came out of the soldiers' quarters, a little peeved to be caught in other than their uniform, and no time to change. They wore khaki breeches and sweaters and a sort of knitted khaki night-cap.

The corporal did not look too well-disposed. He was tall and cadaverous, with huge black eyes switching perpetually in the sockets. We had entrusted Jemil with the note Salim Bey had made out for us, but apparently Salim Bey's warrant did not run far out of Akaba. He made straight for us, though his eyes did not once seem to focus us. Out came the implacable word. The air was sulphurous with it before he shaped it.

"*Jehudi?*"

"English! English!" cried Jim and Lucas with some fury. But I saw red. I tore my wallet from my pocket and snatched out the Storrs letter to the Emir. There were two sheets of it. My hands were trembling so violently I could hardly unfold them. It seemed to me that we were entitled to some civility from this minion when we bore with us a letter to his prince from one of the most distinguished of living Englishmen.

"*Shuf!*" I cried, thrusting the letter under his nose. "Storrs Pasha! Emir Abdullah!"

A little taken aback, he took the letter from my hand. His eyes crossed so swiftly over the first few lines, I was convinced he could not read. His eyes rose from the paper, and for the first time tried to focus mine.

"*Tayib! Tayib!*" he said. "Good! Come this way!" He gestured us to follow him to the office. He could not immediately adjust his manner to the altered situation. If he was a native, he was a good instance of the character imputed to these people by Laborde, their mixture of contempt and fear. He asked for tea to be brought to us, and sent a man to help Jemil unload our stuff from the car. There was, at the moment, only a table and a chair in the room.

"Would they like beds?" the corporal asked Jemil. The floor was cement. Lucas had no objection to cement. Jim had no more than a little.

"Yes, we would like beds!" I said firmly. I felt the emirate might well go as far as that. We proceeded to prepare ourselves a meal.

" We're lucky! " said Lucas, somewhat diffidently, and half
under his breath.

" What do you mean lucky? "

" Did you forget the passage in the letter which goes on
about your Jewish ancestors."

" Yes," I admitted awkwardly. " As a matter of fact, I
did."

" It's a good thing he couldn't read," said Lucas.

" Yes. It's a pity we can't, either."

" It ought to be quite easy to work out what part of the
letter it is," Jim pointed out.

I took the letter out of the wallet. There were only a few
lines of Arabic on the top of the second page. They evidently
corresponded with the final compliments and greetings.

" So it must come into these seven lines at the bottom," I
worked out. " Ten at most. A pity they're there. It would
have been a useful letter in an awkward spot."

Lucas somewhat lugubriously agreed.

" We can't rely on the whole population being unable to
read."

I sighed. " ' A long line of illustrious Jewish scholars,' " I
quoted. " A bit ironical, isn't it? "

" Listen! " cried Jim. " Why not turn the sheet back about
here, see? " It was Jim who brought up the constructive ideas
from some reservoir of wisdom at moments of strain. " And
just hold the letter, see? Say it's important—private—
politics."

" I think you're right," I said slowly. " Private, that's it.
In a very real sense. In a sense the world no longer recognizes.
High politics! "

" You mean you'll hold the sheet with the part turned
back," asked Lucas, " while the other fellows looks over your
shoulder? Won't that make him really suspicious? Don't you
think he might insist——" He stopped.

" I hadn't thought of that," I said, a little crestfallen.

" Someone's coming."

We saw through the open door a little man in a fine silk

abayah descending from the road towards our quarters. He looked a suaver type of man than these officials.

" Good-evening," he said in English. " I come in? I schoolmaster."

We welcomed him heartily. Someone to talk our own language! But how delightful! A cup of tea? No, thank you. A cigarette? No, thank you. He did not seem disposed to accept hospitality. Perhaps he wished to confirm it.

" You come to visit Petra? "

" Yes."

" You come for follow Nebi Musa? "

" Yes."

" I help. Very pleased help."

" We shall be so grateful."

" You go Amman? "

" Yes. But later. After Petra, after Shobek, after Madeba."

" Nebi Musa in Shobek? "

" Yes," I said eagerly. " Not far. Khirbet Feinân."

" You see His Highness? "

" Yes. We hope to."

" Oh, you see His Highness! "

He stood about drumming with the toe of a patent-leather shoe on the floor. I realized what he had come for. They had sent him to check up on the mysterious document we carried with us. He was not going to ask us point-blank for it. He was the schoolmaster, not the police-officer. But it was clear he did not intend to leave the room without seeing it.

" Yes," I said airily. " Here is a letter. It is from the great Storrs Pasha. It is for His Highness." I realized in that same moment that if he was to see the letter at all, it must be handed over to him. It was impossible to invite him to read it while I still held it in my hand with the genealogical paragraph bent back. If we showed we distrusted him, he could not fail to distrust us.

" Look! " I said. " This part at the bottom is private. Message between Storrs Pasha and Highness." I bent it out of sight. " You see? "

" Certainly," he said. He took the letter from my hand and read it till the last visible line. He was too gentlemanly to show that he was curious about what followed, though it might be presumed he was. He handed the letter back, then said cordially:

" Very glad. A great honour. Can I help? I help."

He bowed, shook hands, went off up the path again, then disappeared towards the village.

In fact, we saw very little of him after that. We met him in the village that evening, but his greeting was perfunctory. He had been detailed to do a somewhat unpleasant duty, and he had done it. Really, nothing more could be expected of him.

While we ate our meal, the men brought in three beds for us, with planks for mattresses. They filled a basin with the water of Moses. Below the window, the water of Moses was singing down the gullies. We did not doubt we could sleep well that night, planks or no planks. The meal over, we went down into the village, a conglomerate mass of mud huts, slashed with two or three tortuous streets. Some of the house-walls were daubed round fragments of old stone, from which it was to be gathered that El Dji was once a grander place. It was not grand now. The houses were mean, the streets full of smells. El Dji was rich in cattle, as we already knew it to be rich in barley and fruit-trees. The animals seemed to share the houses on equal terms with the humans though some, a little more supercilious, seemed to prefer the roof-tops to the foetid interiors.

In addition to their beasts and terraces, the people of El Dji do quite well out of Petra. They see to it you hire guides and animals, whether or not you feel you can do without them, and the money is pooled among the villagers. They must be so prosperous, you find it puzzling they are content to live in such squalid hovels. I was reminded of certain Osage Indians of Oklahoma who had become wealthy from the oil found in their reservations. They live in one-roomed shacks not less squalid than these Arab hovels, with high-powered Hollywood limousines drawn up beside their door-steps. The Indians get away in their limousines and the Arabs of El Dji in their goat-hair tents. They are, in fact, a semi-nomad people, like most of the villagers in these parts; they spend as little time as possible in their homes. I do not believe it is the open sky that calls them, and the wind's lash. They dislike each other only a little less than they dislike the foreigner. There is elbow-room in the desert.

Now and again as we turned a corner, we came upon a little tattooed girl with hennaed hair who, at the sight of us, fled screaming. The boys stood their ground, and stared at us with that insistent mixture of contempt and fear. One young man standing on a roof-top, tending a black calf with a white head, played with the idea of discharging a pebble at us from his catapult. He looked immensely like the young David, outlined against a stormy sky with rain brooding. But he was not David. He was Moses.

" Musa ! " a female voice screamed at him from inside one of the hovels. " Musa ! " He let the catapult hang limp from his fingers, and contented himself with sticking a tongue out at us.

" Musa ! " another voice cried, further down the street, admonishing or summoning some other Moses.

" Harun ! " we heard later, and more than once " Harun ! "

" Musa ! " we heard again.

" Josephus was right," I murmured to my friends. " And Eusebius and Dean Stanley. Petra must be Kadesh-barnea, after all. Listen! The whole place is clamorous with Moses and Aaron! "

" Musa ! Harun ! " we called out to the rocks about us.

" Musa ! Harun ! " the rocks answered again.

CHAPTER EIGHT

§ 1

WE found the young man apportioned to be our guide waiting outside our door next morning. He, too, was Musa, but he was the least Mosaic creature in all those regions. He went back before the Israelitic irruption, before the Edomite occupation, to the days of the Horites, the original inhabitants, who were troglodytes, dwellers in caves. He had wild black eyes, and wild black hair, escaping in ringlets from under his yellow head-dress. His golden-black *abayah* swung behind him as he walked and as he walked, he sang. He had a loaded carbine slung over his shoulder, which he would remove from time to time in an access of animal spirits. and whirl round his head like a bandleader whirling the baton. At these moments the voice would issue shrill and thin from somewhere high in the caverns of his nose. There was a bandolier round his waist, bulging with cartridges. His footwear consisted of two oblong pieces of outer tyre, with toe and heel straps made of the cloth lining. He left a track like an eccentric motor-car in the Nabataean dust.

We had agreed to try and get to the top of Jebel Harun that first day. There was a sense in which that was a duty rather than a pleasure. The more we had pondered the character of the High Priest during this journey, as it emerges both from Holy Writ and the legends which have gathered round his name, the more immense our reverence for Moses had become, the more non-committal our attitude towards Aaron. However, as I have said earlier, it was incumbent on us to try to get to the top of that mountain, even if we had a lot of reservations about it. From what we had read and heard, we gathered it was possible to buy your way to the top, though that could not be guaranteed. But that seemed deplorable from various points of view. They would want a lot of money from three infidels, which might have seemed worth paying, if the shrine had any intrinsic beauty, but it had not. It seemed to us a matter for the benevolent offices of the Emir Abdullah, whose guests we had already been that night. It would be wise, we thought, to be as casual about it as possible.

" Jebel Harun! " I said to Musa.

The fellow snapped off his song like a glass rod and looked at me, as one quite unable to believe his senses.

" Jebel Harun! " I repeated.

He gave one searching look into my eyes, then bounded off like a young stag to a group of elders who had called to pay their respects at the police-post and see what manner of bipeds we were. There was a lot of whispering and head-shaking, punctuated by sudden spurts of angry noise. It did not look too good, we thought. The corporal came over to us, his men following, the elders drew up the rear. Other elders came. El Dji had gathered something was afoot.

I took out the emiral letter.

" Look! " I cried. " To the Emir himself! "

Infidels might be infidels, but there was no getting away from irrefutable black and white. There was more whispering, more spurts of angry noise, then some bright intellectual had an idea. Why not telephone Maan?

There was an immediate stampede towards the telephone. It took a long time to get through, but contact once established, everybody seemed determined to maintain it for as long as possible. Now and again an elder, possessed by a sudden necessity to communicate his point of view, pushed one head from the mouthpiece and installed his own. The issue, I should have thought, was simple; but I was wrong. A good many minutes later, the convocation streamed away from the telephone and rejoined us.

No, alas. We were not to be allowed to ascend Jebel Harun. We might gaze on it, if we cared to, from one of the other peaks, Jebel ed Deir, for instance, but no more than that. It was sad, it was to be regretted, but——

The fact was, the corporal accurately pointed out, it was

SHOBEK

a letter *to* the Emir, not *from* the Emir. An academic distinction, we thought, but not one to be argued at that time and place.

We set off for Petra and Jebel ed Deir in Musa's Dunlop track.

§ 2

The road from El Dji descends rapidly towards the clefts in the mountains. The well-banked terraces pursue the descending slopes. The women and girls hack away with mattocks at the brown crumbly soil. The women and girls climb the paths with donkeys tripping delicately before them, loaded with great piles of greenstuff from the damp nooks below. The women and girls work. The men are too grand for that.

On an isolated hill ahead of us rises a crusaders' castle, but we have no eyes to spare for it, having seen crusaders' castles before, and knowing that further lies something not yet experienced by us, and not often to be experienced elsewhere —an architecture which is almost Nature itself, Nature which is almost architecture.

Some little distance beyond the first view of that castle, we see a tomb, and then a temple, which are the outliers of Petra, its precursors. The first of these is not a tomb, but a series of tombs, the Harabt er Ramleh, with a forecourt, and with a sort of Doric pillars cut out of the mass. The other is more grandiose, the Temple of el Gradji, more starkly hacked out of a mountain-side and rising in four storeys to its culmination in four of those pylons which the mind recognizes at once to be Nabataean, of Petra, a thing which it has for years, perhaps, hoped to look upon and now, at long last, sees.

Yet the mind registers with alarm its disappointment. These laborious, and in fact well-proportioned, cuttings may be Nabataean, but they are not Petra. They are merely in academic detail different from rock-hewn work seen earlier elsewhere. They look secondary, like a photograph, rather than the thing itself.

Oc

The traveller continues on his journey, a little perturbed. The growing wealth and variety of greenness he encounters as he descends will shake him somewhat out of his foreboding. By the time he has entered the gorge, the Sik, and continued but a few yards along it, he will be in such a state of delight, or it may be terror, he will completely have forgotten the apprehensions that that outer tomb and outer temple evoked in him. If ever he remembers the mood again, he will realize it was due to two causes. One, that tomb and temple lack the colour without which Petra is not Petra; they are merely the carved desert, part of its substance and hueless with its lack of hue. Second, they are outside. The enchantment begins the moment you set foot in the gorge, not a moment before. It is as if a portcullis came down behind you, after you have passed through.

It is not easy to compute how long the gorge is with all its sinuosities—some three or four miles it may be. The walls are some two hundred to two hundred and fifty feet in height, sometimes coming so close that two men on horseback can hardly ride abreast. Anciently the waters of Ayun Musa were dammed outside the Sik and carried towards the city through a duct that pierced the mountain just north of it. The Sik was therefore the royal highroad into Petra, and some of the square slabs that paved it are still to be traced.

You plunge at once into greenery, a hundred sorts of fern and moss in the crannies of the rock, maidenhair and hartshorn, moonwort and adder's tongue; at the base of the rocks as many odorous or flowering shrubs and tufts and single flowers, wild fig, oleander, broom and acacia, fennel and arum lily, narcissus and asphodel. Here creepers hang in gushes as if the rocks had sucked up the waters of Moses and gave them out again in greenery. Here the root of an oleander thrusts backward into the path like the forked tail of a great lizard, which, as it darted into a crevice, was petrified there. A wild fig seeks to embrace the cliff behind it, with last year's leaves lingering among the shoots of the new.

But it is not the greenery that transports you, for you have seen richer stuff and will see it again. It is the colour, of course; than which you will see nothing richer in the world anywhere; or I have not, at least. The colour does not unfold slowly, like the first bars of an overture. You enter with one step into the very heart of the movement, all the instruments in full career. The dominant note is rust-red, or the rose-red of the Newdigate line, if you prefer, though it is useless to specify a dominant shade of red, when the redness slackens or deepens, blazes into orange or subsides into purple, as the excluded sun moves across the sky. But often enough some other colour than red provides the basic key; the colours orchestrate themselves round an apple-green, or a crimson-lake, or a daffodil-yellow. The modes in which these colours arrange themselves are so various that they simulate the appearances of things organic and inorganic and textures which vary in consistency from rusting steel plates to butterfly-wings almost in the act of fluttering before your eyes. Here you have the grained greens and blues of watered silk. Here is fresh-sawn wood in concentric circles of pale and paler yellow. Here is a quick flurry of blue-grey and white markings like a shoal of mackerel, in sunlight here, in moonlight there. The Sik is a Champs Elysées of colour. He is a hardy painter who passes this way, except at night, and quickly.

Half-way along the Sik another narrow ravine bears down on it. At their point of meeting, the façade of a great temple is hewn out of the rock facing the interior. It is magnificent, it is overwhelming, with its fine ruby columns, its sculptured frieze, its upper pediment interrupted by that gay and knowledgeable cupola crowned by a great urn. The thing might have been built by some lordly Italian bishop late in the sixteenth, or early in the seventeenth, century. But in point of fact it is the Temple of Isis that Hadrian built when he came this way in the second century and impressed the Nabataean workmen to carve for him a temple out of a mountain, for in such carving their great skill lay, and give it a semblance of some building on a Roman hill, the Capitol, or the Aventine.

Isis? Hadrian? It will be wildly easy in Petra to stray wildly far from Jehovah and Moses. I must beware of other gods and other conquerors.

" Khaznet Faraun ! " a young voice cries suddenly. The sound comes out of the thick boskage which swathes the lower levels of the crimson pillars. It is rather an inhuman sound, almost like a bird cheeping.

I look round swiftly. No, that is not the black-ringleted Musa. He is a few yards away from us. He has been oddly silent for some time. Perhaps the Sik oppresses him. Besides, his voice is not young. He is a grown man, being full eighteen. Nor will he on any account demean himself to act the guide. He has a carbine. He is a man of El Dji of the terraces. And in any case, what difference is there worth pointing out between one hacked-out hole and another?

" Khaznet Faraun ! "

Some small Bedu boy of the caves, doubtless. We listen hard. He says no more. He remains invisible. He says enough to remind us we are nearer Nile than Tiber. This is the Treasury of Pharaoh. In that great urn above the cupola Pharaoh hid his jewels, when Moses and Aaron turned upon him in this valley. Do you see those pot-shots in the urn? Many a subsequent Musa and Harun has sought to smash the casket and retrieve the treasure. There are other traces in the wadi Musa of Musa's tale. Did I not see sculptured on the right-hand wall of the Sik a six-branched candlestick failing by one branch only of the sacred Menorah Moses made in the plain under Sinai?

We continue, swishing through oleander and asphodel. Four women come up toward us in single file, each driving a donkey before her laden with broom. Their faces are unveiled, their feet are naked, their bodies are swathed in voluminous black gowns embroidered at the hems. Their eyes stare straight before them, as if, in fact, we are invisible. For they are the living ladies of Petra not yet dead; before we are visible, we have two thousand years to go.

Here, then, is the end of the gorge. Here is Petra in its cirque of hills. Here is Petra which *is* its cirque of hills. It seems to us it is worth waiting for, these two thousand years.

§ 3

It is so strange, so beautiful, so complete, so lonely. For six hundred years the place completely passed out of the ken of the West, from the year when the traveller, Thetmar, in 1217, visited the city he called " Archym, the metropolis of the Arabs," entering it by a gorge " very high, narrow and horrible," to the year 1812, when Burckhardt alighted upon it, journeying between Syria and Egypt.

It is so lonely. It is so lonely still, you feel another six hundred years might have passed by without its re-discovery, if chance had not brought Burckhardt. There are a few Bedu families of the Bdul tribe that inhabit its caverns, and flicker about between the greenstuff and the water; but these no more impair its loneliness than the bats who live with them in the caverns or the sand-martins who nest on their outer surfaces.

It is complete. As you emerge from the Sik, its impact upon the senses is sudden and absolute, that same impact of terror and delight with which New York assails the traveller, when he first sees that more than earthly pyramid of towers possess those unfamiliar heights of sky.

It is beautiful. It is like a vast crater, brimming over with light and colour, with the dark leaves of lilies and the slim branches of oleander paddling far down in the concave bottom. The mountains, being of such a colour, of such a height, and standing about the plain in such a posture, divided from each other by their profound ravines, would in themselves have been of great beauty. But mountains used as the basis of an art and the medium of an architecture are of a beauty not to be surpassed, while the shapes that have been imposed upon them are of the most notable proportion and dignity.

It is, perhaps, impossible to isolate the essential quality of a given beauty, in sound, or stone, or whatever it might be. Something is sometimes achieved by pronouncing what it is not, what it is felt not to be. I should say that the beauty of Petra is essentially pagan, idolatrous, something as completely non-Christian as it is non-Jewish and non-Islamic. The Islamic shrine connected with it is beyond its frontier, on the summit of Jebel Harun. Despite its wealth of water, the Arabs have kept shy of Petra during all the long centuries since Mohammed, in a country where each trickle of water is jealously accounted for. Thetmar, the last of its Christian pilgrims before the darkness fell, voiced a repugnance which Doughty expressed in striking and sonorous language. A " gorge very high, narrow and horrible " said Thetmar of the ravishing Sik. But listen to Doughty.

" Strange and horrible as a pit, in an inhuman deadness of nature, is this site of the Nabataeans' metropolis; the eye recoils from that mountainous close of iron cliffs, in which the ghastly waste monuments of a sumptuous barbaric art are from the first glance an eyesore."

I do not quote this passage intending disrespect to the towering genius of Doughty. I quote it chiefly to prove how unchristian the quality of the place is, when to that great Christian it is so horrific. But it seems to me inevitable it should provoke reactions so extreme, in one direction or the other. It seems to me also that a minute analysis of that judgment, that is, of the reasons that impelled it upon Doughty, would provide a basis for a truer appraisal than yet exists of " Arabia Deserta," which is hard to rank at all unless you rank it one of the world's major epics.

I have talked of the beauty, the completeness, the loneliness, of Petra. There remains its strangeness. It is strange; the world does not even know the name of the place, or rather the name by which its own makers called it. Certain early Christian writers, following Josephus, declare its primitive name was Arekem (hence " Archym " in the traveller, Thetmar). But Arekem seems to have been no more than the Aramaic name for Kadesh, with which Josephus confused this place. The word " Petra " is the Greek rendering of the Hebrew " Selah," of which we learn that it was taken from the Edomites by a King of Judah. How the Edomites he defeated named it, we do not know, nor how the Nabataeans named it who followed them.

Not less strange than their nameless capital are these same Nabataeans. They were an Arab tribe, who had lived in the Arabian desert for centuries, indistinguishable from their fellows; until, when the Edomites were given possession of the south of Palestine as their reward for helping Nebuchadnezzar destroy the kingdom of Judah, some impulse seized upon those dim people of the further desert. Finding the stronghold of Petra void or unguarded, they possessed themselves of it and made it the astonishment we know. They became merchants. Petra became the warehouse and clearing-chamber of the caravans going north and south and east and west. Their predecessors doubtless had already carved a few tombs and shrines in the living rock, but the main impulse was Nabataean, and remained Nabataean to the end, though it was to embody Egyptian and Greco-Roman influences as time went by. It was a colossean impulse, inscrutable, that spends itself as mysteriously as it is engendered. There are moments when, gazing round a little helplessly, you declare Petra a city of claustrophobiacs. Intoxicated by those wild draughts of colour, the encircling summits pressing home upon their skulls, they hacked and hacked away at the mountains with the desperate repeatedness of madmen, making one façade and another façade—façades only; they were not interested in interiors, which they left meagre and monotonous; they moved on to the next mountain and the next façade.

But, that mood over, you realize the Nabataean impulse was, in fact, something grimmer and more controlled; controlled, for you do not produce such ordered beauty in sporadic frenzy; grim enough, for all those carved mountains, or most of them, were houses of the dead.

Day by day the sun illumines them with gold and fire, and

in its season the moon visits them with pale terror. The tomb-makers have gone long ago, but the tombs seem likely to endure till the next buckling of this planet's crust.

§ 4

Petra is a place of strange gods and the dead worshipped as gods, as little Jewish in mood as Christian. It is odd, therefore, that it should be widely rumoured in these parts that the few families of Beduin who live in its caves have Jewish blood. So we first heard from the lips of Ibrahim the Chaldaean, whom we met at the moment of our egress from the Sik.

He was waiting there for us. He was attached to the camp run by the people from Amman. Yes, it was still there, two billowing white pavilions spread under the rust-red cliffs. They looked very white and impermanent. You said to yourself: " The host of Israel has found its way into Petra after all. Surely that is the tent of Aaron the High Priest. They are laying out his garments, and he is to proceed in them to the top of Mount Har. And then Moses will strip him of those garments and put them upon Eleazar his son."

But that was not the tent of Aaron the High Priest. It had been designed in Cairo for a later notable, Ibrahim the Chaldaean told us, the Kaiser Wilhelm, who visited Petra in 1898.

Ibrahim was a young man with an astonishingly old face. His nose was as bold as any cliff. His face was lined like an ordnance survey. He seemed to me to carry the whole history of these regions in his face. He had been a Horite, a cliff-dweller, and then an Edomite, when the host of Israel marched into Edom. He became an Israelite; then Christ came, and he became a Christian. Then Islam came, and he became a Muslim. For the time being he was a Christian again.

" Your face is a map of all Palestine," I ventured.

" Excuse me," he insisted. " I am an Iraki. I am from Chaldaea. The patriarch, Ibrahim, he was just a boy from one of our villages. Excuse me."

He had an inexhaustible supply of knowledge about Chaldaea, Canaan, Egypt. Nabataea, above all, Nabataea. It might not have been accurate, but it was copious.

"Excuse me," he would begin. "When the Nabataeans opened it up the country . . ."

"Where do they come from," I asked, "these Beduin in the caves of Petra? They have fuller faces than the Beduin in the high desert."

"Excuse me. It is foolish. People say they are original Nabataeans. Excuse me. They are Jewish mens."

"Jewish men? Did Musa and Harun leave them here when they passed through these parts? "

"No. Please. Excuse me. I do not think the Jewish mens come this way. I think if they come this way they not go away again." (That was a thought which had occurred to me, too.) "They go up top way by the mountains. Excuse me. These Beduin in Petra—their name is Bdul. Excuse me. I will tell you. Long time ago in the Khyber country . . . that is, India, yes? There lived some Jewish mens in the Khyber country. Five hundred and seven years ago." (He was very precise in his figures.) "They look like Indian mens. But they are Jewish mens. Excuse me, you cannot see it any difference. They have one sheikh. He change it from Jewish to Mussulman. So they call him Bdul, which mean ' change.' You see? Excuse me. He went to do big *haj* from India. From Mecca and Medina he wish to go to Jewish city, Jerusalem. He only get to Akaba. Excuse me, he get sick, he stay there.

"And then, you know, excuse me——" He paused. It really sounded as if this time the expression were not a form of words. "Excuse me, he fall in love with daughter of Emir from Akaba. He is Emir's nice best son-in-law. Other sons and other sons-in-law, they not like that. Excuse me, no. So he go away from Akaba up into Arabah, and he has family and founds three tribes, the el Faquir Bduli and the Abu Jdel and the Semakhin Bduli. And the Semakhin Bduli settle by Mount Hor with animals in 1831. And in 1913 they come into Petra and live in cave. But they are Jewish mens. The Howeitat not like them. It is a sad for them."

"Yes," I agreed. "It is a sad for the Jewish mens now all the world over. The Howeitat not like them. There are many Howeitat up and down all the countries."

This exposition had taken us across the arena to the base of the opposite mountain. As we approached, a woman of the Bduli emerged from her cave, with small terra-cotta lamps to sell us, and coins, and the broken limbs of small eidolons. Her husband kept himself some distance apart, with the family goat; he would not let himself be involved in petty trafficking. Her children came out after her, a girl of fourteen, and two small boys, about seven and six. Her eldest child, a boy of fifteen, had died a few days ago and they had placed his body in the male cavern of the Bduli high up in one of the gorges. When this girl dies, they will place her in the female cavern, said Ibrahim.

"I hope she will not die," I said. "She looks so beautiful."

"Excuse me," said Ibrahim. "They die very easy. Like butter."

The girl recognized the tone of admiration in my voice. It was not the first time she had heard it. She was ogling now one, now the other of us, bewitchingly, from under her long black lashes. She wore a yellow kerchief round her head, and a voluminous gown of black cloth, brightly embroidered on the front and round the hems. The sleeves of some lower garment she wore were embroidered, too.

"She has no husband now," regretted Ibrahim.

"What? She has had a husband already?"

"Not one. Four. Excuse me. She is naughty girl. So one husband say go. Two husband say go. Three husband say go. Four husband say go. Now she has no husband."

"It will not take her long to find a fifth. Divorce is very easy among the caves of Petra."

"Very easy. Husband say go, wife go. Finish. Excuse me. You see small boy? This one Matrud. It mean go. When he is born, father not like mother. He say go. Easy, just like you say."

"Ask Matrud what he wishes to do when he grows up."

"He wish to get married."

"Ask him would he like to go to great big city, when he grows up, to Amman."

"He says you mad. What for go to great big city? His father has goat. Some day he will have goat. In great big city no goat."

"This other one is very quiet. Why does he not speak or smile?"

"Little Mohammed! He is very sorry. His great friend die."

"His great friend?"

Ibrahim shook his head sadly. "You see garden near camp?"

We had already seen it, with its paved paths and bright borders and blossoming shrubs and flowering plants in tins. Behind the garden two or three caves had been boarded up so that they looked like huts with small windows.

"Tufik el Afraoui make it." He dropped his voice, but the small Mohammed heard the name. He turned his face away. "He was Druse from Lebanon. Please, he spend a lot of money on women and drink. He is Mussulman. At forty-eight, he become Christian and come to Petra away from world. If mens come to see Petra and give him money, he give money to Bduli. He is good when Bduli sick and dying. He pay fifteen piastres for Mohammed and bring him up like own son. He cut Mohammed's hair like Englishman and put him on Englishman's suit. He get much Englishman's suit from Peake Pasha. And then, excuse me, four week ago, he himself get sick. He take Bible and read and read, three days, and then he is tired and fall asleep, and not awaking.

"And so mother coming for boy and take him back to cave. And she take off Englishmen's suit and he wear Arabi suit. And he very sick for friend. It is sad. He will die."

"No!" I protested. "No! You mustn't deal out death

like this!" I lifted my hand to my forehead as if to brush away a skein of spider's web.

"Excuse me," said the Chaldaean. "I see all in stars."

"I want to take a photograph," I said hurriedly. "Will you tell them?"

Ibrahim told them. There was great excitement. The four-time-divorced maiden clapped her hands and danced.

"Wait!" she cried. "Tell them to wait!" That was the obvious meaning of the words. "I go! I come back!" She disappeared into the family cave.

It was obviously some special piece of finery she had gone off for. We speculated what it might be. A ribbon for the hair? A gaudier kerchief? A sixpenny bead necklace some-one had given her?

It was not. The girl took her place in the centre of the group. Then she lifted the huge folds of her gown from about her feet. She looked down proudly towards her treasure, pointing at it with her forefinger.

"Look!" she cried. "Beautiful! No?"

The treasure was a large pair of brown male boots, gaping wide open between toe and sole.

"Beautiful!" we murmured, "Beautiful!" meaning not only the brown boots. We meant also the blue orchid in the blue shadow of her gown; the filmy smother of tamarisk behind her shoulders; the soaring red mountain which was the front wall of her house. We meant herself, too, our Peggy Hopkins Joyce of the caves, our troglodyte Cinderella.

§ 5

Musa was standing on a rock, waving his carbine about his head and singing.

"Is he happy," I asked, "that he is always singing?"

"Excuse me," said Ibrahim. "He always sing. Happy, unhappy, always sing. Now he is happy."

"Why is he so happy?"

"He love nice girl, excuse me." Then he dropped his

voice. "Hush. Her name it is Enhaye." He spoke as before.
"When he has crop in ground next month, he will marriage
with nice girl."

"Will you translate that song for us, Ibrahim? The one
he is singing now."

"Musa!" cried Ibrahim. "Sing slow! Gentlemen want
I should explain." Musa said nothing for some time, but
looked fixedly on the ground, making patterns in the sand
with his right foot. Then Ibrahim pressed him again, and at
last he came over. I felt a spasm of guilt to force a few minutes
of self-consciousness on so spontaneous a creature. At last he
repeated the verses, slowly, looking the other way.

"It is song to camel," Ibrahim explained, "shall take him
to nice girl. It go like this." He translated it line by line:

> *Run, run*
> *Oh my camel*
> *Run*
> *As the free bird flies.*
> *Last night*
> *My eyes did not close.*
> *Though sleep offered itself to them,*
> *They would have none of it.*
> *Oh it is pleasant*
> *To talk with my true love*
> *Of this thing and the other.*
> *Oh my camel,*
> *Run,*
> *The Arabs are not far.*
> *We that seek love,*
> *Wait in hope always,*
> *While in our veins*
> *The red blood flows.*
> *Run, run,*
> *Oh my camel,*
> *Run,*
> *As the free bird flies.*

This first song instantly passed over into a second, the last note of the old prolonging itself into the first of the new. But the mood had changed somewhat, or it was less consistent.

> *The roots of love*
> *Entwine in the heart*
> *Like the roots of trees.*
> *Woe to us lovers,*
> *It is none of our asking.*
> *But Allah wills it*
> *To Whom be praises.*
> *Dost thou flee,*
> *Oh maiden?*
> *But thou art foolish*
> *Above all women!*
> *Behold the youths,*
> *They keep their distance,*
> *They will have none of thee!*
> *Alas, oh woe to me,*
> *How she is beautiful,*
> *How she is lovely!*
> *My heart is in flames*
> *With my fiery love for her.*
> *Behold her breasts,*
> *They are firm, they are round,*
> *Even as pomegranates.*
> *And her deep eyes are like*
> *Small cups of coffee.*

Musa's voice died away. We waited. He did not embark into a third song.

" Will he sing us another, Ibrahim ! " I asked.

Musa understood the tenor of my question.

" No ! No ! " He tossed his black ringlets into the air.

We waited several minutes in silence, with a sense upon us that listeners had come out of the caves to listen, thousands

of listeners from all the ranked tiers of caves, and that soon
they would creep back again.

" Well now, Musa," I said, " shall we go to the top of Jebel
ed Deir? They will let us go no nearer than that to the grave
of your great-grandfather, the Sheikh Harun! " I turned to
Ibrahim. " And thank you, Ibrahim. Thank you, and
good-bye till later."

" Excuse me, good-bye," said Ibrahim. " You come to
spend night in camp? Not go back to El Dji? "

" We do not go back to El Dji. We spend the night with
you."

" You sleep in tent? You sleep in cave? Excuse me."

" We sleep in cave, Ibrahim! "

He went up to prepare cave. Jim detached himself from
Matrud and Mohammed, with whom he had managed to
carry on a brisk conversation, despite his meagre knowledge
of the Bduli version of the type of Bedu Arabic spoken in these
parts. We set off, the print of Musa's tyre-shoes leading the
way.

The gorge of ed Deir thrusts due north through the wall of
hills, hung with coloured tapestries. The path leads upward
by great swirls of carved stairway, spread over with a stair-
carpet which neither wears nor ruckles, more ravishing than
any woven in Bokhara or Samarkand. Less relevant stair-
cases start out in the centre of every rock-face, leading from
nowhere to nothing, with sudden breaks on to breathless
vacancy. Carved on the foreheads of perpendicular cliffs are
shrines and cells which would seem to have been accessible
only to a race of winged men. At an elbow of the mountain
is a shaded ledge, where water sweeps into an antique cistern
through cascades of maiden-hair. Here we took luncheon in
a bay of laurels, looking down along the way we had come
into the valley of the preposterous city. While we sat there,
a group of Arabs in European clothes came plodding up the
stairway, and seeing us, talked in low tones to each other and
looked immensely disagreeable. Then a spokesman came

forward and inquired in English, truculently: " Who killed Christ? " a bitter variant of the native formula: " *Inta jehud?* " It seemed an ungracious thing to puff the stale dust of theological acrimony into so sweet an air, cooled with water and maiden-hair and laurels. Lucas and Jim managed to assure them that our party was, on the whole, guiltless in the matter, and the Arab gentlemen were somewhat softened. They were officials, most of them Christians, from the up-country towns, Tafileh and Kerak. They, too, were allowed nothing more of Aaron's tomb than a view of it from Jebel ed Deir. But they were at one with their Muslim kinsmen in their intolerance of Christ's people and Mohammed's mentors. They climbed on, and left us a little saddened, wondering whether there was any cranny in the rocks in any mountains so secret that the smell and smoke of race-hatred could not find it out.

We followed some half-hour later and came out upon an arena sown with wheat and ranked round with spires of asphodel. Here is the Temple of El Fatuma, the vastest of the Petra monuments. This, too, like the Treasury of Pharaoh, is crowned with a huge cupola, and from this cupola we heard, one minute after we reached the arena, a music so astonishing that each of us looked quickly at his two fellows to assure himself Petra had not knocked him silly.

> *Onward Christian soldiers*
> *Marching as to war*
> *With the cross of Jesus*
> *Going on before.*

The melody came out to us like a flung streamer and fell at our feet. Then once again. It was a man, not an instrument, a man whistling. It seemed to come straight out of the cupola, like a bird's song out of a cage.

" The Arab Christians! " said one of us.

" Of course! "

" Of course! "

It was a queer thing, none the less, to be taken back

GREETING IN SHOBEK

suddenly from Petra to a Methodist Chapel in Oswestry on a Sunday afternoon, to a camp-fire sing-song in a Grasmere meadow, to a Salvation Army meeting over against the Marble Arch. Yes, it was one of the Arab Christians signalling his theological at-one-ness with us, by means of an esoteric pass-word, an initiate's theme-song. No truck with Jehovah of the Hebrews, Dushara of the Nabataeans, Allah of the Muslims. We are all Christians together.

Or perhaps it was not so strange. All the rocks surrounding the arena were honeycombed with the cells of early Christian hermits. From this complex of cells the temple and the moun-tain get their name—Ed Deir, the Convent. The name of an Abbot of the Convent is on record. (The name is Musa, of course.) Perhaps it was the Abbot Musa whistling " Onward Christian Soldiers "? Is that too fanciful? Then and there, in Oswestry by Petra, nothing seemed too fanciful.

But the truth was we were coming free from Dushara and all the Nabataean idolatry. We were making for the tops again. And not many minutes later, we were so free of Petra, it might have been five countries away.

We came out suddenly into unconfined air. Brown eagles were slowly circling under our feet. Below their unquivering wings, red sandstone peaks and grey limestone flanks tumbled down into the sweltering trough of the Arabah, here wider than we had hitherto seen it. Rivers of heat slid sluggishly along its devious channels. Far off, beyond the gulf, the blunt tops of Et Tih extended in phalanx. Only southward the view was checked, where Jebel Harun was blocked against the intense sky, holding up for all Islam to see, the white tomb which houses the bones of the Sheikh Harun.

Gebel Musa having been, in a certain sense, a perquisite of Christian monks since the sixth century, we had been per-mitted to climb to its summit, where Moses is stated to have received the Decalogue. But we had come away unhappy. What was wrong? What was inadequate? Gebel Musa is a noble mountain; if it were even four times its height and so

Pc

ranked among the world's highest it would not be nobler, in form, in symmetry. Yet it is not adequate. It is not adequate to the Decalogue or to Moses. So Heine unforgettably phrases it:

> *Wie klein erscheint der Sinai*
> *Wenn der Moses darauf steht.*

We had, on the other hand, not been permitted to go to the top of Jebel Harun, but it was not for that reason we were disappointed in it. It would be more correct to say we were, in fact, not disappointed with it. It seemed merely to have no connection at all with the Mount Hor of the Bible. A Muslim sheikh was buried there, not Aaron the Levite, High Priest of the Israelites.

As we stood on the summit of Jebel ed Deir looking towards the summit of Jebel Harun, we felt far removed from the lunar strangeness and secrecy of Petra. But for me the distance was at least as great from the Talmudic warmth and intimacy of my boyhood kitchen in Doomington, where my father of old time would tell us the tale of Aaron's death. I closed my eyes on the hill-top above the hovering eagles and tried to recall his voice and the details of his narrative. But I could not, and it was not easier that same night, lying in my Nabataean cavern carved out of a Petran cliff; nor was it at all easy for many a night thereafter. But I will tell it in this place, for there will be no other, and it is already late enough. We are on our way to Moab, are we not? And Aaron has died some time ago, and the host has come down the Arabah a second time southward to Ezion-geber and gone northward a second time up the Arabah and has encamped at Zalmonah. And the host has now moved forward from Zalmonah, and it is high time we came up with them in Punon-Feinân.

And it is written (my father recalled) that the Lord spake unto Moses and Aaron in Mount Hor, by the border of the land of Edom, saying, Aaron shall be gathered unto his people; for he shall not enter into the land which I have given unto the children of Israel, because ye rebelled against my word at the waters of Meribah. Take Aaron and Eleazar his son, and bring them up into Mount Hor: and strip Aaron of his garments, and put them upon Eleazar his son: and Aaron shall be gathered unto his people, and die there.

And even as the Lord commanded, so Moses did, and the three went forth from the camp even to the mountain and climbed to the top thereof. " And wherefore," asked Aaron, " hast thou brought me here? And wherefore hast thou bid me wear the eight garments of my priesthood? Wherefore dost thou look so strangely? "

And the heart of Moses was nigh to breaking, and well might it have been that Moses, too, had died upon that mountain, were it not decreed he must die a lonelier death on a further mountain. And Moses turned his head away, and could not answer that questioning save with further questioning. " Hath the Lord put something into thy keeping, Oh Aaron my brother? " And Aaron answered: " Yea, verily. The altar hath He put into my keeping, and the table of the shewbread." And Moses asked again: " Is there no light he hath put into thy keeping? " And Aaron answered: " Yes, verily. Nor one light only, but seven lights, the seven lights of the candlestick."

And Moses sighed heavily, for he perceived he could not lighten his task by this dark questioning, such was his brother's holy simplicity. And even as he spoke, lo, in the summit of the mountain a cave opened before their eyes, wherein, it was manifest to Moses, Aaron must enter and die. " Wilt thou go in, Oh brother Aaron? " he asked, and all the woe of all the world was in his heart. " As thou biddest, Moses my brother," and Aaron entered the cave.

And now Moses was sore perplexed. For the charge was laid upon him to strip Aaron of his eight priestly garments and clothe with them Eleazar the son of Aaron. And how might this thing be done without grieving his brother piteously? Wherefore he said: " Lest this should be an old cave, and there be graves of dead men there, wilt thou not strip thee of thy garments, Aaron? " " As thou biddest, Moses, my brother."

But it would have been unseemly that Aaron should have been buried naked, even as a child is born, after a life so long and virtuous; wherefore the Lord wrought this miracle. Even as Aaron stripped off one of his garments, so the angels spread over him a heavenly garment, one following another, till eight were taken off and put on. Moreover, this further miracle was bound up with that other, that the inner garments should be removed before the outer, so that when Eleazar at length stood fully clothed in his father's garments, he should be wearing them in their due order, first first and last last.

This thing done, " Wilt thou stand, Eleazar, at the portal of the cave," said Moses, and the two passed beyond the threshold, and out of sight. And there, within the hollow of the cave, behold a couch was spread with fine linen, a table set up, a candle lighted, and all about was the exceeding glory of angels. And still Aaron knew not what thing his brother must needs say to him, only that the Lord had bid him say it. Whereon he reproved him gently, and a smile of exceeding sweetness was upon his face: " Wilt thou not speak to me, Moses my brother? Even if it is of my death thy lips must speak? "

And Moses hid his face in his hands. " Of thy death, Aaron, my brother. It is even so."

And Aaron took his brother into his arms and kissed him, and laid himself down upon the couch. And the table was spread, as it were, with the good things of all the world, its harvests of grain, its harvests of fruit, baked meats, and all manner of spices. And the light of the candles shining together was like the stars whose flame is increased in the blowing of a strong wind. And even as Aaron had kissed his brother, Moses, so the Lord kissed Aaron his servant, and Aaron was no more. In that way it is appointed that the Lord's holiest shall pass away, not through the Angel of Death but through the kiss of God. As it had been with Miriam their sister. As it was to be with Moses.

And Moses bowed his head and turned and walked out of the cave. And a great cloud came down over the cave. It was not seen again by mortal eyes.

CHAPTER NINE

§ 1

IT was not in Petra I recalled that Talmudic tale of Moses and Aaron and Eleazar, with its mediaeval subtlety and freakishness and piety; nor in Shobek, nor Tafileh, nor Kerak, nor Amman, nor the steep valleys between, nor the wind-battered high places, not anywhere in Edom or Moab.

Above all it was not in Petra. We came down from Jebel ed Deir, and went to our beds in our hacked-out caverns. It was not that night I recalled the Talmud, staring out through the embrasure roughly squared by Nabataean stone chisels two thousand years ago, staring out upon the carved hills haggard with moonlight. It was not the next day, when we climbed to the place of sacrifice and leaned over the trough which carried the blood away of who knows what wild obla-tions to what wild gods. It was not on the evening of that day when we sat on the coloured steps of the theatre, with Musa singing to his true love from out of a covert of tamarisk, and the colour on the stone so like the minute down on a peach or a butterfly's wing, you felt you could recompose its light and shade by passing your finger-tips over it. It was not the day after, nor the day after. We left at length, but we had not spent those days and nights either with the host of Moses or the fabulists of the Talmud. We were far removed from them.

So on a certain morning we returned to El Dji, where we had left the greater part of our things in the charge of the police post, and found Jemil waiting for us, who had spent these intervening days in his home-town of Maan.

" To Shobek, Jemil! " I said. For our journey was now to Khirbet Feinân by way of the wadi Shobek. This time no sandstorm, at least, would oppose our journey thither. The distance to Shobek was not great, some twenty miles or so over a track which has been recently put to rights. We thought it likely we could get horses at Shobek to take us down to Feinân, and the horses would automatically provide us with both a guide and a certain amount of protection. We were ready to waive the protection, but our letters from Jerusalem had suggested rather forcibly we should not go off into the blue without somebody, preferably a police officer, to give an eye to us. The horses seemed a good way to do without the police officer.

Lucas suggested walking down to Feinân, spending the night there, and walking back again, but it did not seem practicable to descend and ascend those colossal ravines with the requisite amount of kit. It would have to be horses.

The journey was not exciting. More likely, we were so buffeted with the excitements of Petra that we were not capable of appraising it. The hills were several times so steep we had to get out and walk while Jemil laboriously chugged to the top.

" If that man were normal he'd have his car decarbonized or something," said Jim severely. I pointed out that it is the norm to be an Arab in Arab regions, but he was of the opinion that not to be British was to be below par anywhere. Similarly the Romans must have thought who laid down the road we followed for long stretches of the journey, and built the block-houses whose obstinate ruins cluttered the hill-tops.

As we climbed, the air swept about us in cold currents. Patches of snow lay in the angles of the hills, though the bottoms were green with tracts of barley. On the right hand and the left the wadis circled round and were enfolded in the mass of landscape. Once or twice we rose high enough to command all the circlings and enfoldings so that the eye followed a wadi's whole history till it died out upon the Arabah. Herds of goats that seemed as small as ants threaded the slopes obliquely and the far cry of goatboys was like a sound muted by fathoms of water. Partridges thudded up from beside the road, teal flapped over and down. Once a hyena came from behind a sandy hill, looked at us shame-facedly for half a minute in the hope we could forgive his existence, then slunk away.

The country now became wooded in fretful patches of oak and terebinth, like a scalp that retains some of its hair, and would be covered with a good growth again if someone did something. Then once again the huge landscape parted, so that the eye could ride mile upon mile down to the Arabah; this time it rode further, into northern tracts of grey heat not glimpsed till now. Here a series of dull cones stood out like pumice islands in a sea. The sea was not grey with the Arabah's gravelly greyness. It was white, with a sickly leprous whiteness. It was the Ghor, the accursed region southward from the Dead Sea, where deep down the charred ruins of Sodom and Gomorrah stifle in salt.

And beyond the Ghor, the Dead Sea. And flowing into the Dead Sea, the Jordan. *Gird your loins, Israel!*

Then still once again the landscape folded round upon itself and extinguished that wadi; and we moved further north, inward from the ridge of the plateau. Then suddenly the earth fell before us into a great arena, where diverse wadis met and swept together, as it were, all their scourings of chalk and rubble to make a breast-like hill commanding all that country. And on the top of that hill was a circuit of stout stone walls, embayed, enkeeped and battlemented. And that was Shobek, Shobek not of the desert, not of Islam, Shobek of the Crusaders, of the Christian swashbucklers that had captured Jerusalem, stretching forth a mailed fist south-ward towards the unconquered and unconquerable spices of Arabia.

Yes, it looked very strange and alien on that hill-top, like something transported by wizardry from Castile or Piedmont or the marches of Scotland; as all these Crusader's castles in Asia Minor do, at Acre, Kerak, Shobek, Akaba, built by European minds of no delicacy, that knew what they wanted and by Christ's blood would have it. It was of a solidity repugnant to the desert, where fleetness, transportability, are the virtues that count—not thick boots but the naked foot, not beams and stone walls but goat-hair tents.

It was Baldwin the first, first King of Jerusalem, who built the place and called it Monreal, the Royal Mountain. History has no record of an earlier city than his, and there are no remains earlier, though one or two bemused scholars have, of course, placed Kadesh-barnea there. But it is tempting to play with the fancy that the Israelites coming northward along the ridge of Edom saw a strong place on that hill-top staring down on them and so removed incontinently down the wadi to encamp at Punon. One of the Latin fathers tells us there was a Roman fortress fifteen miles north of Petra, which he called Thaiman. There is a certain duke Teman mentioned in Genesis among " those that came from Esau." It was from the terror of Teman, sitting in his fortress Thaiman, to be called Monreal later, to be called Shobek later, that the host fled again into the way of the Arabah. But that is dimmest conjecture. Early in the twelfth century Baldwin built the place. Before the century was over Saladin had captured it, at least the fabric of it, after a bitter siege. But it remains Baldwin's house, a Crusader's strong place, though not much of the original stuff is extant. Saladin did not capture the whole of it. Lawrence sending his Arabs to capture it from the Turks was striking a blow not only for Allenby, but for Baldwin's ghost still after all these centuries haunting his mountain. The present denizens of Shobek seem as fierce as any in those parts, but they are not at ease there.

Here was Shobek, where we might be able to hire horses to take us down to Feinân. As we descended into the valley we looked round for horses, and saw some grazing in good pastures. There were thick woods, too, and terraces well planted with fruit and wheat. Very dizzily the not-well-banked road climbs round and round the hill. I was glad we got to the top without mishap, though it did not seem we were going to go scatheless much longer. The car came to against a massive wooden gateway, the one entrance into the fortress. It was shut with a sort of resoluteness, as if it was intended it should stay shut. Two or three dozen Arabs were gathered together on the minute area of flatness in front of the gate, ranked shoulder to shoulder as if another assault was intended in another siege of Shobek. A supplementary group was extended on a low stone-banked platform that shored up the main wall beyond the gate. They looked heavy and not friendly, silhouetted against the vast sky.

We exclaimed " Salaam! " encouragingly, as Jemil braked, but the response was inconsiderable. Then a few sallow hook-nosed faces thrust towards the windows, and Jemil uttered some words of explanation. Then we got out and fumbled for papers and smiled energetically. A tooth or two displayed itself in response. Then " Emir Abdullah! " I said, " Emir Abdullah! " And " Beake Basha! " said Lucas. " Beake Basha! " And Jim began to put a comb through his hair, which was all over his face. And altogether it was felt we had not got a couple of big guns hidden in our kit, and the atmosphere lightened somewhat. At this moment a handsome fellow in fine white silks came out from a postern-door in the gate and advanced salaaming pleasantly.

" How are you? " he said. " I am schoolmaster."

That was fine. They seemed to be useful fellows, these schoolmasters, a link between two worlds. In a few minutes everything was easy. We had explained about Moses and our journey and horses and Khirbet Feinân. The line of Arabs along the platform took their pistols out of their holsters and fired them at the sky, evidently to assure us they did not intend to fire them at us. A small man, a sort of town janitor, produced a large wooden key from the recesses of his clothes and held it up before us, intimating Shobek was open to us, we could take our ease there.

" We will have tea in school-house, yes? " said the school-master. " Then we will look round town. Then, perhaps, horses will be ready, yes? "

That suited us well. We passed through the gate and

climbed two or three narrow ill-paved streets and entered the school-house. The schoolmaster went in front, behind us followed the whole male population of the town, which had by now assembled, some two or three hundred of them. There was not room for everybody, so a sort of representative senate entered, the most venerable of the sheikhs. The schoolmaster took his usual place on the dais, the rest of us sat down at the desks, the three strangers at the top of the class, as it were. Two or three small boys had managed to insinuate themselves into the room, but these were expelled with ignominy. There was something quite grotesque about it all—the globe, the blackboard, the kindergarten animal charts, the top boys from Europe, the bearded boys from Asia, black-bearded, black-eyed, bristling with knives and pistols, the flowing robes tucked into the well of the desks.

Tea was brought to us and was drunk gravely, then grave conversation followed. It was understood a youth had gone down into the valley to see about those horses. It used to be big forest round Shobek, said the schoolmaster, but all burned up for train in Hedjaz Railway during war. There used to be special little line between Shobek and Railway. Always used to be many robber in forest. So Mansur, brother of Saladin, built castle, to look after Mussulman people. Still there is wolf and hyena in forest and sometimes leopard.

It was not only grotesque. It was a little uncanny, too. The sheikhs did not utter a word, but gazed at us with eyes that were set like black glass in their heads, unblinking, turning neither to right nor left. We finished our tea, and the schoolmaster rose and said, shall we look Shobek. We rose. The sheikhs rose, too, and stood silent as images, while we went out. We felt we preferred them in their earlier more turbulent mood, firing pistols and wagging beards. We wandered round the walls, saw the ruin of an early church, were shown with pride a subterranean staircase that thrust down into the bowels of their hill towards some far perennial spring. There were fig-trees in the valley below and ancient olive-trees. It looked a long way down from the top of the wall to the bottom of the valley. The slopes were very steep. We could make out the grazing camels, small as toys. There were horses, too, but not for us, not yet.

We were standing in a redoubt at that moment, overhanging a slope as steep as any.

" Look ! " said the schoolmaster. " Here we throw down Turks ! Before the War we have Revolution. Turks want women to bring up water. Not good. So we throw down Turks ! Look ! "

I looked, got a bit dizzy, and turned away. It seemed very matter-of-fact to our friend to throw down Turks over wall. I was pleased there were no odd Turks about.

We returned to the schoolroom and resumed our conversation. It was less brisk than before, and it had not been brisk then. We did not have much more English and Arabic between us, and not more than a limited stock of subjects. There were long intervals of silence. The horses seemed a long time in coming.

" Excuse me," I said at length. " Is there any news about those horses? "

" No, not yet. Excuse," said the schoolmaster. " Soon it will be. Perhaps more tea, yes? "

We had more tea. We were getting a bit restless. If we were to get to Feinân and back in the same day, we ought to start moving. The idea of spending a night either at Feinân or Shobek was in different ways oppressive. The immobile staring sheikhs were rather nerve-racking.

Jim tugged at my coat.

" Look ! There's Jemil at the door ! He keeps on walking up and down ! He's getting quite worried ! "

" What's he got to be worried about? We can't be long now."

We were long now, quite long. The afternoon shadows were lengthening. Horses? No horses. Not yet. Then Lucas crystallized the situation in a word.

" Kuntilla ! " he murmured.

" I rather agree with you," I murmured back. The idea

had, in fact, been in my mind already. It began to look as if we were as likely to get horses in Shobek as we got a goat in Kuntilla, and for the same reason. It was not intended we should have any.

But the lonely officer in Kuntilla had kept us there merely because he liked our company. Could it be said of the sheikhs of Shobek they liked our company? Could it even be said of the schoolmaster? He seemed pleasant enough, but so, for a time, had the other schoolmaster, in El Dji. They were strange fish, these schoolmasters. You felt you had something in common with them, because they talked a few words of your language. But had you? You began to feel that their dislike for you was even more intense than that of their fellows to whom you said " Salaam " and they said " Salaam " and that was all there was to it. The little they knew made them thank Allah the more devoutly they were not such as you were, unbelievers, outcasts. They stretched out a hand, but it was only to push you away, not bring you in.

Horses? No horses. If you couldn't conscientiously say these people were keeping you here because they liked your company, what were they keeping you here for?

But there *were* horses. You could see them far down in the valley. It was a long way down from the top of that wall to the bottom of that valley. " Turks! " the schoolmaster had said. " Here we throw down Turks! "

" Ha! Ha! " I laughed aloud, and checked myself at once, as one does when one coughs during a service. The black eyes looked on unblinking.

" What on earth's the matter? " asked Lucas.

" Nothing! " I said. " Nothing! " As if people could throw people off walls in present-day Transjordan, the Transjordan of Colonel Cox, Winston Churchill, the Emir Abdullah. It was too stupid. My hands and neck were getting very clammy.

" He's looking awfully worried! " said Jim.

" Who? " I asked.

" Jemil! "

" It *is* getting late, isn't it? "

" It *is*, isn't it? "

It *was* getting late. But we were set on getting to Feinân. It would be very disappointing to fail to get there a second time. It had been bad enough to fail a few days ago when the sandstorm had turned us back in the Arabah, though in our heart of hearts we had not really thought we would get there. It would be really painful not to get there from Shobek. Nowhere else on the journey would we be so near, according to the map. But perhaps, when you really got down to it, there might be an easier way, even if it were longer.

What about Tafileh, for instance? That was the place we were making for that night. It was a good distance further, but it was more of a place altogether. Perhaps we could somehow fix things up in Tafileh.

Suddenly Tafileh became a haven, a warm light to make for across inhospitable waters.

I got up from my desk at the bottom of the class, and went up to the dais where the schoolmaster sat, as if I had an exercise to give him.

" Excuse me," I said. " I think, perhaps—if you don't mind—we'll move on to Tafileh."

The schoolmaster shrugged his shoulders.

" Well, if you not wait for horses—— "

We shook hands with him, salaamed to the assembling sheikhs, bowed and walked out. Most of them bowed back, few said anything.

" They seem disappointed we're going," said Jim.

" Yes. We hardly gave them a chance, did we? " I turned to Jemil. He looked very relieved. " We can get to Tafileh, before nightfall? "

" I think."

" To Tafileh, Jemil! " I said.

§ 2

We were going on to Tafileh for one or two good reasons. It was the natural place to make for going north from Petra on this side of the plateau. There was no inn there, so far as we knew, but we had a note from Salim Bey for the Officer of Police there, one Abdullah Bey Rihani, who was a Christian, we had gathered. He ought to find us a shake-down at least as comfortable as the one we had had in El Dji.

We were also en route to Tafileh because the word had been taken to be a signpost to direct the traveller along this section of the Mosaic journey. The opening words of Deuter-onomy, it will be remembered, are as follows: " These be the words which Moses spake unto all Israel beyond Jordan in the wilderness, in the Arabah over against Suph, between Paran and Tophel, and Laban, and Hazeroth and Di-zahab." *Tophel, Tafileh.* There is enough similarity between the words to have convinced some scholars they mean one and the same place, though Sir George Adam Smith insists grimly that they correspond neither in spelling nor in situation. Perhaps, not in spelling; that is a specialist's matter. But the insistence that they do not correspond in situation is not formidable. The Deuteronomic writer seems to name these places, rather because he has heard them spoken about at some time or another than because he hopes to convey some accurate information about the place where Moses actually was when he delivered his final discourses.

We get some further encouragement to identify Tophel with Tafileh from the fact that in the plain below Tafileh, a couple of hours' distance away, you come upon a place-name, Imeh, which it is possible to identify with the station of Iye-abarim, called also Iyim, where the host encamped between Oboth and Dibon-gad. Dibon-gad can be identified, too, and with certainty; it is the heap of ruins to-day called Dhibân, some four miles north of the wadi el Mojib, the brook Arnon of the Bible.

In other words, we get a whole sequence of place-name correspondences from Punon to Diban-gad, all in the same general line northward through Edom and Moab, lying down in the Arabah or over towards the western edge of the plateau.

We get Punon-Feinân, Oboth-Oueibeh, Tophel-Tafileh, Iyim-Imeh, Diban-gad-Dhibân. It is true that apart from the last, which is not doubted, none of these correspondences can be stated to be an academic instance of phonetic trans-mutation (though phonetics is by no means such an exact science as it is held to be by some of its doctors). But the cumulative effect of these conjunctions is formidable. If they do not provide us with an actual chart of the northward wanderings, they do seem to establish that they took place on the westward, and not on the eastern side, of the plateau. It must be remembered, too, that the journey now is more properly to be described as a march, or series of marches, than a wandering. The Israelites had their bellies full of compassing Mount Seir. They wanted to get on with it. Nothing could have been less likely to get them on with it than a journey along the eastern fringes of Edom and Moab, as desolate a waste as any they had yet encountered, with wells as few and far, and with enemies ready to swoop on them from either hand, and no escape from them. It is true that the march along the western fringe would have taken them through some of the best country of Edom and Moab. But that had by no means been prohibited them. They were told: " Ye are to pass through the border of your brethren the children of Esau, which dwell in Seir." Later: " Vex not Moab," they were instructed, " neither contend with them in battle." Still later, it was Ammon they must not vex, nor contend with in battle. But the contending, alas, came from the other side, as it has so often come in Israel's history; and the westward line of march would have given them swift access to deep wadis, where they could at once defend themselves easily and where there would be ample supplies of water for themselves and their animals. As perhaps was the case with a retreat from Shobek (as it is called to-day) to Punon, from Tophel to Iyim.

Well, we had been twice baulked of following in their traces to Punon, would we have more luck from Tafileh, we wondered?

ATARGATIS, THE FISH-GODDESS

The road wound dizzily round the Shobek hill and down into the valley among the figs and olives. Lucas had not been quite following what had been going on in my mind and Jim's, up on the hill-top. He is not susceptible to that sort of panic. I told him that Jemil looked very apprehensive, too. He was about to say something a little caustic, when he suddenly uttered a loud shout.

" Stop ! " he cried.

The car stopped. He flung himself out of the car and down on to the ground. It was as if he had suddenly remembered an act of prayer he had criminally neglected. Jemil unconsciously ducked his head, as if there could be no other explanation than that a bandit was awaiting us with a cocked gun behind a rock.

But it was neither of these. It was a scarlet anemone, the first scarlet anemone we had seen yet upon the journey. It was more of an excitement to Lucas than any danger he might run or any other form of religion. It was spring, spring in the Near East. From this moment he kept his eyes close to the ground, as if the host had left a trail of flowers along the way they had passed, and that was the way you might establish it, by keeping up the scent from anemone to iris, from iris to lily.

A flower was Lucas's major sensation on the journey between Shobek and Tafileh, mine was a mountain, the Jebel Dana, the highest mountain in these parts. Indeed, it cannot be said that intrinsically one is more miraculous than another, in this case still less, when the colour of flower and mountain was almost identical. High over a green valley hangs the red mountain. Straight towards the hazy Arabah thrusts the deep valley, flanked by sheer precipices, enriched by woods and waters. Some distance from the valley-head, on the southern slope of the wadi, the village of Dana spreads out fanwise on a fan-shaped buttress of rock. It is some little distance below the tops and an immense distance above the valley. It looked so lost, so improbable. We wondered if the race of men that had built it, had died out long ago, and in this fine air the place endured in immortal suspension; or if there were men still

Q c

there, were they men quite like the rest of us, did they love and hate, hunger and thirst, as we do? A foolish speculation—but the place looked so lost, so unreal; we were not to guess, were we, that we were to find the lost place—lost no longer, yet not a whit less improbable?

And we sped northward again, up on the tops and down into the valleys and up on the tops again. And this region, between the wadi Dana and the wadi el Hasa, the frontier between Edom and Moab, is called to this day the land of Djebal, by which name also the Psalmist called it, when he detailed the enemies of Israel—Edom and Moab, Gebal, Ammon and Amalek, that had said: " Come and let us cut them off from being a nation; that the name of Israel may be no more a remembrance." Soon, on our left hand, across a great tract of dusking air, on a plateau cut off from approach on all save one side, we saw a pale smear of hovels the name of which at this day is Buseir, at one time Bozrah, chief among the cities of Gebal, pride of Edom. But it is not proud now, and as the Lord foretold, speaking through the lips of Jeremiah, so is it: " a desolation, a reproach, a waste." It is no more than a pale smear of hovels across a gulf, and hardly more, or even less, are the tabernacles of Edom and Moab, of Ammon and Amalek. But Israel is not yet cut off from being a nation, and its name still is something more than a remembrance, and will, it is likely, for some time so remain.

It was dark when we climbed to a ridge whence we saw Tafileh spread out below us, flat roofs, steep streets, a fortress commanding the further skyline, a light flickering here and there at a threshold or behind a barred window. A breeze was blowing, bringing up to us the smell of gardens and flowing water and the aromatic wood, *ar-ar*, a sort of juniper, they burn in their braziers.

Jemil went down to report our coming to the police-post and bade us wait for him. It was pleasant in a slightly breathless way, to be left there, on the edge of a strange town, without any knowledge of where we would spend the night, what sort of people we would meet, if any would deign to meet us. We had a note for one Abdullah Bey Rihani. He was a Christian. But the Arab Christians of Tafileh and Kerak whom we had met in Petra had not seemed to us excessively agreeable. And he might not be there.

But he was. He came striding up the road beside Jemil, a handsome figure in a khaki coat and riding-breeches. He came up toward us and shook our hands warmly, addressing us in English. He did not use many words, even in his own language, but we knew at once we were with a friend, and with a person of rare quality.

"This way," he bade us. "My house is down there along the road. Please come. It is all yours." His voice was gentle as his eyes, but you felt both held immense reserves of firmness and energy.

We followed him, and a minute or two later stood at his door. We entered and found ourselves in a small courtyard with rooms on the left and right.

"Please, you will sleep here." He pointed to the room on the left. "All waiting," he said. There were beds, with rolled-up mattresses, and eiderdowns and blankets and sheets folded up on window-ledges. There was a wash-stand and water-jugs. "They will make ready for you. Come over here, please."

We crossed the courtyard and found ourselves in a big sitting-room warmed with a stove and copper brazier. There were easy chairs about, draped with the skins of animals and woven cloths, and several fine rugs from Persia and Bokhara on the floor. An *ar-ar* tree stuck in a petrol-tin served as a hat-rack. The frilly coloured paper draping the tin, the bright appliqué cushions and the vases of artificial flowers indicated, it might be presumed, the feminine touch. But the masculine note predominated, the long antique rifles, inlaid with tortoiseshell, the squares of wild animal skins tacked against the walls. Under an arrangement of four ostrich-eggs was a photograph of Abdullah taken many years ago in the desert with his brothers Feisal, Ali, and Zeid. Abdullah appeared

again, now become Emir, this time with Peake Pasha. Abdullah Bey spoke of Peake Pasha with such devotion that it became possible to see how the Arab Legion, a body, after all, of
no more than twelve hundred men, maintains public order
over this vast territory.

" You will sit down, please? " We sat down while he
trimmed the lamps. Then he assembled cups and poured out
coffee from a pot that seemed to stand in perpetual readiness
among the embers of a brazier. I remembered that I had a
letter for him from Salim Bey, but it seemed gratuitous to
produce it, as if I felt that his hospitality needed a formal
symbol to fasten on to. I mentioned the other documents,
half apologetically, and he smiled, he waved a hand. We
were strangers, and Englishmen, Peake's countrymen, come
up out of the desert. How should we do anything but break
bread together?

" So you follow after Moses, yes, the Prophet of the Jews? "

It was the only time the word " Jews " was uttered between
us. It was unspeakably refreshing to hear it uttered without
a hiss of hatred.

" Yes. You have heard? "

" Oh yes," he smiled. " We must learn about travellers, it
should not come harm to them. Moses, he was here? You
think Tafileh is Tophel, like it says in the Bible? "

" How well you know your Bible! "

" I go to Greek school in Jerusalem," he said. " I learn a
lot, but no, not about Tophel. Since I come here I learn
much."

I told him the place we were most interested in getting to,
this side of the wadi el Hasa, was Khirbet Feinân, which we
took to be the place of the encampment at Punon. I told him
of the efforts we had made to get there, both from Akaba and
Shobek, and said we still intended to get there, though it
meant going back a fair distance.

" We get horses," said Abdullah Bey quietly. " We go."

" But I never had any idea——" I began to protest.

" Please. We go. How not? What? They are not friendly

at Shobek? " We were all making various sorts of noises to express our delight, and he wanted another subject. " Perhaps you not understand them plain," he suggested.

" Perhaps not," agreed Lucas, looking at me pointedly. That had been his idea, too.

" What are the people of Tafileh like? " I asked hurriedly.

" Oh, the people of Tafileh! " He railed at them a little, saying how lazy and contentious they were; perhaps things were too easy for them, there was too much water, too many animals, they did not need to work hard enough. His own heart was out in the desert wadis and the waste places; his men looked after Tafileh, they did it well. He would set out on horseback with a round or two of bread in his wallet and a rug strapped round his shoulder, or perhaps not even that, and he would sleep where he would find himself, in a mud hut, a goat-hair tent, or under a rock. He had come upon certain old sites, of which only the Beduin knew, and not many of them, and they were not great talkers. He began speaking of them, and almost he forgot there were people in the room with him. He got up from time to time and fingered a moulding, a carved head, that had come from this place and another place, more particularly from one called Khirbet-at-Tannur, somewhere to the north, where the wadi el-Âban runs into the vast trench of the wadi el Hasa. So lonely the places were, only a stray goatherd, and he but rarely, had set foot there, for many centuries now, since the idol-breakers in their first frenzies threw the idols from their altars and choked the wells and razed the walls to the ground. But the time had been when the Nabataeans had gone forth there in procession, the priests going before, and the novices leading the garlanded beasts to sacrifice, and the worshippers going after. A long time ago that was, a long time ago. He seemed to have an especial devotion to the Nabataeans, he was their latter-day champion.

It was a little uncanny to hear this police-officer, this tough desert horseman in breeches and leggings, talk so raptly of forgotten shrines, of extinct races and gods, like some devoted little spectacled scholar out of a museum.

" It is beautiful, this lion's head, no? " he asked, turning to us, as if remembering our presence again. It was a fearsome creature, with a great snub nose and glaring eyeballs and exposed fangs. It may have been the spout of a conduit at the angle of a wall. " Grand! " we murmured. " Grand! "   A moment later he was in the further corner of the room, where three fragments of square pillar standing on top of each other made a sort of altar, supporting some invisible object draped over with a cloth. He caught the cloth up in his hand, but stood hesitating for several seconds, as if it was not without difficulty he bared the hidden object to strange eyes.

" It is the fish-goddess! " he murmured.   " Atargatis! " Then he removed the cloth.

But in the short lapse of time between his enunciation of the name and his lifting of the cloth, a picture of another fish-deity and another votary took possession of my mind. We had just landed on the beach at Akaba. An old man, wrinkled as a tortoise, stepped out of a coracle painted blue and white. In that same moment he held up before us a great greeny-blue fish that seemed made rather of bronze than flesh. A moment later, another fish-worshipper came up out of the desert, in a loud chariot emitting smoke and fire. This was a younger man. He was wearing short trousers and an open shirt. He proposed to build fish-temples in Akaba with ice to keep the deity cool and fresh. He was a Crusader, like his ancestor, Baldwin of Jerusalem, who also loved fish well; loved fish too well, and so had died of a surfeit of them.

" Is she not beautiful? " asked Abdullah Bey Rihani, in this shrine of the fish-goddess, further north, in Tafileh.

She was very beautiful, despite injury to her nose and chin. Backgrounded against a large shell, she stood out in full relief from a soft white limestone block, some thirty centimetres high, and rather more in width. Her broad forehead was half-covered with two masses of hair that rippled in waves from a central parting, and fell in two thick braids each fastened with a shell. There was a sort of headcloth folded over her hair. There were still traces of paint on her lips and in the hollows of her eyes. But it was the two fishes that most interested us. Broadening from their narrow tails, lying mouth to mouth above her head, symbols of fertility, seals patent of her godhead.

" She was Astarte," said Abdullah Bey, " she was Ashtaroth. She made a travel from the Syrian sea. And here she is Atargatis." He stopped and sighed. Then he shook his head and laughed a little awkwardly, as if he felt he had been remiss in his duty as host; he had been too solemn for too long.

" From Khirbet-et-Tannur," he said, " she go further, no? " He looked at us quizzically, out of the corner of his eyes.

" Further? " I asked, puzzled.

" She go as far as Akaba, no? "

We paused. We were quite silent for some seconds.

" You mean——? " I stammered.

" Oh please, it is nothing! Come! I will see if supper is ready. I am sure it shall be ready by now." He saw we were a little perturbed. " Please, please! " he begged us. " I make joke! Why shall you not go fishing in Akaba? " He went out.

" Good old Rolfe! " I said, with a trace of bitterness, perhaps. " I had a feeling the smell of his fish would come after us! "

" What an Intelligence Service! " marvelled Lucas.

" I wonder what they think we're after in Feinân! " I exclaimed. " We're showing a lot of keenness to get there! "

" Oh *we'll* never get to Feinân! " Jim said brightly. " It's not that sort of a place! "

" Don't be absurd! " I exclaimed. " Of course we'll get to Feinân! We've got to get to Feinân! "

" Well, it's quite true," observed Lucas, " we've not had an Abdullah Bey till now to see us through."

Abdullah Bey re-entered.

" Please it is ready! " he said. " Come! "

We followed into an inner courtyard, which had a further couple of rooms on the left hand and a kitchen on the side facing us. There was no door to the kitchen and you could see two charcoal stoves glowering red-hot. It seemed unlikely that those stoves had lit themselves up and fed themselves. We went into a dining-room and found a pleasant table spread for us. It seemed unlikely, too, that the meal had prepared and spread itself. Probably the feminine hand which had been deduced in the sitting-room was responsible for both the fires and the meal. We did not feel ourselves slighted by this with-holding from us of Madame; we were merely a little surprised, perhaps even a little saddened. It was sad that the Muslim taboo should operate in a Christian household. It must be a little dull for Madame, we thought.

We sat down to a beautifully hot plate of vegetable soup steaming on the table, followed by a dish of boiled spinach, boiled rice and chopped meat, flanked by great bowls of sour milk. A dim little girl appeared and disappeared, carrying dishes in and away. The bread was the best we had eaten since Suez. We drank tea, supplied from our own store, the one contribution we had been permitted to make. The tea-pot was covered with an immensely Cheltenham hand-embroidered cosy, which we were certain Abdullah Bey had not with his own hand embroidered. For dessert we had enormous Jaffa oranges, that had crossed the Jordan to us, impatient that the vanguard of the host had not yet crossed the Jordan to them. During the course of the meal, the door opened, we caught a glimpse of the knuckles and fingers of a female hand, we heard a soft voice whisper: " Abdullah! "

" Excuse me! " said Abdullah Bey and rose, was out of the room a minute or two, then came back and sat down again, saying not a word, as if he had not been out at all.

It is sad, indeed it is sad (I said to myself) that the body of a Christian woman must be reduced to four fingers and four knuckles round the edge of a door.

She was reduced to even less than that, some minutes later. I said we had some brandy left, might I not go and fetch it, we would celebrate our meeting in it. I went, and reaching the inner courtyard, caught a swift glimpse of a woman issuing from the sitting-room. The woman paused for one moment, then turned back into the room, noiselessly, like a shadow.

Please, please, my heart begged. I am not so dangerous as that. Really I am not.

We went back into the sitting-room to smoke and discuss plans for the expedition to Feinân. We would go back by car, Abdullah Bey proposed, as far as the head of the wadi Dana, under the lee of the great red Jebel Dana which had so impressed us. At that point we would pick up horses, which would have set out from Tafileh a good many hours earlier. The beasts belonged to Sheikh Saleh Pasha, one of the leading notables of the town, from whom it would be quite simple to hire them. The sheikh never had any objection against doing anything he got money for. He would be in here any moment, in fact. We could fix things up there and then. I said how kind it was of him to have lost so little time in the matter. Abdullah Bey smiled. No, he had not sent for the sheikh. The sheikh always came bustling up, the moment anybody arrived or anything happened. He must have been out to-night, or he would have been here already.

And even as he spoke, we heard a noise like a rowdy political procession coming along the road. It stopped outside the door for a few moments while a loud voice detached itself from the hubbub. The loud voice embarked on a brief monologue, which might have been a religious exhortation, but was, in fact, no more than a valediction. The hubbub withdrew along the way it had come, the loud voice passed through the door-way, into the courtyard, and flung open the door of the room we were sitting in.

A small man entered, indecently small considering the volume of noise he had been expelling. He was swathed round in a thick brown *abba* to protect him from the evening cold. Through the opening of the *abba* glimmered a rich *kibr* of pink silk shot with silver. His feet were shod in a pair of tangerine-coloured button-boots. His beard, like his pink silk *kibr*, was shot with silver. His eyes were black as jet beads. His hands were gnarled like the roots of olive-trees.

He did not pause at the door. He came straight in, roaring "Salaam! Salaam!" as if he were trying to make his voice heard on the deck of a ship in a howling gale. Introductions followed. We roared "Salaam! Salaam!" our voices involuntarily raised to the pitch he had set. He consented to sit down and take a cup of coffee, though it was obviously an enormous strain to do anything that required such unemphatic movements. He rapped out a series of questions at Abdullah Bey, who tried his best to frame one answer before the next question overwhelmed it. No attempt was made to pretend it was anything but ourselves he was asking about. His immensely bright eyes raced like a couple of hares between our faces and Abdullah Bey's, then back again. Now and again he would interrupt Abdullah Bey's explanation with a single lone shout of corroboration, once or twice he went even further. He took the words out of Abdullah Bey's mouth and completed his sentence for him, as if, really, he knew far more already about the strangers than the Christian, both because his own wits were far less slow, and because he had his own secret supplies of information.

The upshot of it all was favourable. Abdullah Bey was *tayib*, the Nebi Musa was *tayib*, each one of us in turn was *tayib*. The commendations were rattled out like machine-gun bullets. We would have horses to-morrow. They would be the most *tayib* horses in the neighbourhood. We were his blood-brothers. All the English were his blood-brothers. We must without fail come and have coffee with him before we left.

"Salaam! Salaam! Salaam!" he hurled at each of us. He flung the drains of his coffee into the back of his throat like a pellet, and sped to the door again, the tangerine-coloured boots leaving a flare behind them like two meteors. Then he was gone.

None of us said a word for some minutes. We had a distinct sense that the lamps, the cups and even the lighter pieces of furniture were still rocking. We felt we ought to give them a chance to settle down.

" Phew ! " someone said finally.

" Exactly ! " someone else confirmed.

Abdullah Bey smiled. " He is rich ! " he said. " You cannot make noise like that if not rich ! "

I agreed. " And you cannot wear boots like that either."

" He has several wives. Most live away in country, fifteen kilometres away. They are Beduin women, with faces tattooed very blue. They live in small mud house with donkey. He calls them when he wants them. He has also grand house and garden here in Tafileh, with boy children, all clever and beautiful and learning English. Principal wife, she is here, too, she is a good wife. She gets corn to eat, others get barley. He bring her from Nazareth for one thousand pounds. The money is from Lawrence money, given during Revolt. Much useful, Lawrence money."

" Lawrence money? " I repeated. " You mean, of course, Colonel Lawrence? " He had had to hand over a great deal of money, I remembered, at one time or another, to various sheikhs up and down the country to win their support, or at least their benevolent neutrality. (The traces of Lawrence, I said to myself, are certainly more palpable in Tafileh than the traces of Moses in Tophel.)

" Yes, of course, Lawrence. You remember, he fought big battle here? I show you. He give father of this sheikh fifteen thousand pounds, they say. Yes, fifteen thousand pounds. No wonder many big sheikhs love Lawrence. But that sheikh is clever with money. He know how to keep it. Many sheikh spend it quickly on wives, and wives die. Now his son has the money. He spend one thousand pounds on one good wife. He is satisfied. She is worth the money. The other wives are like animals in stable."

Yes, he is satisfied. I wondered if Lawrence would have been quite so happy. A little disillusioned, I suppose, but he would have seen the wry humour of it. " We wanted no rice-converts," he had written. " Persistently we did refuse to let our abundant and famous gold bring over those not spiritually convinced. The money was a confirmation; mortar, not building stone. To have bought men would have put our movement on the base of interest; whereas our followers must be ready to go all the way without other mixture in their motives than human frailty."

Well, it was not rice that the Sheikh Saleh Pasha of Tafileh had bought with his Lawrence money. It ran to something more handsome than that.

We went out for half an hour or so before turning in. It was cold. The ridge was alive with advancing and retreating mists, like bodies of troops deploying against the town. At one point we cut across a stony flank of hill to cut off a loop in the road, and found the stones were tombs. Some belated mourner, or a watchman, it may have been, sprang upon us suddenly, and poked the muzzle of a gun into our ribs, yelling at us loudly for the infidel tomb-robbers we were. The men have lusty throats in Tafileh, we thought. So, too, have the dogs. They were at it all night long, defying each other to do their worst, and they did it.

They did not prevent us, however, from having a good night's sleep, embowered as we were under ornate mosquito-nets. There were no mosquitoes, but the nets were evidently a mark of esteem, and we spread them carefully round us as if we were at the heart of the jungle.

The dogs were still at it when we got up, rather louder, and even more of them. Above the half-blocked window the sky was a solid grey, for last night's floating mists seemed to have consolidated. It did not look too promising for the excursion to Feinân.

" Perhaps it will clear up during the morning," I said.

" I've read somewhere, if it once starts, it goes on for three days and nights," deplored Lucas.

" I told you we'll never get to Feinân ! " croaked Jim. " You'll see."

" Don't ! " I protested and turned away.

There was something going on in the house, the air of excitement spread through our closed door. There was a going to and fro along the outer and inner courtyards, a moving of furniture in the room opposite, a beating of rugs.

" You see? " I said. " They're preparing! "

But no, it was not for the departure to Feinân they were preparing. As we sallied into the courtyard, Abdullah Bey came down toward us resplendent in his full uniform. His eyes were shining with emotion, though he managed to keep it out of his voice and demeanour.

" A message came through from Kerak," he told us. " Peake Pasha is on his way. He is going for a holiday with his young wife to Akaba. They are just married. It shall be like a honeymoon. They will stop here for coffee. You will take coffee with Peake Pasha and wife, yes? "

We told him how pleased we should be.

Then his voice changed. " But, please, perhaps we cannot go to Feinân till to-morrow. You will not mind ? "

" Please ! Please ! " we begged.

He looked up into the grey sky. " Perhaps also the weather it will be better later." I thought his voice lacked conviction. " Well, come now. Breakfast is this moment ready. You shall make a good breakfast."

That we did, of fried eggs, olives and small egg-shaped cheeses soaked in olive-oil. Two walls of the room were flanked with mattresses, with a pile of rugs neatly folded on each. In one corner of the room a sewing-machine stood undraped, with a length of material caught in the needle. We were being permitted, with discretion and silence, to perceive further aspects of the feminine element in action. Above the breakfast-table was a small framed lithograph of the Virgin and Child which, we could have sworn, had not been there the night before. Even with us westerners, these Arab Christians could not abandon the habit of wariness their residence in a Muslim world imposed on them.

After breakfast, we moved to the sitting-room, where we found cups and plates set out, and fruit and home-made biscuits and cakes. But still Madame delayed her appearance. Abdullah Bey put in the finishing touches, with the dim little girl helping. At last, some twenty minutes later, we heard voices at the outer doorway, the gentle voice of Abdullah Bey, a gay pleasant clipped English voice, two female voices. Then at length the party of two British, two Arabs, entered the room where we stood waiting, a little apprehensive.

We did not need to be. The utmost cordiality and ease reigned at once.

" Here is Madame Peake Pasha, here Peake Pasha, here my Madame," said Abdullah Bey. He was very proud and happy. The inference that might have been drawn was that Madame had been away up-country, and it was most fortunate she had arrived at the very moment the Peakes arrived, too. She was an extraordinarily beautiful woman. She was big and shapely with a grand carriage of the head. Her dress was of grass-green cut in excellent style. Her features were straight and her skin of a faint-flushed marble pallor. She wore great loops of jet-black hair like a crown. Even at that busy moment of hand-shakes and greetings, I could not but be aware of a certain resentment against this pusillanimous eastern custom, involving Christians, we saw, as well as Muslims, which will prevent a creature so lovely as this from bestowing her loveliness on the world, and glowing in the warm breath of the admiration she must evoke. It did not seem just that such generosity of beauty must be diminished to a voice calling on the further side of a door and four fingers clasped round the edge of it. The woman's demeanour was as natural as her appearance was noble. She acted the hostess, she smoked, she talked, as self-possessed as any western woman in a metropolitan drawing-room.

It is all a paradox and a mystery, I said to myself. Enough. This is the legendary Peake Pasha. How lovely this other woman is, too. Two women cannot be more unlike, the one pale as magnolia petals, the other fresh as the petals of a wild rose, but how lovely both!

And this is Peake Pasha, very trim and smart in his Colonel's uniform and astrakhan hat, sporting the badge of the Arab Legion. His wife wears the badge as a brooch, patterned in diamonds. He is about fifty, his face as rosy as his wife's. His moustache, too, is trim and smart. His eyes are blue and bright as pebbles. His manner is breezy, almost jaunty. He drops his g's, like a member of the Bullingdon who is cut out to be M.F.H. of the Heythrop Hunt. You would not guess, if his legend had not gone out before him, what power of personality he has, what talent for organization. The first is attested by the breathless worship of Abdullah Bey, no swooning fourth-form schoolboy, either, with a crush on a Sixth Form prefect, but a tough one, hard as nails, yet capable of revering a brave and a just one, when he finds him. The second, the talent for organization, is attested by the *pax romana* of all this country, only two decades ago a pleasaunce for the wild raiding and counter-raiding of uncontrolled and uncontrollable tribesmen.

You would not guess, hearing those almost Berkeley Bar accents, he is also one of Lawrence's paladins, as well as Peake Pasha in his own right, needing no deflected rays from an earlier shining. But he was, of course, that persistent exposer of himself that Lawrence tells us of, the assaulter of stations, the demolisher of railways, the co-inventor and co-planter of explosive " tulips " that blossomed so disastrously for the enemy's rolling-stock out of the fabric of steel sleepers.

There was little time to remind him of these things, and little disposition on his part, I should think, to talk of them. There was much they had to say to each other, the two men, the two women, in that brief time. There was a wedding-gift to hand over, a fine grey-silvery rug of lynx, put together out of the skins of beasts Abdullah Bey and his men had shot. The lining was a handsome brocade quilted by Madame. We managed to get a certain amount said, too, about Jebel Harun and Nabataean goddesses and the children of the caves of Petra whom Peake had fitted out in Norfolk suits. I forbore to tell him that he was endangering the salvation of the Muslim troglodytes, who were inclined to revere his eikon, if they could get hold of it, as the Greek mountaineers do the eikon of the Lordos Vyron. He regretted he had not been on hand to achieve a safe-conduct for us to Nebi Harun's tomb, which he himself visited with some regularity, and which, he agreed, lacked the Hebraic note. He wrote a note for us commending us to the goodwill of the Legion. There was a final breaking of cake, a final cup of coffee.

" We'll have to be goin' now! " he said. " Better be goin' before that rain starts comin' down. The road will be like Seccotine."

The Peakes rose. There were good-byes. Their long black car slid down the ridge and out of sight, with the Union Jack bannerol fluttering bravely above the mascot. By the time we had returned to the sitting-room again, Madame was gone. From that moment till the moment of our departure we saw no more of her again than a shadow disappearing across a threshold and four fingers round the edge of a door.

It was agreed, for one reason or another, that the departure for Feinân should be postponed till next day. The rain-clouds still hung over the mountains, and did not look like shifting unless a strong wind got up; perhaps a wind would get up at nightfall. The packing was going to be a bit complicated; we would have to make provision for wet weather, cold weather and hot weather, all within the space of a single ruck-sack apiece. We wanted to look round the town, and make a few calls. And finally, there was some delay about the horses, which would have to set out a good many hours before we did. Our blood-brother, the sheikh, talked more volcanically than he acted. It was thought it would be a good thing if we paid our formal visit to the sheikh.

The dim little girl was sent down to the sheikh in ample time to warn him we were on our way; but when we got there there was such a spick-and-span look about everything, you had the feeling that all the wives had been mobilized and put to work dusting furniture and polishing floors. There was no doubt at all. Tafileh was en fête that day.

There was nothing hole-and-corner about the sheikh's residence; the Lawrence money had been put to good account. There were a good many rooms, but we only came to close quarters with the state reception chambers. The windows were curtained with yellow silk and the window-bays festooned with rich pink drapery. There were half a dozen brand new Hedjaz rugs on the floor, and a great central table with ornate legs, spread with a fringed and embroidered Indian table-cover. Between the table and the window a gate-legged teak-wood stand supported a huge Benares tray in turn supporting a huge Benares coffee-pot. But the clou of the room, its particular glory, was the series of mahogany chairs, uphol-stered in brown plush, which flanked all four walls shoulder by shoulder, excepting for the few feet the door needed. It was as if the sheikhs of that neighbourhood reckoned their wealth in terms of mahogany plush chairs, and the Sheikh Saleh Pasha was determined to show he was the equal, if not the master, of any.

The sheikh was not alone in receiving us. He had a small handful of his sons dotted about the chairs at irregular intervals. They were charming and very shy, pale-faced and long-lashed. One or two of them talked English with a very pure accent. The sheikh himself was extraordinarily subdued. Perhaps that was the responsibility of entertaining three Englishmen; perhaps the display of his own wealth always had a slightly awe-inspiring effect on him. It was suggested also that he was setting a good example to his sons, or, alterna-tively, that his thousand-pound wife was somewhere in the offing, keeping a debit and credit account of his social behaviour. At all events, he was very subdued. That is, for the Sheikh Saleh Pasha. When he did talk, he talked like a factory-siren at eight o'clock. Then he checked himself, put his hand to his mouth, and his eyes rolled in his head left and right, a little fearfully.

We drank coffee, smoked cigarettes, and nibbled at small sweet biscuits. But that was not all. We had received those things at the hands of other hosts. The pièce de résistance was a large blue tin of Mackintosh's Mixed Caramels, which were handed round reverently, rather as if they were a plate of braised peacock's tongues, and were received by us gratefully,

Rc

for we had not had any for a long time. The unwrapping of
the caramels became something of a rite; as we placed them in
our mouths, the sheikh looked into our eyes carefully, to see
how we appreciated them, and when one or the other of us
tried to make some observation during the process, he shook
his head and bade us desist, mere politeness must not prevent
us from enjoying our Mackintosh's to the full.

It is safe to say we never enjoyed them so much before, and
perhaps never will again. We rose to go. The sheikh uttered a
loud lament, but a brief one. There was much hand-kissing
and lifting of hands to hearts. We were at least as much his
blood-brothers as before. It had all been a great success,
Abdullah Bey assured us. We would have our horses in good
time.

As we ascended to Abdullah Bey's home again, we looked up
into the heavens and around upon the hill-tops, to see what
hope the heavens held out to us. They held precious little.
Only north-westward the roof of cloud lifted, where beyond a
deep and winding wadi you could make out the southern
reaches of the Dead Sea, gleaming like a sheet of molten
brass. You almost felt you could see the steam rising from it
and that the smell of the furnaces was in your nostrils.

§ 3

Abdullah Bey turned us out very early next morning. It
was cold. The air was still thick with cloud, with torn fringes
hanging almost motionless. A feeble suggestion came from
somewhere that perhaps the cloud would break when the sun
came out, but Abdullah Bey gave the idea short shrift. He
was not merely our host now. He was the leader of an expedition. And the horses were already on their way.

As we moved southward again along the track by which we
had come, the fissures in the cloud filled up, so that the
country a hundred yards on either side was almost invisible.
The acute twists of the road were rather frightening, for it
looked as if Jemil were heading rather for infirm cloud than

firm earth. A narrow triangle of goathair tent suddenly poked its peak up toward us, and a head thrust out from under the peak. He looked like one of Aladdin's *djinns* condensing out of mist in a magic bottle. He was a stone-breaker, said Abdullah Bey, an old friend of his. It was reassuring to know that people were giving the road some attention, though it did not feel like it. He is very useful, said Abdullah Bey. It is through people like him we know what is going on, if there is some movement somewhere that there should not be.

" Allah go with you! " said the old stone-breaker.

" Allah might," I murmured. " But it looks as if Jehovah won't! If it gets any worse, it'll be quite obvious He doesn't intend us to get to Punon! First the sandstorm, then the panic. And now——"

It got worse. A coppery glow began to suffuse the cloud-scape. A really fearsome storm was brewing in the east, though in the west the opacity melted for a few minutes, so that we could see Buseira again on its lonely ridge and, on the flanks of the hills beyond, the straggling outline of a forest of black trees—Cedars of Lebanon, we were told they were; no other grow in all this region, and these would not have survived much longer if the authorities at Amman had not come to their assistance.

On the left hand beside the road was a saint's tomb. The saint, Hodifeh, had been sent by Mohammed northward into Syria to spy out the land and he had been martyred here. Was this, I wondered, a reminiscence of the tale of the spies Moses had sent northward into Syria to spy out the land for him? Some kilometres further was a place-name that seemed to embody another Biblical reminiscence—Khirbet Ru-ath. There is no such name elsewhere at all, said Abdullah Bey, and it is said that in this village dwelt Ruth, the Moabite woman, who married the son of Naomi, and went with her to Bethlehem at the time of the harvest of barley. But this is Edom, I murmured, not Moab. He did not seem to hear me. If it was often such a weather, he went on wryly, it is not strange Ruth should want to go away from Khirbet

Ru-ath. But up there were many olives once, Abdullah Bey said, pointing through the mist, so the place is called Khirbet Umzueitini, of the little olive-trees. And a Greek church was there, and in the floor is many bits of stone—how do you call them?—mosaic. Would you like to see mosaic? I have once or twice travelled the length of a whole country to see mosaic, so I was not averse from plunging across three hundred yards of cloud. As we padded forward a shudder shook the clotted air. A yellow flare blinked as if somewhere a vast furnace-door had been opened and shut off again. A second or two after we reached the Byzantine ruin the cloud split into a million points of rain. I have never known so sudden and devastating a deluge. This was no time to hunt for fragments of mosaic, and the rebounding rain would have made them invisible. We turned and pushed forward through the solid downpour, finding two gay streams to wade across between ourselves and the car, where all had been gritty desert before. In that brief interval a good deal had happened to the motor-track, of which at best the surface is a perfunctory affair. It was now like thick vegetable soup, like a choked drain.

We got into the car, not one of us saying a word. Jemil started up and tried to move off. It seemed just about as clear that we could not get to Feinân as that water is wet. How could we get to Feinân when we could not even get to the head of the wadi Dana? How could we get to the head of the wadi Dana when our wheels were just about as stickily embedded in the road as a fly's legs in a flypaper?

It all looked pretty grim. The rain looked as if it was set for days and days. Even if the car could get moving, I did not like the idea of driving along a road where it was impossible not to skid and where if you skidded you were bound to fall over a precipice. No, things did not look too hopeful for Feinân.

I breathed a word about the horses. Abdullah Bey said it could not be said where the horses were. We had perhaps passed them a long time ago.

" Please push! " he said.

We got out into the vertical and horizontal stream and pushed. We did not get any wetter, for we were even so soon already as wet as might be. We heaved and pushed for a long time and at last got started. With a vague curiosity we looked to see if Jemil had had instructions to turn the car round back towards Tafileh or keep her headed towards the wadi Dana. He kept her headed towards the wadi Dana.

To us it was all a little exciting, though it had its gloomy aspect. Abdullah Bey was treating it very soberly, although his mouth was a little closer set than normal.

" I wonder . . . " I ventured to ask after a few strenuous minutes. " I mean, is it far? "

" Not far," said Abdullah Bey shortly. " We have luck. In a few minutes it shall be Razhadiyeh."

It was not a few minutes, but we got somewhere soon. We slewed the car round on the right hand and found ourselves among a litter of Roman stones, some of which had been set up by the Turks to make a khan. The khan too was roofless, but there were one or two roofed-over holes in an old crypt, where somebody seemed to be living.

" Hi! " cried Abdullah Bey, peering into the blackness. " Come out! "

A splay-footed hunchbacked little creature came out, rubbing his eyes, looking a little surly and frightened.

Abdullah Bey gave him certain instructions. He looked less frightened when he saw it was Abdullah Bey.

" We will take things from car now! " requested Abdullah Bey. As we did so, the hunchback took off his over garment and spread it beside the car. Then we loaded it with our kit and stores. It made a colossal bundle, considerably bigger than the hunchback. Jemil and Abdullah Bey helped him to lift it to his shoulder. He staggered off, bent almost double under the load.

" He can't carry that! " I exclaimed in dismay.

" He can carry twice as much! Jemil stay here till we come back! We go now, yes? "

Razhadiyeh was not a palce to linger in at the best of times, least of all in that rain, which was cold as well as fierce. Our feet and hands were quite icy. Shoes and gloves were as useful in keeping the wetness out as tissue-paper. Our teeth were chattering. It seemed a long way indeed from the sweltering drought of the Arabah.

" We leave Jemil *here*? " I asked, a little faintly.

But Jemil looked quite resigned. He had no overcoat, he was still wearing his brown gymnasium shoes, he had no food as far as we knew. His sole luggage seemed to be a small pink blanket.

" He will be all good here," Abdullah Bey assured us. So would he have been himself. I realized as never before the extraordinary talent these people have for accepting life as it comes to them without the faintest whisper of remonstrance. We insisted on leaving some stores with him, though he protested quite genuinely. He would not have us deprive ourselves. We, on the other hand, did not think it right he should live on grass for the next few days, so we carried our point.

We set off. We kept on the north-south track for some time, how long it was impossible to compute. It felt like a very long time indeed. We were on our way to Feinân again, under the captaincy of so immensely competent a person as Abdullah Bey. We should have been pleased and excited about it, but we were not. At least I should say I was not. Jim wasn't happy, but he was bearing up. Lucas, on the other hand, was very happy, I think. He had all his soul craved for. He was walking, not riding. He was wet, cold, and uncomfortable. If it was possible, he was going to be more of each before he was through. Yes, he was happy.

As I say, I was not, despite the presence of Abdullah Bey. In a tussle between Jehovah and Abdullah Bey, I felt the first would win every time. At last we slewed round from the motor-track on to a mountain path, if you could call a track that series of small waterfalls and shifting slithers of gravel. We were in the wadi Dana. We were, in fact, making for the village of Dana, where we would spend the night, perhaps the next night, too. Abdullah Bey could not promise us we would be comfortable, exactly. He rather thought we would be the first westerners who had ever spent the night there. But at all events we would have shelter from the rain. We would get a little drier, too. Sheikh Suleiman would look after us.

Dana? The village of Dana? Now I was feeling very wet and feeble and impotent, rather like an animal being pulled to market by a ring in its nose. Yet the mention of the name Dana produced a queer sensation in my spine, which was odd, I thought, for it had been so rained upon, it felt about as sensitive as a length of chewed string. Dana. Yes, I remembered. Some distance from the valley-head, a little below the tops and an immense distance above the valley. Looking so lost, so improbable . . . as if the race of men that had built it had died out long ago. Looking so *unreal*. . . .

Yet for us it was to become so real that we were to be first of westerners to spend the night there. Real enough to produce a Sheikh Suleiman for our special benefit. But I still had the feeling that Dana would remain unreal to me, however closely we rubbed beards with Sheikh Suleiman.

As we descended, the invisible walls of the valley gave us a little shelter from the icy wind, though the quantity of rain did not abate. Our boots became as soft as blotting-paper, with the sharp stones poking through the welts. Our garments clung to us like another skin. After a time the cloud thinned. Great slabs of rust-red precipice became palpable across the width of the valley, abruptly separated by sharp slabs of cloud. It was as if a company of giant scene-shifters were wheeling sets of cloud and mountain into position. Now and again they unrolled a backcloth, now they let it fall again. On both sides of the mountain the streams ran like mad things. Once, quite fantastically, the whole cloudscape west of us parted, so that two vast walls faced each other, like the two walls of water that flanked the Israelites when they went down into the Red Sea. There, at the end of that plunging valley, beyond the red screes, the bronze-green glistening woods, the leaping streams, there was Punon, the goal of this thrice-attempted journey. If only those walls of cloud remained apart, we would forget everything, our aching limbs, the stones in our boots, and run, and run, and get there . . . it looked so near, if only those walls of cloud did not come together again.

But they did, like colossal gates closing. Never did Punon seem further away.

Now at last the mountain-side down which we were scrambling became a little less primordial. Here, it seemed, the earth had been banked up, had it not? Yes, this was a terrace, with a scraggy growth of barley clinging to the reduced soil. The range of vision went further. Sheltered by that rib of hill, was a grove of olive-trees, poor things, but olive-trees, none the less. Then we turned the flank of a valley, and behold, spread out fanwise on its fan-shaped buttress of rock, lord of those rickety olive-trees and that thin barley, here was Dana.

We stopped a moment and looked down on it, hardly more credulous of it than before.

"Look!" Abdullah Bey said. "Where we sleep!" He pointed out a mud-hut on the hither fringe of the fan. "That is Hotel Bristol," he smiled. "Proprietor Sheikh Suleiman! He is great man in village, he come from big town, Maan. He has two rooms, one for family, one for us. Only house in Dana with two rooms. Very comfortable."

We scrambled down the hill after him, till we got to a point above a low embankment which made one side of Sheikh Suleiman's yard.

"Stop here, please!" requested Abdullah Bey. "I tell them!"

He leapt down into the yard and disappeared round the angle of the hut. The air was pungent with the smell of animal droppings. The rain was coming down less gustily, more implacably, than before. It kept on coming down a long time, and Abdullah Bey did not reappear. No sound penetrated Sheikh Suleiman's thick walls. What is going on there, we wondered, why this deathly quiet? Nothing can have happened to Abdullah Bey? No, no. To anyone else, not to Abdullah Bey. Was there anything to be done? There was nothing to do but to stand and be rained on. The mud nosed through shoes and stockings and took possession of the spaces between toes. That seemed, somehow, the crowning discomfort. The world had become very dark and chilly and forlorn.

"He's a long time," said Jim. "I don't like all this!"

"Nor me either!" I muttered.

Not even Lucas had the ill grace to say he was still enjoying himself.

At last Abdullah Bey reappeared. "It take a long time to make clean!" he apologized. "Please come!"

We jumped down into the yard, which was so sticky with mixed mud and ordure that we could hardly move our feet. In the wall round the corner there was an open doorway with smoke indecisively filtering through into the surrounding mist. Abdullah Bey stood at the threshold motioning us in.

"There is fire!" he exclaimed cheerfully. "Sheikh Suleiman not in yet. He come later. Family all in other room."

We stooped under the low lintel and stood choking for a minute or so, blinded with the acrid smoke. The rain dripping from our clothes made the floor almost as pasty as the mud outside. We managed with a little effort to get our shoes and socks off. They felt as heavy as the roots of a tree.

We advanced further. We could make out two dim figures lying on their bellies puffing away at the fire, which consisted of a bundle of damp twigs laid down in the centre of the room, with a raised earthen rim to show that was the hearth. It was not warm yet, but it was at least dry. The floor was very clean. Round three sides of the room a series of gaily-coloured mattresses were laid end to end, each with its padded head-rest and heap of quilted blankets. We peeled off our clothes and proceeded to wring them out like dishcloths, leaning over the threshold into the yard. Lucas had been wearing a huge furry coat of the type known as "teddy-bear."

It had absorbed so much moisture, it fell from his shoulders like a sack of coke.

The two young men, exhausted, turned their mouths away from the reluctant fire. Abdullah explained they were the son and nephew of Sheikh Suleiman. They smiled at us shyly and switched their mouths round towards the fire again. When that was going, one filled a couple of basins with water from a huge hairy goatskin, the other trimmed the lamps. We washed, took possession of a mattress each, then opened up our rucksacks, and put on a garment or two not to shock our hosts with nakedness, though it would have been pleasanter to wait till something had been dried out a little. A few more visitors came in, bowed gravely and sat down in the corner of the room towards the doorway. They looked on, saying nothing. It was odd, this quietness—not disturbing, merely odd. It was impossible to feel disturbed with Abdullah Bey by your side. Somebody coughed. It sounded like a child's cough. But there was no child in the room. Then we saw, with eyes for the first time capable of seeing, that the wall at right angles to the doorway did not go the whole way up to the vault of the roof. It was, in fact, no more than a partition, with small holes let in that served as store-places. The family was evidently on the further side of the room.

" There is a child there, yes? " I asked Abdullah Bey.

" Many children," he smiled. " Plenty children, perhaps ten. Very quiet people in Dana. Also goats there and chickens."

Yes, it did not make them any more real, these people of Dana, that ten children could maintain an almost tomb-like silence, with their goats among them, and their chickens. A young man brought in a petrol-tin without top or bottom and set it round the twigs to condense the fire, which now had some heat and body.

" Isn't it interesting," whispered Lucas, subdued by that ecclesiastical silence, " how important a place petrol-tins occupy in the life of the desert countries."

" Yes," I agreed. I thought the subject a trifle academic.

" They make roofs with them," he continued, " even whole homes; every sort of ironmongery, flower-pots, braziers."

" They will have to make boots out of them," I spluttered, " for to-morrow's journey to Feinân."

" To-morrow's journey to Feinân," repeated Jim hollowly.

" We're going to Feinân on horses," said Lucas. " We won't need boots."

Still they kept on coming in, the silent ones, and bowed, and took their places alongside the wall. The water was ready for tea now. Tea was brewed and our three enamel mugs went solemnly from mouth to mouth and round to our mouths again. Then Abdullah Bey proffered cigarettes from the store he had thoughtfully brought with him, which they smoked, smacking their lips faintly. Then, when the cigarettes were half smoked through, they extinguished them, and placed the remnants carefully in their wallets.

" Sheikh Suleiman will be here soon," said Abdullah Bey. " They have gone for him. He was a long way down the wadi, in tent."

Then at last he came, bearing another mood with him, with three or four attendants laden with brand new quilts to make our night more comfortable. There was a good deal of hand-kissing and invoking of Allah to bless us, and altogether he was a more metropolitan person, coming, in fact, from Maan, the most amiable of its products. As for Abdullah Bey, it was clear the sheikh loved him like a brother, for he threw his arms round him again and still again, resting his beard now on his left shoulder, now on his right. Those transports over, he stood a little distance away, looking down on us benevolently, where we sat round the fire preparing our meal. His eyes gleamed black and friendly; the dark tracts of his beard, heavily streaked with silver, looked quite blue. It was not his house any longer, he declared. It was ours, all ours.

From time to time other sheikhs came in to pay their respects to us, having come great distances across the still undiminished storm. When we had eaten, they permitted themselves to join us at tea, sitting there gazing at us, without hostility, without any emotion it was possible to give a name to. But when the last mug of tea had been drunk and we were beginning to arrange ourselves for the night, an episode occurred, a spit of temper and loud noise, which, dying down as sharply as it arose, made the dream-like silence more dream-like than before. Suddenly, one of the nameless sheikhs rose, and faced Abdullah—a tall fellow, he was, white as flour, with a nose like a scythe. Without warning, he launched into a fierce harangue, his voice with its first syllable attaining its top register. He continued so for half a minute. Then Abdullah rapped out a few sharp words: " What? Have you no shame? "

The man stopped, a word broken off in mid-air. He stared back haughtily into Abdullah's eyes. Then he gathered his garments round himself, and swept out through the doorway. A second later it was as if the man had not been there. Abdullah Bey went on rolling his puttees round his legs, Sheikh Suleiman poked at the fire with a twig, the other sheikhs sat inanimate, shoulder to shoulder. The complaint, as we learned later, was that another of the sheikhs there present had turned his donkey loose in the complainant's patch of garden. It was one of Abdullah Bey's functions to smooth out differences of that sort, but in circumstances he deemed more suitable.

It was getting late now; we were all very tired. The visitors began to withdraw, each bowing toward us and kissing the back of his hand. Then only Suleiman was left, who, seeing we were quite ready for sleep, turned down the lamp and went over to Abdullah Bey's mattress and squatted down beside his head. Then they started whispering, those two; hour upon hour went by, and still they whispered. It was not a sound to keep one awake. It became part of the mist-muffled silence, as the glow of the smouldering embers in the hearth became part of the darkness. Suleiman was giving an account (we learned later) of all that had happened in that territory, all that was happening and seemed likely to happen. The officers of the Legion have a confidence-man in each

region, and in Dana he was Suleiman. The whispering went
on like rustling leaves.

I fell asleep at some time, for when the fleas awoke me it
was dead silent and pitch-black. I had nothing on, having
learned from Lawrence that nakedness is the Arab defence
against a verminous bed. It was no defence for me. I found
myself embossed and smarting all over with bites. As I
caught one flea, all his friends attacked me in other quarters.
I was agonized for sleep, but sleep would not return. Out in
the yard a cow mooed for her calf; but the calf was snuggled
up warmly against the sheikh and his family, and only replied
once or twice and then was silent. All my other home-mates
slept. I slew one flea, and another, but they came still. I
switched my torch on between the rugs, and frightened them
away for a time, for they feared light more than my inexpert
fingers. But they came again. Again I thrust at them with
my pole of light.

" Oh blease, blease! " the voice of Lucas remonstrated,
picking itself heavily out of the glue of sleep. " Garnt yer
ztudy mab tmorrer? "

The voice subsided. I thought if I burst into tears, I might
feel better; tears, alas, would not come. I was sliding off into
sleep, when Suleiman jolted me with a sudden gabble of
prayers, which seemed to go round and round in his mouth
like a top. A baby whimpered. A dog growled. Then silence
was complete again, and blackness. When Suleiman's prayers
awoke me still again, his voice was resonant and musical.
He knew what he was doing this time, he gave each syllable
full value. He stopped. I slept. I must have slept or Abdullah
Bey could not have awakened me.

" Time to get up! " he proclaimed. " The horses will be
here now! "

I did not get up. I hated those horses with a devastating
hatred. Somebody uttered the word " Feinân," but even that
did not quicken my heart-beats. Lucas and Jim rose and
walked over to the doorway.

" It's foggy! " said Jim. " You can cut it with a knife! "

" Told you so! " I muttered. " Can't stand up 'gainst Jehovah ! "

I slumped again. They had to kick me hard before they could get me up, which must have been some time later, for by then there was a certain amount of light in the room, and a fire crackling on the hearth. There was coffee for breakfast and bread and strawberry jam and cold boiled cauliflower. I was not still dreaming. They were both there, strawberry jam and cold boiled cauliflower. I was very stiff as I pulled myself along towards the fire, but not so stiff as I was to be before the end of that day.

Sheikh Suleiman was in fine form that morning. His prayers must have done him good, for he had had not much more sleep than I, though he was doubtless used to less.

" Look! " he cried, tugging at his beard. " Can nothing be done with this devil's spawn? How they breed! "

" The sheikh means those grey hairs! " explained Abdullah Bey. " He is very angry on them! "

" Sheikh! " I repeated. " Sheikh! He is getting old. He is getting old. Like French *vieillir*! "

The others looked at me with expressions of alarm.

" You remember? " I went on dimly. " Fellow told us in Cairo. *Châhha* means to become old. Like French *vieillir*. So *sheikh* doesn't mean ' big shot,' only by extension. Means man become old. Like Suleiman! Grey hairs in beard. Sheikh! See? Ha! Ha! "

I tittered. It was rather fun catching the word out, as it were, when it wasn't looking. I think Jim murmured something about taking a pulse. Then Suleiman suddenly emitted a torrent of sharp protest.

" No! No! " he cried. " Not old! Not a bit of it! " He had understood exactly what I had been driving at. He was not an old man. He was a *waled*, a boy, stronger than any boy. He opened his mouth to show how perfect his teeth were, how dazzling white. He was strong. Who was stronger in all the country? That was why women loved him—he smiled a little salaciously—but not men. Oh no, not men!

They were jealous of him! They hated him! He inclined his head in my direction and carried my fingers towards his scalp.

"You see? Bullet here! Sword-cut here! What other man could have been wounded so and lived? Old, eh? Old!" He wagged his finger at me reprovingly, then pulled his garments down below his neck. "Tell him about this one!" he requested, and thrust my fingers into the hollow of some old gash. It had been made when he was young, Abdullah explained, and an orphan. A man, a grandson of a pig, had stolen a patch of ground from him, thinking he was so young he would not protest. But, indeed, he had protested, and that lustily. So the piece of offal had slashed at him with a scimitar, and marked him all the way from the collar-bone to below the navel. The blood had spurted like a fountain. "Sphur! Sphur!" The bystanders had gone away leaving him for dead; but when he came to, he had taken a burning brand and sealed the wound with it, that it should not go green. So it was clear, was it not, he was a great one even when *waled*. But he was not less *waled* now. These grey hairs, they lied, they lied! Was there any decoction made by the wise men of our land that turned grey hairs black again?

But more than that, we said. Grey hair could be made not only black, but red or golden, at will. It could be restored thick as a fleece to scalps bald as an egg. They published photographs which proved these things. Could such things lie?

Suleiman sighed heavily, then he motioned to us to bring our heads closer. "The fact is," he whispered, "I am in love again. She is a lovely one. She is fourteen. Fain would I marry her, but she cannot abide these grey hairs, these cheats, these liars." He twitched his head round nervously, for fear he had spoken too loud, but all seemed as before behind the partition. "She has gone to Palestine," he said, "with her father, for they are poor, and he seeks a rich man for her. But if Allah finds me this black-making decoction, I will go after her, no man shall stand in my way." His eyes flashed. He threw his head back magnificently.

At that moment, a word was uttered from behind the partition. Suleiman, the word was; a woman's voice uttered it. Suleiman rose, looking shamefaced and rather frightened. He went out of the room. We did not see him again till we were ready to set out on the expedition.

"It will be hot later," promised Abdullah Bey. "Very beautiful."

I looked at him with an unenthusiastic eye. It might have been he, not I, who was on a journey in the steps of Moses the Conqueror, and had insisted on getting to the station of Punon at the cost of any discomfort.

"Horses are waiting," he said.

We set out, the path leading along the outer rim of the edge. Below us the deep mist heaved like a sea. There was still no other side to the valley. It was cold and damp. I moved very awkwardly in my clothes, which were in some parts still damp, in others baked hard as boards. A company of men and animals was waiting for us in a small clearing. It included Suleiman on a donkey, a Circassian Corporal of the Legion, Musa by name, on a horse, and four other horses with a couple of Sheikh Saleh's men in attendance. Musa had brought over Abdullah's horse for him, a handsome and mettlesome grey mare. The moment he got into the saddle, you realized a horse's back was his real element, as the water is a swan's. Jim's and Lucas's animals had a certain amount of spirit, mine not so much.

"Ready?" called Abdullah Bey.

We were ready. And once more, now a third time, we set our faces for Feinân. The first part of the journey was the stiffest, the descent to the water-course. The mountain-side was not only very steep, but, being exposed to the weather in a way the rest of the wadi was not, was caked with a layer of loose rubble, which went crashing with every other step down into the blind depths below. It did not take me many minutes to learn to hand myself over completely to my horse's guidance, who, if he seemed now and again to go out of his way to choose a particularly giddy bit of scree, clearly knew much more about it than I did.

Before long the mist became less dense, so that we could see the eye-level slopes across the wadi. At the same time we entered into a boskage which went on thickening as we descended. The boughs and leaves were dark and fresh with the cloud which had steeped them for many hours. It stretched out towards us blossoming branches of wild white pear and pink almond blossom. It spread a starry blanket of white and purple and golden flowers in the niches of damp earth between the boulders. The perverse rancour against Punon with which I had started the day was, in fact, already beginning to wear thin. It was quite shot to pieces as by a salvo of blue bullets when suddenly, in a single moment as it seemed, we had emerged from cloud, which stood like a vast wall above and behind us, and we gazed straight up into unmitigated sky. On our right soared enormous precipices of bright red sandstone, shored up by colossal buttresses, and separated by gorge after gorge abruptly descending. The left-hand mountain was grey, less spectacular, of a slope easy enough to allow a grey-green scrub to overspread it, though there, too, the lateral gorges were very fearsome. Far off, at the end of the wadi, the Ghor simmered like a sea of mercury punctuated by the sharp cones of hills. Southward, still further, light on the Negeb was pale pink, shadow was lilac.

" I was wrong," I reflected humbly. " There was no opposition between Jehovah and Abdullah Bey. Abdullah Bey is His trusted agent. It was the Lord's will that we should fail twice to reach Punon, that we might approach it the third time by this thoroughfare of titanic beauty. It was the Lord Himself who isolated Punon in my heart's map from its equally dim peers, Rimmon-perez, and Tahath, and Mithkah. And if Feinân (as modern speech renders old Punon) has not even a piece of odd-shaped scrub to distinguish it from the desert half a mile left and half a mile right of it, the thrice-essayed journey has more than repaid itself, both in its two failures and in this third attempt which seems unlikely to fail now."

Sc

Lucas drew rein on a spur ahead of me.

"Look!" he cried. "Do you see? That eagle! Golden-breasted!"

Yes. I saw. An eagle, like a piece of the cliff that had detached itself and put on wings. An eagle that had gilded its breast because it was spring, and he wished to look a fine fellow in the eyes of his mate.

"Listen!" cried Jim from a spur behind me. "Do you hear?"

I turned my head. I could hear the water running down the ravine, as before, and the noise that there always is among leaves.

"The water, you mean? It's fine!"

"No! Listen again!"

Lucas heard it at that same moment.

"Cuckoo!" he cried excitedly.

Then I, too, heard it, the double valve of sound opening and shutting upon the incredulous air. Cuckoo of the heathery moors of Ross-shire, cuckoo of the sedgy Sussex marshes, cuckoo of Punon of the far-wandering Israelites.

"What is it? What wrong?" called Abdullah Bey anxiously, galloping down from a rather flimsy looking ledge where he had been prospecting. We must have looked a bit silly, each gaping on his spur of rock.

"A bird!" I cried. "Like in England!"

He stiffened suddenly on his horse.

"And that?" he cried, pointing to a place high up on the opposite mountain. "Is that like in England? Ibex! You see?"

The others saw; they saw his fine horns, they said. I, alas, did not. We touched the horses' flanks and went on again, the hooves clicking musically on hollow rock. Abdullah Bey rode on ahead, went skirmishing up the hill, cantering down the mountain, suddenly came up on us galloping from our rear. He must have covered several times as much ground as we did on the journey. He drew rein once or twice to point out to us traces of the Roman road which once came up this way from the Arabah—the remains of a causeway, the remnant of a bridge over a small gorge. If the Roman road had been here, I asked myself, why not that " king's highway " regarding which Moses had sent messengers to the King of Edom, asking might he go by it, turning aside neither to the right hand nor the left?

" Why not? Why not? " clucked a covey of partridges our hooves struck up from the undergrowth.

Why not, indeed, excepting that the way is very steep. But what road is not, leading up from the Arabah to Edom's high places?

The going became more difficult down by the watercourse, where we often had to duck and dodge to prevent the spiny branches scratching our faces or dragging us from the saddle. Frequently we had to draw rein within a foot or two, finding ourselves on the brink of a sheer cliff, and there would be much scouting and hallooing about the adjacent slopes to find out how we could get further.

But once the hallooing came from far off, further than the furthest scout of our own party. Was it an echo? The men from Tafileh looked at each other dubiously for one brief moment, as if they thought there might be a *djinn* haunting these slopes. But the men from Dana at once hallooed back, making a trumpet out of their hands.

" Later ! " gestured Sheikh Suleiman, who happened to be beside me at that moment. He made a diving movement with his hand towards a point some distance down the wadi. For the next hour or two the voice kept pace with us across an enormous gulf of air, slowly descending, slowly approaching. Then at last the voice put on substance. A young man stood out on the skyline, with bare feet and flung hair. He delivered a few words to our company, a message and an invitation.

" His father lives high up in cave," explained Abdullah Bey, " on opposite side of mountain. He shall slay sheep for you, in your honour. We shall have banquet when we come back."

The lad dwindled up the mountain-side again. We continued down the stream, beyond thickets of broom and oleander, into lower, hotter airs, where the bamboo grew rank, marshalling the spear-tips of its leaves.

He shall slay sheep for us. We shall have banquet when we come back.

How did that dweller in a high mountain-cave know (I asked myself) that strangers were abroad in his wadi to whom he must do honour? Has the tale of our being here already reached him from far-off Dana still buried in its cloud? Keen of eye as an eagle, has he sighted us from his eyrie? Why am I not more excited about it? I have never sat down before at the mouth of a cave in a high mountain, to a sheep slain specially in my honour.

Or perhaps I have . . . wandering with my forbears, long ago in these regions. . . .

" Look out! "

The thrust-forward arm of a tree tore at me and almost had me off. It was Suleiman's arm miraculously projecting from twenty feet off slewed me round into the saddle again. We went on, for another hour, another two hours. I was getting very stiff and saddle-sore. I was relieved when at last the watercourse opened up. We came down the last ledge of the foot-hills, we were cantering upon more or less level ground. But we were still several hundreds of feet above the sweltering level of the Arabah, which steamed north and south, several miles ahead of us. The plain opened out into a great amphitheatre, closely overhung on the south by the red mass of Mount Shobek, guarding access into that wadi Shobek down which we had earlier proposed to journey to this place. Further away on the north Jebel Dana dwindled into a few low ridges and a last outcrop of isolated pyramidal hillocks. It was bakingly hot. The sun rippled and dazzled along the rough plain. We were in the way of the wilderness once more.

" Look! Do you see? " called Abdullah Bey, wheeling his horse round. " That little hill in front! It looks all black, yes? That is Khirbet Feinân! " He drew rein beside me. " You

are happy, yes? What you wished to see, yes? Feinân!
Punon!"

I was almost too racked to say how happy I was, and how
grateful, to that annuller of sandstorm and panic, driver ahead
through pelting rain and opaque cloud. I smiled at him
wanly. We cantered on. Some minutes passed.

"Look! You see? All is Feinân!"

He pointed left and right of us, ahead and behind us. I
became aware this was no mere primordial rubble over which
we had been riding for a little time now. Men had lived here
once, if it could be called living, a city had been here. There
were shards underfoot, and here and there a worked stone.
There was a sense that a street may have been here once,
a building there. Here was the lip of an old reservoir, here
several feet of wall still standing of a church in one place,
of a fort in another. It had been clearly a vast city, or rather
a vast mine-head. Everywhere the scoriae of copper-smeltings
glistened evilly, piled together in small mounds at the entrances
to mine-galleries. It had been a city, it had even been a
bishopric, but they had served not Christ here, but copper,
in an anguish made only tolerable, because, being so extreme,
it could not last more than a few days, and you were a dead
man. Dead men, all of them, whether criminals sent here
because of their crimes, or martyrs because of their faith.
Here died the Christian martyrs condemned by the pagan
emperors, Maximinus and Diocletian. Here the Catholics
were sent to die by the Aryan schismatics. St. Sylvanus and
thirty-three of his companions were beheaded here, the
Egyptian bishops, St. Peleus and St. Nile. All of them died,
soon and terribly; only copper lived on. And then even
that died, and the husks of it only remained, like heaps
of blue-green beetles baked rigid for all time in that gross
heat.

We had drawn up now to the central hill we had seen from
far off. A citadel had crowned it once, which commanded
the region for leagues round. Now all the slopes were cluttered with its ruin. The others had dismounted. I found

I could not dismount, and the Circassian Musa lifted me off, nearly as rigid as a carcase a butcher lifts from a hook.

We separated. It seemed that each of us wished to savour in solitude the strange and bitter flavour of the place. To the Arabs (I said to myself) this is Khirbet Feinân. To the Christians it is Phaenon of the Christian martyrdoms. But I have come here chiefly because it was Punon, where the Israelites pitched their tents . . . *And they journeyed from Mount Hor, and pitched in Zalmonah. And they journeyed from Zalmonah, and pitched in Punon.* There is still water about in stagnant patches, the seepage from the flow of the brook Dana. There is still a little meagre pasturage, where even now our beasts were grazing, with our men lying down beside them, taking their ease.

Here, then, the host of Israel briefly lingered, and passed on . . . *And they journeyed from Punon, and pitched in Oboth.* Now three hours northward lies the wadi Oueibeh. But if Oboth and Oueibeh are the same word, as has been conjectured, they came south again, did they, to take the king's highway up the wadi Dana? So I moved on, pondering this matter, till I came out under the northward side of the hill. And in that moment I saw a sight and heard a sound which made it seem as if the Israelites had not yet moved out of Punon.

A dead man lay on a crude stretcher, covered over with a single blanket. Not many yards away a small group was working at his grave. They must have been resting from their labour for some time, for as I came round into view of them, they took up their long-handled spades and got down to their work again, keeping rhythm with a chant the while, one man leading. With big boulders and a mud cement they had made a sort of culvert the width of a man's body. As I stood there, they shovelled the body out of sight, and walled up the open ends of the grave, each man bringing up his own boulder. Then the leader put into position at the head of the grave a stone larger than the others, marked with a tribal arrow— the arrow of the Howeitat it was; with such an arrow the men of the tribe of Dan or Zebulun might have marked their graves. The place was a cemetery, I saw now, and a few yards away among the graves, a woman sat on a rug crouched over her knees, swaying forward and backward, forward and backward, uttering a faint moan so high-pitched it was almost beyond the range of hearing. Her eyes were shut, her whole face was shut and expressionless, like the blank stones round her. A few yards further, a hobbled goat and kid wilted at their tether.

He was very weary, I thought; he had been wandering a long time and come a long way. Perhaps this is the last of them all to die, the last of those older ones, concerning whom it was written: " Your carcases shall fall in this wilderness; and all that were numbered of you, according to the whole number, from twenty years old and upward, which have murmured against me, surely ye shall not come into the land, save Caleb the son of Jephunneh, and Joshua the son of Nun. But your little ones, which ye said should be a prey, them will I bring in, and they shall know the land which ye have rejected. But as for you, your carcases shall fall in the wilderness."

And as I stood there, recalling those words, the men finished their work, and came over towards me. They did not seem to resent it that a *rumi* had stood there watching them, per-haps because they must have sighted Abdullah Bey and been aware I was there under his auspices. So they came up friendlily, spitting on their hands. They poked with their thumbs behind their shoulders.

" He won't get out of that in a hurry," they intimated. They pushed imaginary stones before them, and shook their heads. " He will not find them at all easy to move, should he think of trying."

" And that goat and that kid? " I asked, pointing.

They made the gesture of a knife drawn across a throat, and of blood flowing over the newly made grave. No, I said to myself, no. It is not thirty-three centuries since the time of the encampment at Punon. It was only yesterday, and the host has not yet reached Oboth, even.

I said good-bye at length to the men above the ground, and the man below it, and went on my way. I joined Lucas and Jim on the broken arch of a Roman aqueduct; where a Bedu close at hand looked at us wryly, and we found we were once more treading on graves. We wandered about for some time more, for Abdullah Bey seemed to have various affairs on his hands, not all archaeological. We saw him outlined now against one horizon, now against another, galloping tirelessly. He came up to us at length, and asked were we satisfied, had Punon been what we had expected it to be. It had been more, I thought. He said the return journey would be harder and longer than the coming here. So we moved back to the small spread of grass where we had left the horses grazing and the men resting, and rested, too, and refreshed ourselves, under the vast red shoulder of Mount Shobek.

" You shall not eat much, please," begged Abdullah. " The old man is killing sheep on mountain. If you do not eat much, he will be not happy."

We thought there would be no difficulty in eating much sheep by the time we had returned over the plain of Khirbet Feinân, and struck up through the long foot-hills, and come out at length among the precipices. We permitted ourselves, therefore, a goodly amount of bread and bully-beef, and washed them down with a draught of Dana water, now become very brackish. As for myself, I wondered vaguely if I felt so stiff now, how would I feel by the time the day's ride was over. I wondered also who those people were who had suggested we would not get to Punon, the forces of Jehovah being arrayed against us. They were pusillanimous people, I thought, not to be encouraged; and I moved from the morsel of bully-beef at my mouth a hairy caterpillar marked with bold bars of red and black. The little tract of sour meadow was alive with them.

So we rose at last, and turned our backs upon Feinân, and our faces toward the sheikh, our host. It was a comforting thing to get out of the baked plain, and into the shade of trees and the sound of water. For an hour or more we kept to the side of the wadi by which we had descended, and then found the sheikh's son waiting for us at the point where we must cross. The valley-bottom was ablaze with flowers, which seemed to have sprung up in these few hours, lilies and blue irises and white and golden crocuses. So attacking slope upon slope, each steeper than the one before it, we turned the flank of the mountain and entered a deep gorge of pale pink and yellow limestone, with the sandstone peak of Jebel Dana due north of us still holding three-quarters of the sky.

We had arrived at our trysting-place. In the belly of the mountain close at hand gaped a large cave and a smaller one beside it, both walled up for a yard or so at their entrances, except for the narrow space left for a doorway. Further away was a small plateau swung out over the gulf, where a dozen or two goats and sheep grazed. Between the caves and the plateau a broad ledge ran for some thirty yards or more under the bulge of rock, then petered out into a goat-track. The ledge had been swept meticulously clean, with the swept twigs and droppings piled up on either extremity. Half the ledge had been spread with bright rugs laid end to end. It looked so hospitable and luxurious in that austerity of sky and mountain, we could not refrain from crying aloud with pleasure.

As we dismounted, our host appeared at the entrance to the greater cave, which was clearly the living-place, and came over to us. He was an extremely old man, bent almost double, with not more than two teeth in his head. Zaheb was his name. He was shivering with excitement; it was to be presumed he had not known so great a day for many years, if ever at all. It was honour enough to entertain Sheikh Suleiman, head man of Dana, once resident of the famed city of Maan. But to entertain Abdullah Bey Rihani, Chevalier of Tafileh, protector of the innocent, scourge of the evil-doer, what language could rise to it? And when that same not only came himself, but brought great lords, albeit *rumis*, from far lands further than Al Qoods—it was more than he could do to keep the tears from his eyes. He kissed their hands, fondled them, and it was a grief to him that he had so few rugs and such poor ones to spread out for their comfort.

Abdullah Bey conveyed our great pleasure. Suleiman announced jovially, by Allah, he was hungry! By the beard of the Prophet, when would a man's thirst be slaked? Then he made a quip or two, being a renowned comedian, then sang a line or two from some ditty. Tittering, his head wagging from side to side like a balloon, the old man at length made off to the caves, where one woman was baking bread and two or three others bent over a cauldron, stirring its contents lustily. From within the caves, the sound came of chickens clucking, calves mooing, children crying. There was great excitement. But not enough for old Zaheb.

" Get on with it! Will you be all day? " his gull-like voice protested. " Do you not know what manner of guests we have? Get on with it, you bags of bones! "

So we sat down and waited, in that eagle's eyrie, in the high-hung wilderness. As we waited, a fawn dog came out of one of the caves, smelled us, then withdrew again, barking loudly. Then the lad who had guided us here brought some drinking-water in a goatskin; it tasted of the goat a little, but it was cold and refreshing. Then a great tin of *leben*, sour milk, was passed round, then bread, to each one of us four or five rounds, very thin, but tough and spongy. Then at last the cauldron was brought over, sizzling hot, the sheep slain in our honour.

Suleiman thrust his nose down through the sharp steam. " *Tayib! Tayib!* " he cried, and bade us smell in our turn. *Tayib!* " we cried also. It smelled good indeed, the great bed of rice, the yellow sauce, the piled hillock of mutton. The contents of the cauldron were now ladled into two basins, one for Abdullah Bey and ourselves, the other for Suleiman and his friends.

" This way! " suggested Abdullah Bey, considerate of our strangeness, and tore off a piece of bread and wrapped it round a chunk of meat, and lifted it to his lips. We followed suit. Then having waited politely till each of us had taken a mouthful, the others set to, throwing their sleeves back, and thrust their bare arms into the scalding cauldron. They ate with great gusto, and at enormous speed, kneading the rice and meat into moist balls in the palms of their hands. A minute or two later we, too, were doing the same thing, set off by Abdullah Bey, who in a moment's absent-mindedness had forgotten to make use of his bread fork-spoon. It was pleasanter like that. Our drawing-room manners were a little invidious. Sheikh Suleiman, his mouth dripping fatness, beamed at us delightedly the whole time. Every now and again, having discovered a particularly tasty morsel in the depths of the basin, a piece of heart or kidney, he would hand it over to one or the other of us, with loud commendations.

Our host did not sit down to the repast with us. Perhaps he thought it would be presumptuous. Perhaps there was too much to do, and it would not be seemly unless he did it all. There would be more bread to bring, or more water. From time to time he would pour a mug of hot *leben* over the two basins, threshing it into the meat and rice with both hands.

At last we could eat no more and Suleiman's basin was quite empty, and now, but only now, our host sat down to the festive board with us. He gathered round himself all the empty utensils, and proceeded to lick them dry, to show that that which he had set before us was the best he had, and for so humble a person as himself even the last lickings of the dishes were ample feast. There were one or two wooden dishes, and these he scoured with his knuckles, screwing them into the grain. Then he sucked his knuckles dry, and smiled at us. His face was quite radiant, as he sat cross-legged by the edge of the shelf, his arched back outlined against the further mountain. In the abyss an eagle sailed indolently, as if he too had eaten enough and was at ease.

So we said good-bye at length to the sheikh of the precipices, and once more he kissed our hands and fondled them, his women looking on dimly from the darkness of their caves.

It had been a strange meal, not to be forgotten easily. After such poetry, all eating will be prose, I thought.

We descended obliquely to a point higher up the wadi where we could ford the stream again, and continued for three hours or so, slowly ascending. To me it seemed longer than that, for I had developed a large saddle-sore, which every movement chafed. At length it seemed no time at all. I was jogging on and on, in a dream of fatigue. That went on for I do not know how long. Then someone bade me look up.

" Dana! " they said. " We're home! "

I looked up. The mountain looked so vast and vertical, the place so inaccessible, it seemed merely funny.

" Nobody could get up there! " I said. " Not without a cable! "

But we got up there, of course, and dismounted. I should of myself say I was dismounted. It seemed a long way between the little clearing on the rim of the village and Suleiman's house, but we got there, too. The sheikhs began to file in at once, but polite conversation was neither expected nor attempted. I turned to the wall and slept. Punon became one again with Kehelethah and Makheloth, not even a bubble on the surface of the waters that engulfed me.

§ 4

Sheikh Suleiman drew me aside next morning, as I was about to mount. He took hold of his beard and pushed it nearer my eyes, so that I should the better note the grey hairs that did him such wrong.

" You will send? " he murmured. His eyes sought mine anxiously.

" I will," I promised, " by Allah! " And having left the earlier Prophet behind me on the summit of Mount Nebo, I went over the river to Al Qoods to fulfil my vow to the later Prophet. But alas, I cannot say if Sheikh Suleiman of Dana has received that bottle of hair-restorer, and, if he has, whether it has made his grey hairs black again.

So we climbed up out of the valley on to the top of Edom again, and I drew rein and looked back for a minute or two at the village of Dana. It is really there, I said to myself. I have a friend there, Sheikh Suleiman by name. I have eaten and drunk in his house. I have been flea-bitten there.

That may be true, I said to myself. But it is the same as before, as lost, as improbable. It exists. It does not exist. And yet, I mused, is there any discovery of new truth in that? Cannot the same be said of Birmingham?

Abdullah Bey rode beside me for a little time.

" So you have seen Punon, yes? " he asked a little mischievously.

" I will not thank you——" I began.

" Please, no! " he said hurriedly. " And now? "

" Back to Tophel. And we may catch a glimpse of Iye-abarim. And so at last to the brook Zered, and Edom is behind us, and Moab ahead."

" There is something I show you before we get to Tophel. Tell where you think the Egyptians follow the Israelites? "

" Well, according to the Bible, they got no further than the Red Sea."

" Ah yes," he said secretly. " But some escaped. They followed into Edom, all this way; further north still, so far as Buseira."

" As far as Buseira? But what is your authority for that? " I wondered if it was an over-ingenuous reading of some inscription, or some pretty local legend, perhaps.

" You will see," was all I could get from him. " You will see."

We found Jemil where we had left him in the ruined khan of Razhadiyeh, sitting on a fallen lintel. You could not have told whether he had been sitting there five minutes or five weeks. He looked a little sad, perhaps, but quite resigned, as if he would have been quite ready to wait another five weeks.

" What have you been doing, Jemil? "

The question seemed to surprise him.

" Drinking tea," he replied at length.

We got back into the car, which had not suffered from its torrential drenching, and covered the ground between Dana and Buseira now a third time. A track debouched from the road and led up to the narrow saddle connecting the Buseira plateau with the main massif. Buseira is a doleful collection of mud-huts now; gone are its palaces, now " a desolation, a reproach, a waste and a curse." The princes no longer walk about there, glorious in their apparel, in dyed garments, like them that tread in the winefat. The whole plateau is littered with ruin, that dates from several antiquities, Edomite and Nabataean and Byzantine. None has withstood the curse.

The villagers had seen us coming from far off and gathered round us as we got out of the car. They plucked insistently at our coats. They almost wept with excitement. They had not the reserve of the people of Dana.

" They want we shall eat," said Abdullah. " But not now. Come. You remember what I tell you? About the Egyptians following the Israelites to Buseira? You shall see at once."

We followed him along the ridge of the plateau northward, where every step kicked up the rubble of fabulous centuries, a painted potsherd, the grit-encrusted glass bottom of a bottle. Here and there were the bases of ancient columns or the rims of old cisterns long since blocked up. At one time, as it seemed, the whole plateau-top was protected by stout walls, which remain at their stoutest at the northern edge. There we stood at length, the vast valleys swinging round us on all sides. Ahead of us soared a great mountain.

That was Jebel Dehal, Abdullah pointed out, and below it wound the wadi Oueibeh, the name of which, according to certain writers, preserves the name of the encampment at Oboth where the host pitched their tents after the march from Punon.

" Many ibexes are there," he stated. " I shoot."

" Yes, but the Egyptians——? " I reminded him.

" Ah yes, the Egyptians ! " His eyes twinkled. " Look ! Do you see far down ? Stones and foundations, like it was a camp there ? "

I would not have perceived unaided that those stones must have been put there by the hand of man ; but they had, it was indisputable.

Abdullah Bey looked round among the men and boys that had followed us. Then, hearing a noise of bells he waited a moment, and a goatherd and his goats coming up from the valley came into view.

" Ho, Arab ! " Abdullah called out to him. " Come here ! "

The young man came, a little nervously. He was a primitive-looking youth with ebony eyes and hair like dyed flax. Abdullah plucked his cloak and pointed to the shell of ruin down in the valley.

" That place—what name has it ? "

" Ramissis ! " said the goatherd.

" Ramissis ? Who is Ramissis ? What is Ramissis ? "

The goatherd looked round miserably. That was all he knew—the name of the *khirbet* was Ramissis. That was all that remained of the pomp of Pharaoh and the havoc of his war, a breath of sound on a barefoot goatherd's lips.

" It seems you may be right," I said at length. " The pursuing Egyptians may have come as far as this. Although you'd think they'd build their night quarters out of less durable material."

" We know that Rameses the Second went north as far as Moab," Lucas remembered. " The word ' Moab ' is mentioned for the first time on one of his monuments. Perhaps there was first a camp down there, and later a fort. Though, of course, it was Meneptah, not Rameses, who went chasing the Israelites."

The matter could not be pressed, I thought.

" Ah well, if the Egyptians are coming up after them from the bottom of the Red Sea, it's time the host started moving. They ought to be thinking of crossing the brook Zered. But there won't be any rest for them there, either." I paused. " Not anywhere," I added a moment later. " Not anywhere."

To reach Ramissis from that point was a difficult undertaking. We would come closer to it later in the day, Abdullah promised. We returned to the huddle of houses and lunched in the schoolroom with the schoolmaster and a small brighteyed sheikh, who, we soon gathered, was Abdullah's local confidence-man, as Suleiman was in Dana. Other sheikhs came in continually.

" That small one knows country very good," approved Abdullah Bey. " Up till ten months ago, he was big cattle-thief." He patted him on the back affectionately. " Nearly all cattle-thieves. Now less and less." It seemed to us a fair epitome of the new conditions. Abdullah bade us look through the window. Two women had issued from a house opposite and were spreading out great lengths of black goathair tenting. They were to be dried and mended against the forthcoming exodus into the open pastures. Abdullah hoped it would be a better year for them. The last had been a very bad one. One of the sheikhs there present had had four hundred sheep. Of these over three hundred had died in the great snow-blizzard. The man's voice broke as he told us the tale of it. In his efforts to rescue his animals, he had been snowed up in a cave, and nearly frozen to death. When his son located him and dug him out some days later, he was already stiff as a board. Three thousand sheep in Buseira alone died in that snowstorm. Very bad, protested Abdullah, shaking his head sadly. Thousands of years they manage sheep, yet in bad weather sheep die like flies. Bad weather coming often, too. Well, perhaps it shall be better now. Perhaps new government will see it shall be better. Very bad, he repeated, sighing deeply.

A great wind arose while we were at luncheon, that seemed to claw fiercely at the meagre fabric of modern Buseira, as if to tear it about and hurl it where the debris of ancient

BANQUET ON JEBEL DANA

Bozrah lay. Isolated as it was on that bare plateau, at the meeting-place of the wadis, any movement of air became a storm. It was a melancholy luncheon all in all, and we were relieved to be on our way again. The horses were waiting for us some miles further north, where we took a track that disappeared into the wilderness of the western plateau. The idea was, as we had been told, that we were to see Ramissis at close quarters. But in fact it was the name of Ramissis which was the excitement of it, not its few formless stones, a thing which Abdullah Bey understood clearly. It was that we might see another place than Ramissis that he took us on that last detour, according to his cunning method of progressive revelation.

I will say at once the emotion this new place aroused in us was comparable with any we experienced on the journey— the emotion of being on the summit of Mount Sinai, or of first seeing Petra, or of wandering on the rolling tops of Pisgah. But in those three cases, the imagination had already dealt with the experience, however falsely or clumsily. In this case the eye and the heart had not been prepared. At a certain moment the place had not been there; a moment later it was there with all the authority of solid rock, with all the unreason of a mirage.

The name of the place is Selah; but it is a name of the order of Ramissis, not shown on maps, a word that has chanced to survive on the lips of goatherds from one epoch to another, thin as wind, and as immortal. Selah, you say to yourself again. The name evokes a swift response. It is recorded on divers occasions in the Bible. As in Isaiah: " Send ye the lamb to the ruler of the land from Selah to the wilderness, unto the mount of the daughter of Zion." Or in Kings: " He slew of Edom, in the valley of salt, ten thousand, and took Selah by war." Elsewhere, where the original has the same " Selah," the scholars have rendered it as " rock," as in the sublime passage of Jeremiah: " Thy terribleness hath deceived thee, and the pride of thine heart, O thou that dwellest in the cleft of the rock, that holdest the height of

Tc

the hill: though thou shouldst make thy nest as high as the eagle, I will bring thee down from thence, saith the Lord."

Now it is usually thought that by that "rock" the town known to us as Petra was meant. But is it not also possible that the place still called by the name "Selah" after these thousands of years have gone by was meant? For though Petra evidently was far the bigger place, Selah may well have been as big as Bozrah, a city which could evoke the most grandiose anathemas of the Prophets. It was predominantly, like Petra, a Nabataean site, as the little excavation that so far has been carried out there has proved. But enough Idumaean shards have been found there to make it possible, at least, that the place was the Selah of Edom. This, I think can be said too: in Petra it was chiefly the tombs and temples that were carved out of the encompassing rock, the dwelling-places were for the most built in the open arena. Selah is nothing but a rock, a single carved mountain, a city of refuge, it might be, when the land was hard-pressed by war.

We came upon it suddenly, turning a shoulder of the slope we were descending.

"Look!" Abdullah bade us. "Selah! You remember? Selah!"

We looked, and marvelled, and were silent. At first the eye saw only a most strange mountain on the further side of a vast and profound ravine, a great flat-topped rock rising from the centre of it like a round tower. It was almost completely isolated, accessible only by a single traverse of rock, the cliffs of it nearly vertical, lapped round by a stillness and secrecy which imposed themselves as almost visible, like a mist. Its broad uneven tops were rounded in a series of flat domes at different levels, as if the thing were made of a different substance from the mountains in all these regions, and therefore time and weather had handled it in a way quite peculiar to itself.

After some time the eye made out that men had had the handling of the mountain. It began to isolate squared windows and doorways cut out of the solid rock and carved stairways dizzily ascending. When you make the precipitous journey thither, you find wells and cisterns and fragments of walls, you find altars waiting, as it seems, for the due sacrifices to be set down on them, that day or the next day, to Du-shara or Atargatis.

Impregnable the place must have seemed to the makers of it, the holders of the heights of the hill, the dwellers in the clefts of its rock. They had made their nest truly as high as the eagle. But it had not been high enough. I will bring thee down from thence, said the Lord. And the carved square windows of its houses stare like the eye-sockets of a skull. And Edom shall be a desolation, the Lord said. No man shall abide there, neither shall a son of man dwell in it.

Now there is a village facing Selah on the south side of the valley. It has existed no more than three years, for only so recently some families of the Beni-hamidi tribe, who had been pure nomads till then, built themselves a few mud-huts to live in during part of the year. They have incorporated the name of the strange dead city in the name they have given their village: Douweikhli-Selah. We drank tea with the villagers, and they told us mournfully of the plague that had halved their numbers in this brief time. And looking between their sallow faces and the spectral city opposite, I could not but recall the fullness of that old curse.

" Edom shall be a desolation; every one that goeth by it shall be astonished, and shall hiss at all the plagues thereof."

Should I come this way again, I darkly mused, three years from now, how many families would I find still extant of the Beni-hamidi that built themselves the village of Douweikhli and added the name of Selah to it in their folly?

§ 5

So we left Selah and some hours later were back in Tophel-Tafileh again, in Abdullah Bey's carpeted and cushioned sitting-room, where we drank tea, self-brewed as it seemed, flanked by platters of self-served cakes. The roaring sheikh came in again, and there was a good deal of important stamping of documents in respect of our horses, but we were not so deafened by him this time, for our ears still retained the roaring of the wind about Buseira. The bed-sheets were balm to my sores. We slept like three babes.

We had made our way to Feinân-Punon, despite sundry discouragements. We had passed close to Oboth-Oueibeh. There remained one more station, Iye-abarim by name, before we reached the brook Zered, now called the wadi Hasa. The brook Zered behind us, we should pass by the way of the wilderness of Moab, as the Lord had enjoined on us.

Abdullah Bey proposed to take us that day to Khirbet-et-Tannur, the Nabataean site where he had discovered the fish-goddess, Atargatis, whom he had unveiled for us with such reverence the evening we first met him. Khirbet-et-Tannur stands at the confluence of the wadi el-Âban and the wadi Hasa. At that point he would leave us, to go forward lonelily for several days among the wild wadis. We would go forward into Moab, into the noise of the battles.

I mentioned to Abdullah that one or two scholars had identified Iye-abarim, the next station after Oboth, with Imeh, some kilometres north of Tafileh, according to the map. Would we get a glimpse of Imeh, I asked.

"Not many people," mused Abdullah, "but bad." He was speaking for the moment rather as a police-officer than an archaeologist. "I have to punish Imeh men very strong one month ago. But they fight good, yes, they fight good." He was also disposed to see virtues where he could find them. "Without the Imeh men Lawrence not winning the battle in Tafileh here."

Lawrence! We were not by any means to leave Tafileh in the steps of that earlier warrior, without being reminded we were still in the steps of that later one. We were shown the house he lived in, after the Tafileh battle with which he reproached himself so bitterly, for being too victorious in it . . . not a comfortable house, he found, " since to have a fire was to be stifled with green smoke, and in the window-spaces were only makeshift shutters of our own joining. The mud roof dripped water all the day long, and the fleas on the stone floor sang together mightily, for praise of the new meats given them. We were twenty-eight in the two rooms, which reeked with the sour smell of our crowd." It was not comfortable then, it did not look comfortable now. We asked might we enter it, but some taboo, presumably female in some aspect or another, seemed to be exerting itself. We did not press the matter. To make up for this disappointment, Abdullah sought painfully to elaborate the tactics of the battle as we moved towards Imeh. Lucas, as the soldier of the party, seemed to understand what it was about. It remained very dark to me until I re-read Lawrence's account.

The line of Lawrence's Journeys as traced in one of the maps in *The Seven Pillars of Wisdom* a little puzzlingly goes no further north than the wadi Hasa, though in the narrative he tells us of a " personal examination " he made " of the approaches to Kerak, and the ground over which we could later advance to Jordan." Probably the line only indicates the journeys he made with some measure of actual military achievement; a line of his " personal examinations " might have been a very confused and spidery affair.

But the line of his military achievement might well have covered the line of the Mosaic battles between the brook Arnon and the plain of Jericho, if one of the sons of the Sherif Hussein of Mecca had not let him down egregiously. When he set out on his personal examination of the approaches to Kerak, he had left Zeid behind with a considerable supply of gold, the gold which was always necessary to buy the foundation on which an advance might be made. On his return he found the money foolishly frittered away among the local sheikhs. " I was aghast," he wrote: " for this meant the complete ruin of my plans and hopes, the collapse of our effort to keep pace with Allenby." He determined to throw in his hand and break clean once and for all from the Revolt in the Desert. He had fallen into one of his recurrent moods of nihilist despair. " My will had gone and I feared to be alone, lest the winds of circumstance, or power, or lust, blow my empty soul away "; one of those moods in which, con- templating the bodies of himself and his followers, he saw them " with some hostility, with a contemptuous sense that they reached their highest purpose, not as a vehicle of the spirit, but when, dissolved, their elements served to manure a field."

He set off down the one escarpment and up the opposite one for British Headquarters in Beersheba, to hand in his resignation. But Allenby and the Fates willed otherwise. It may be that by the time he got there the mood had gone. He had already seen spring on the hill-tops " surpassingly beautiful," and the " melting snow falling over the cliff-edge . . . in diamond-strings down hanging tresses of green fern." He went back to the Revolt again, by way of Cairo. When he returned to the Desert, Tafileh had lost its meaning and importance. The thrust towards Damascus was made along the opposite side of the plateau. But still, both on this side and the other, wherever we followed the Hebrew, we heard perpetually the rumour of the Englishman's name.

As we left Tafileh on the journey toward the wadi Hasa, on our left hand below us were spread out its vast gardens and olive-groves and orchards of almonds in bloom. Even the metal pipes of the fig-tree branches were beginning to put on the tight clumps of their first leaves. The gardens ceased. The almond-blossom went out like spurts of flame. Below us now was Imeh, Aima, as Lawrence writes it. " The Aima men, who knew every blade of grass on these, their own village pastures, crept, unharmed, within three hundred yards of the machine-guns. The enemy, held by our frontal threat, first knew of the Aima men when they, by a sudden burst of fire, wiped out the gun-teams . . . "

Imeh, Aima, Iye-abarim, thus for a sweet moment or two of belly-crawling and trigger-pulling coming up into history again, and ready now to relapse out of it for another three thousand years. . . .

So past one ruined tower and another, past a litter of black basaltic boulders where the anemones cluster like gouts of blood, past a daring acre or two of barley under a hollow hill, we come out on to the high tops again. And higher than these, slashing across the horizon west and east, lies the line of the further bank of the wadi Hasa. Another wild wadi breaks the plateau north and south on our right hand. This is the wadi el-Âban, which makes like a tributary towards the great central gulf of Hasa.

Some minutes later we had reached the police-post of el-Âban, high on the eastern bank of the wadi, with a wind like the day of judgment howling round it, and the sun sharp as a sword. Four horses were waiting for us, throwing their heads back and pawing at the flinty ground. The men came out of their hut and greeted us timidly, as if they were not at ease in this roaring vacancy. They had a big fawn bitch to comfort them, with three puppies she rolled over and over like balls of down. There were two wind-havocked birds there, with long necks and coppery bosoms, scrabbling the gritty earth. A series of feathered quills dragged desultorily behind them, on a few of which still winked a blue-green eye. They were—it seemed as fantastic to themselves as to us—they were peacocks.

But it was not these we had been brought to see. In the centre of the wadi el-Âban, looking toward the colossal northern wall of Hasa, soared a huge isolated hill. The circular top was crowned with a thick layer of gravel, darker than the sandy-grey slopes. In the folds of the hill the shadows were velvet-black.

"Jebel-et-Tannur!" said Abdullah Bey quietly. "On the top is temple! Fish-goddess comes from there!" He spoke with pardonable pride. He had had an instinct, already sharpened by his experience of the Nabataean mind, that a site so august and difficult to access by men might have been chosen by them for the placing of a temple to their gods. His instinct was accurate. He had discovered there a small Nabataean temple, completely unknown till then, one of the most interesting of all the Nabataean ruins. Hardly a handful of people had as yet set eyes on it. A party was setting out shortly from the American School of Oriental Research in Jerusalem to take full stock of it.

So we set out to pay our respects to Atargatis, the fish-goddess, in her shrine at Khirbet-et-Tannur, not forgetting that the first creature we had met on first arriving in her country, was one of her votaries, an old man in Akaba. The road descends sharply to a pouch of greenness under Jebel-et-Tannur, where a clan of Beduin had pitched their tents under the comfortable protection of the police-post. There were herds of black goats and sheep grazing, and some dozens of camels, many with young. As we approached, a baby camel nearly all legs picked itself up feebly from the ground, and straddled over towards one of the horses. Its eyes were still shut, it looked hardly more than a few hours old. The horse snapped at it and swept on, as if annoyed that he had been taken for a she-camel. The mother-camel came stalking up to the infant, licked it all over, and the two burbled a love duet mouth to mouth. Then the large mouth pushed and prodded the small mouth to the tiny full udder. A spatter of primroses shone under the archways of tall legs. It was an odd mingling of eastern and western spring-time prettiness.

We left the horses at the edge of the grazing, and scrambled up the steep cone, glinting in many places with white lumps of rock-crystal. There were clear evidences of the banking which had supported the path by which the priests and wor-shippers had climbed to their sacred hill. Most of the summit was occupied by the ruins of a small temple, some fifty or sixty feet across, which, it was manifest even to our inexpert eyes, would yield the imminently expected scholars a rich harvest. There was much to see even before the spades had got to work. On the perimeter, having formed a frieze, as it seemed, lay many blocks of stone, rudely carved with vines and rosettes, shells and leaves and flowers. A number of broken reliefs of male and female deities littered the ground, some still intact enough to possess great beauty. It was with something of fear, as well as with a sense of privilege, we found ourselves

assisting at the rebirth, as it were, of these old gods dead two
thousand years, impressed with the signs manual of cults
Hellenistic and Syrian and Parthian, brought from remote
shrines in Askalon and Palmyra to be worshipped here, in this
place of howling wind, on a hill-top in a waste Moabite valley.

Abdullah Bey returned with us to the police-post, and there
we said good-bye to him. He had not got down from his
horse, because, as we perceived now, it was more natural for
him to be on a horse than on the ground. He was going off to
bathe in a hot spring, he said, in a far wadi ; only a few Bedus
knew of it, he thought, and they did not bathe there often.
But perhaps the host of Israel had bathed there, he said
smiling, on the way between Iye-abarim and the brook Zered.
He had nothing with him, not a rug, not a bite of food. He
would be away in the waste wadis for several days.

" Good-bye," we said to him, heavy-hearted.

" Good-bye."

He touched his rein, the horse cantered off, he turned in his
saddle and waved at us, outlined against Jebel-et-Tannur,
which seemed to take him to itself as he passed out of view
down the mountain-side.

We got into the car and took another road down into Hasa.
We came up against traces of the brief and brilliant Nabataean
civilization several times subsequently in the journey. It has,
in fact, been ascertained that it extended far further north
than has been suspected till now, all the way to a line drawn
eastward from the top of the Dead Sea, where it ceases suddenly and completely.

Now there is mention of a certain Nebajoth in Genesis,
a son of Ishmael, who is taken to be the patriarch of the
Nabataean race. But there is no record of any contact between
them and the invading host of Moses. A thousand years were
to pass by after his day before the Nabataeans trekked into
Edom, under the leadership, it may be, of some forever
nameless Nabataean Moses. They and their memorials are

relevant to this narrative for an aesthetic rather than an historic reason. The traveller making the Mosaic journey will see nothing on this section of it which can be compared with the memorials of their brief existence. There are memorials of the Stone Age, but the interest of these is chiefly archaeological; and many of these might as easily be a hundred years old as five thousand, for the Stone Age mind, which still prevails over a great part of the country, expresses itself in the same way irrespective of historic period. These are Edomite and Moabite memorials, fragments of fort and wall, shapeless and characterless. The Roman stuff, as ever, is stout enough, but crude and provincial. The Byzantine was reduced to rubble by the invading Muslim fury. The Crusader fortresses have real magnificence, but they are alien here, and their like is seen as well elsewhere. The Turks have left behind here a block-house, there a khan; they were not builders.

As for the Nabataean memorials, some, like Petra, are known to travellers, others, like Selah and Khirbet-et-Tannur, have only just been discovered. Still others, perhaps equal in beauty and importance with these, still remain to be discovered in this almost unknown land. But they alone would make this Transjordanian journey an immense experience, irrespective of the incomparable landscape which is their background, and the tale which moves quickening from wadi to wadi, to its two finales, the solitary death on Pisgah, the jubilant multitude on the further bank of Jordan.

CHAPTER TEN

A SHORT distance northward from the police-post at el-Âban stretches the limit of Edom, the brink of the wadi Hasa, where the whole land is broken sheer across between the plateau of Arabia and the Dead Sea, like a stone cracked by a great blow. So is it broken once again, by the wadi Mojib, some twenty miles further north as the crow flies. Rather less than half-way between stands the high citadel of Kerak, where we were to spend the night. Both escarpments of Hasa are cloven apart by the lateral wadis that come winding darkly into the huge gulf between their precipices. Between these the road descends and ascends again in a series of sharp hair-pin bends. Along the valley-bottom a stream twinkles under its curtaining of tamarisk and bamboo and laurel into a narrow gorge, then appears again, making for swift asphyxiation in the sulphurous pan of the Dead Sea. There are many oleanders, whence perhaps the ancient name of Zered, the willows. There are hedges of prickly-pear and even a thicket of bananas, so warm and well watered are those depths. On sheltered slopes are shelves of wheat and barley, hanging orchards of silver-grey olive, fig-trees just sprouting, almond and pear in thick bloom. Herds of sheep and goats wind far-off between the patches of grazing, the crying of the herdsmen coming thin and clear like the whine of gnats. More than half-way up the northern ascent the eye is taken by a wealth of mountain which displays a quite academic exposé of its formation, the tawny sandstone base, then a series of limestone levels, on these a layer of black basalt, and finally the desert blanket of marl and loam.

It was not many yards from the northern brink of the ravine Jemil braked suddenly as he turned a sharp bend. The road was blocked by three or four tough thorn-trees entangled in each other.

" *Mish quais!* " reproved Jemil. He wished ill fortune to the mothers of the mothers of the evil-doers.

No, no, I said to the others. They're not playing fair. The hold-ups didn't happen till after Moses crossed the Arnon. Then they kept him busy.

We looked round a little nervously among the boulders. We would have been easy game for anyone with arms. We carried with us on principle a no more lethal weapon than a nail-file.

But no one was there, or no one showed himself. Perhaps we looked too manifestly the countrymen of the fearsome Peake and Glubb. Or it may be that the thorn-trees just fell across the road that way. As we climbed the last few yards, a blast of icy air swept down to greet us from the high plain of Moab.

We had turned and passed by the way of the wilderness of Moab. We had got ourselves over the brook Zered. All the generation of the men of war had been consumed from the midst of the camp, in these eight-and-thirty years since we came from Kadesh-barnea, even as the Lord had sworn. Moab lay before us, the country between the two great brooks, Zered and Arnon. But it was to be an eventless journey, for the Lord had commanded us neither to vex Moab, nor to contend with him in battle, for he was our kinsman, being descended from that first Moab who was the son of the eldest daughter of Lot, brother of Abraham.

It was perhaps a good thing that the Israelites were requested not to vex Moab, for we learn that a people " great, and many, and tall " lived there. The " Emim " was the chronicler's name for them, as fearsome as the " Anakim," he tells us, of whom we have read previously, those gigantic ones of Canaan who struck such terror into the hearts of the spies that went spying out from Kadesh-barnea. Fearsome though the " Emim " were, they were not averse from doing a deal with the passengers and selling them the bread and water they needed on their journey. Their lack of generosity was remembered against them. " A Moabite shall not enter into the assembly of the Lord; even to the tenth generation shall none belonging to them enter into the assembly of the Lord." This exclusion from grace to the tenth generation rings with a mournfully contemporary note.

As to what is to happen when they get to the other side of Arnon, the text is not clear. In one verse the Israelites are informed they will come nigh over against the children of Ammon, who must not be vexed nor contended with, even as the children of Moab, and for the same reason: the land is given to the children of Lot. A few verses later they are once more requested to rise up, take their journey and pass over the valley of Arnon. But this time another people is named for them, and more accurately, as the tenor of the whole narrative makes plain.

" Behold," the Lord proclaims, " I have given unto thine hand Sihon the Amorite, king of Heshbon, and his land: begin to possess it and contend with him in battle." The trumpet is placed to the lips of the trumpeter. All the valleys reverberate with it. " This day will I begin to put the dread of thee and the fear of thee upon the peoples that are under the whole heaven, who shall hear the report of thee, and shall tremble, and be in anguish because of thee."

There has been only one battle till now, and that was long ago in Sinai, at Rephidim, against the Amalekites. Now will the cup of battles be full and flowing over. Long enough has Israel gone thirsty and hungry in the wilderness. It is time to make an end now, though all the cities of Sihon be utterly destroyed, even their women and little ones, also the cities of Og, King of Bashan. It is a sterner leader than the Lawgiver, it is Moses the Conqueror who leads Israel now, for the glory of Jehovah, God of Battles.

As for ourselves, having arrived at Zered, where must we now make for, in this land of frontiers a hundred times confounded and cities a hundred times over razed to the ground? What next place-name survives to this day, out of the old chronicles, attached to new stones or old, or none at all?

The Book of Numbers supplies us with two itineraries. The first, in the twenty-first chapter, is picturesque, but perfunctory; it has large gaps in it. For which reason the Mosaic traveller tends to fix his attention on the second, in the thirty-third chapter, which is a definite attempt to cover the whole journey from stage to stage. Now this second itinerary launches us at once a long way forward from the southern border of Moab. " And they journeyed from Iyim and pitched in Dibon-gad." It does not even pause for an encampment at Zered, but forthwith sends us three miles across the Arnon, into the thick of the battles. (For it cannot be doubted that Dibon-gad, or Dibon, as it is earlier named, stood where now the great heaps of Roman ruins stand, called by the herdsmen Dhibân.) From Dibon-gad the summary continues with express speed. " And they journeyed from Dibon-gad, and pitched in Almon-diblathaim. And they journeyed from Almon-diblathaim, and pitched in the mountains of Abarim, before Nebo. And they journeyed from the mountains of Abarim, and pitched in the plains of Moab by the Jordan at Jericho. And they pitched by Jordan, from Beth-jeshimoth even unto Abel-shittim in the plains of Moab."

And *consummatum est*, lo, the tale is over.

But the indications of the route given in the twenty-first chapter are not quite the same, or it can be said, rather, that the two accounts supplement each other. The earlier route pitches camp in Zered. Thence " they journeyed, and pitched on the other side of Arnon, which is in the wilderness, that cometh out of the border of the Amorites : for Arnon is the border of Moab, between Moab and the Amorites." Then the writer pauses for a moment to quote a few verses from an old collection of songs, to prove his statement about the Arnon being the border of Moab.

> *Vaheb in Suphah,*
> *And the valleys of Arnon,*
> *And the slope of the valleys*
> *That inclineth toward the dwelling of Ar,*
> *And leaneth upon the border of Moab.*

The itinerary then continues: " And from thence they journeyed to Beer: that is the well whereof the Lord said unto Moses, Gather the people together, and I will give them water." Once more the narrative is held up, with the citation of the song that Israel sang at Beer:

> Spring up, O well; sing ye unto it:
> The well which the princes digged,
> Which the nobles of the people delved,
> With the sceptre, and with their staves.

The itinerary then proceeds summarily to the end, mentioning a number of places of which no mention is made in the later itinerary: " And from the wilderness they journeyed to Mattanah: and from Mattanah to Nahaliel: and from Nahaliel to Bamoth: and from Bamoth to the valley that is in the field of Moab, to the top of Pisgah, which looketh down upon the desert."

It will be seen then, that in the one narrative the first place mentioned after Arnon is Beer, in the other it is Dibon-gad. Does one of these impose itself more clearly than the other? Without doubt, Dibon-gad. Beer is a vague name, meaning no more than " well." It is probably an abbreviation of some compound name, perhaps of that Beer-elim regarding which Isaiah raised his ironic threnodies: " For the cry is gone round about the borders of Moab; the howling thereof under Eglaim, and the howling thereof under Beer-elim." No more can be done with the placing of Beer than to relate it on intrinsic grounds to some section of the line of northward march from Arnon.

But Dibon-gad is in a different case. It is one of the very few stations of which we can say with certainty: " This is where Moses came." Or, at the least: " This is the place that was in the mind of the chronicler." We must get to Dibon-gad, then, whatever road it befalls us to take there. Arrived there, as I have said, we shall be in the thick of the battles. We shall be on the site of a town which once was Moab's, as the text teaches us, but by the time the host had crossed the

Arnon, it was the city of the Amorites, of their king, Sihon. And after the host had fought its battles between Arnon and the land of Bashan, it was no more the city of the Amorites. Israel had taken it, and, Gad and Reuben demanding that it should be a city of their portion, they rebuilt it, and it was called Dibon-gad.

Loud were the taunts of the singers of Israel flushed with victory, as they taunted the defeated Amorites cowering behind their stockades:

> *Come ye to Heshbon,*
> *Let the city of Sihon be established:*
> *For a fire is gone out of Heshbon,*
> *A flame from the city of Sihon:*
> *It hath devoured Ar of Moab,*
> *The lords of the high places of Arnon.*

And, turning their thoughts from the Amorite enemy, they sang of Moab, whom the Lord had not spared, it seems, though He had earlier bidden Israel neither to vex Moab nor contend with him.

> *Woe to thee, Moab!*
> *Thou art undone, O people of Chemosh:*
> *He hath given his sons as fugitives,*
> *And his daughters into captivity,*
> *Unto Sihon king of the Amorites.*
> *We have shot at them; Heshbon is perished even unto Dibon,*
> *And we have laid waste even unto Nophah,*
> *Which reacheth unto Medeba.*

So sang the taunters, beating on their timbrels and blowing once and again a single mocking note on the silver trumpets. But not for ever was woe to Moab, nor for ever undone the people of Chemosh. Moab was to rise up again, and the sweet smoke of sacrifice go up again in the nostrils of Chemosh.

So the books of the Israelites tell us, so also a certain stone

The Rock Called Selah

of the Moabites tells us, incised in the tenth century B.C. and discovered in a field in this same Dhibân, which is Dibon-gad.

This stone was discovered in 1868 by M. Clermont-Ganneau on one of the two hills over which the ruins of Dibon-gad lie scattered, a little west of the southern gate. It is a cubic block of black basalt over a yard high and more than half of that wide, with an inscription of thirty-four lines in the North Semitic Phoenician script, in a language hardly distinguishable from Hebrew. The stone was broken to pieces as the result of a quarrel regarding the local pasture-rights between the Beni Sakhr and the Beni Hamidhi, exactly such a difference of opinion as the stone itself, on a large scale, commemorates. But for the most part it has been put to rights.

The stone is called the Mesha stele, and might be called the Moses stele, for they are the same name. It was engraved on the dedication of a temple to Chemosh, still, or once again, a very stalwart deity. It is a signal testimony to the value of the Biblical documents as history, all the more because it tells the tale from the viewpoint of Moab, not Israel, which had been eloquent long enough, and was not to discontinue its eloquence.

This Mesha, as we learn in Kings, was king of Edom, and a sheep-master, so rich in sheep, indeed, that he rendered unto the king of Israel an hundred thousand lambs, and an hundred thousand rams, with the wool. And Moab had for long years endured the yoke of Israel and the house of Omri; whereon, when Ohab died, Mesha rebelled, and Israel and Judah went out against him, having with them this time Edom as an ally. They did not turn the northern end of the Dead Sea, by those plains of Moab where once Moses had scored his final victories. Moab, doubtless, was well entrenched there. They came instead round the southern end, by way of the Ghor and up the plateau of Edom, as Moses had done earlier, on his way to the victories. And the prophet Elisha was with them, and the hand of the Lord came upon him, and there were great miracles. And according to the Hebrew narrative, " they beat down the cities, and on every good piece of land cast

Uc

every man his stone; and they stopped all the wells of water, and felled all the good trees." (As indeed, a hundred invaders have done since, wherefore that land is still such a wilderness.) And Mesha stood at bay in his citadel Kir-haraseth (the same is Kerak at this day) and made to Chemosh the supreme sacrifice and " took his eldest son that should have reigned in his stead, and offered him for a burnt offering upon the wall."

A dreadful act, and none knew that more than Moab. " There was great indignation against Israel." But, as it seems, it was effective. Mesha was unsubdued, " And they returned from him, and returned to their own land."

So the tale is told by the enemies of Mesha. Mesha tells it differently.

" I am Mesha, son of Chemoshgad, king of Moab, the Dibonite. My sire ruled thirty years over Moab, and I became king after him. I set up this high place for Chemosh of Kerichoch, high place of deliverance, for that he hath saved me from every aggressor, and he hath caused me to see my desire upon all mine enemies.

" Omri was king of Israel and long oppressed Moab, because Chemosh was wrath with his land. His son came after him, and he too said : ' I will set my foot upon Moab.' In my days he said this, but I saw my desire upon him and his house, and Israel hath been humbled for ever. Omri had taken possession of the land of Medeba . . . but in my days Chemosh hath dwelt there. The men of Gad had long possessed the land of Abaroth, and I put to the sword all the people of the city to rejoice Chemosh and Moab. I carried off from thence the altar of Dodoh and dragged it before the face of Chemosh in Kerioth, where I made to dwell the man of Sharon and him of Maharoth.

" And Chemosh said unto me : ' Go, take Nebo against Israel.' I set forth by night, and attacked it from the break of day until noon. I took it and slew all there, seven thousand men and boys and women and girls and concubines, because I had vowed them as a vow to Ashtar-Chemosh. I took from thence the vessels of Jehovah and dragged them before the face of Chemosh. The king of Israel had fortified Jahaz and held it during his campaign against me. And Chemosh drove him out before me. I took two hundred men of Moab, all their chief men, and I attacked Jahaz, and took it and added it to Dibon.

" I built Kerichoch, the park wall and the wall of the hill fortress. I built its gates and its towers. I digged the moat about Kerichoch with the captives of Israel. I built Aroer and the road to Arnon. I built Beth-bamot, for it was destroyed. I built Bezer, for it lay in ruins. And Chemosh said unto me, ' Go down and fight against Horonaim.' I went and fought against the city and took it, and Chemosh dwelt there during my reign. It was I who . . ."

The stone records no more of what great things he did, that Moabite Moses five centuries later repaying the Israelite Moses taunt for taunt. The word is now to the Israelite chronicler who lets us know, almost despite himself, that when the prophet Elisha died, Moab once more was so strong " that the bands of the Moabites invaded the land at the coming in of the year."

So for some centuries more the fierce ding-dong continued, but the anathemas of the Hebrew prophets were more potent than the arms of the warriors of Moab. Asshurbanipal, King of Assyria, razed their cities to the ground, and slaughtered their peoples. Some flew to the wild wadis and the holes in the mountains, and these the Beni-kedem found, the Beduin of the great desert of Euphrates, who slew their men, and slew their women, or did not, as it pleased them. There is no more Moab in the second century B.C.

Moab is no more. Israel endures. In days like these, it is possible to hold that to Moab fell the happier lot. But perhaps Israel has endured darker days, yet has not been worsted by them.

The Mesha still is in the Salle Judaïque at the Louvre, which also possesses a large bas-relief of a Moabite warrior, found in that same Aroer which Mesha tells us he built, or perhaps rebuilt, on the road of Arnon. Its date goes back to before the twelfth century B.C., so that it enables us to present an approximate picture, at least, of the warrior who came out against Moses on his triumphant march northward. His uniform has a somewhat composite air, as you would expect in a border people. His plumed helmet is in the Hittite mode, his short breeches Egyptian. He stands there as one overhearing Israel say: " We have heard of the pride of Moab." " And the pride of Israel? " his silent challenge asks.

A less imposing find made some years ago by Dr. Nelson Glueck is at least as interesting. This was the head of a pottery figurine, found among the ruins of el-Medeiyineh, on the wadi Themed, the upper reaches of the Seïl Heidan, the main northern tributary of the wadi Mojib. It is none the less interesting for the identification that has been made, and Dr. Glueck tends to confirm, between el-Medeiyineh and the encampment at Mattanah, which is given in Numbers, following the encampment at Beer, as the second after the crossing of the Arnon.

" The figurine," he writes, " represents a Semitic king or deity. The head is very skilfully moulded, every feature being clearly and boldly delineated. The head-dress is held on by an 'uqal, tied in front with a bow knot. Beside and below the large ears extend long locks of braided hair. The pointed beard, which shows traces of having been affixed after the head was moulded, extends from immediately below the thick bulging lips. The squat nose, bulging cheeks, and large slanting eyes complete the picture."

The picture of whom? Of the king, the sheepmaster, who went out against Moses at Mattanah (for we can be sure that the stations listed now are more likely to have been scenes of battle than quiet camping-places)? Of the later king, Mesha, who went out against Israel?

We do not, and shall never, know. But it is a strange thought that, at this very day, there is no sheepmaster, proud

or humble, in the land of Moab, who does not likewise
wear his head-dress, tied on in front by an 'uqal, a knotted
rope-band.

" To go now? " the eyes of Jemil asked, sitting patiently at
his wheel, on the northern edge of Zered.

" To Kerak, Jemil ! "

So we went forward into Moab, the westering sun on our
left hand, behind us the ridges of Edom dwindling in the
south, and round us the high wind. We were, it was at once
evident, following a Roman road; a sense of Rome, or rather
of some Roman border country, was impressed strongly over
the whole landscape. I have known evenings like this by
Hadrian's wall in the Northumberland fell country, the
tumbled boulders, the green rolling uplands; and there, too,
have seen flocks of birds that had been rooting among the
young crops in sheltered places, flushed upward into the sun
by the approaching stranger, so that their wing-tips and tails
were translucent silver.

Soon, on our right hand, we saw a great area of ruins, lifted
on several hills above the level of the country. It is unjust to
say of one or two of them that they were ruins at all.

" What great city? " I asked Jemil. I had read of none so
near the bank of Zered.

" No great city ! " said Jemil. " Dat Ras ! "

We went over to the nearest of the buildings. It seemed to
us pure Roman, dedicated to who knows what Roman god.
There was no Christian trace in it, at least on the blocks lying
about and on the exposed walls. It had a great archway and
several arched windows quite intact, and a stairway that might
have been built yesterday. The temple gave the impression it
might be rebuilt for worship to-morrow. It housed a herd of
goats with comfort now.

What great city? There is a dim suggestion that it might
have been the Kyriacoupolis of which once mention is made, as
the seat of a Byzantine bishopric. A dimmer suggestion was
made by our host of that night that Dat Ras is a corruption of

Demetrius. There was a sainted bishop in these parts once who bore that name. It is a strange land where monuments survive that elsewhere would create a sightseer's Eldorado, and here nothing is known of them, a casual car may pause there once or twice a month, then go on again.

The road continued through grassy country, with patches of crops here and there. Given half a century's peace, Mesha might again produce his hundred thousand lambs, and his hundred thousand rams, if he had some assurance he might keep them for himself. Some miles further, the illusion of Northumbria burst, pierced by the points of two tall and slender minarets that rose northward against the brassy sky. Near their sharp points their shafts swelled into bulby parapets. Between them two white domes floated. So they do not in Northumbria, along the border country. Nor, for that matter, had we till now seen any minarets in Transjordan, either. It was for that reason these did not seem real at first, and because they were so delicate; the Turks were never prodigal with delicate building in these knock-about outposts, and the nomad tribes do not know how to build monuments more ambitious than their rounded *welis*.

But in this place three great saints lay buried, Jafar and Hodeib and Suleiman, three companions of the Prophet. So in the fourteenth century a governor of Kerak determined to glorify their simple graves by building this mosque over it. And the Beduin still come in on pilgrimage to the mosque of Jafar, though most of it is in ruins now, and half of what is left has become a post of the Arab Legion.

As we came close, the sun's rim was almost touching the horizon. The herdsmen were coming in from the flushed pastures, the bells of the animals making a pleasant noise. Two cows were drinking at a small pool in the open space before the mosque, as out of a vat of molten metal.

The car braked. Two policemen came over toward us.

" *Inta yehudi?* " they asked.

" Sihon and Og! " exclaimed Lucas happily. " I wonder which is which! "

" English! " cried Jim, making a sound like a poem by Kipling.

" Peake Pasha! " I said.

That was the name that brought them to their knees. We went into the police-post and drank tea, and we slapped their backs, and they slapped ours, as if they had long wanted to slap Peake Pasha's back, but this seemed as near as they were likely to get for some time. They gave us cigarette-lighters, and we gave them revolving pencils. A telephone rang, and one of the men answered, " Hello! " exactly as if it were Paddington ringing and Hampstead answering.

And we went on our way again, the sun being quite gone, but the sky remained tremulous with the after-glow. And after a little time, a huge red disk of moon came thrusting its way round the shoulder of a hill. As she climbed into the sky, the flush faded, the dry seas and windless continents took shape. The whole plateau was powdered with her silver, like a morning hoar-frost.

And we descended at last, and climbed again, the deep gorge out of which Kerak rises, girt round by its walls, with the great hulk of its citadel looking fiercely down on the southern approaches, as if Moses and his host were still on his way here.

It was a breathless ascent, taken somewhat fiercely, as if Jemil could not else hope to reach the top. There was a square tower hanging over us on our left hand. A moment later the great wall soared between us and the black night.

Two policemen came up out of the shadows. " *Inta yehudi?* " "English!" said one of us. Peake Pasha, said the other. All was well, the policemen said, the Nazarene was awaiting us.

We had heard dimly from Abdullah Bey of the Latin mission at Kerak. There were many Christians there, and two priests. There might be beds for us there, he thought. But he was not sure, there might not be room. Perhaps we should have to sleep at the police-post.

But we did not. The Nazarene saw to that. The mission lay

quite close to that high tower, itself called the Nazarene. As we stood blinking a little helplessly in the sudden light, he came up to us, a small man, smiling jovially, with a pointed red beard, somewhat thin and straggly, as a young man's often is. It was a rather simple rustic face. His eyes were bright blue. His black soutane lifted a little in the wind, like a ballet-skirt.

" Hello, you chaäps. You moost be a bit hoongry. Coom and haäv soom groöb."

This attempt at a phonetic transcription is a clumsy, I admit even a wanton, exaggeration. But that was how my ear registered it, my ear that had had to make do so long with Jim's Rochester Home Counties and Lucas's South African Cambridge. It was Lancashire that came out so friendlily towards us over the high-slung platform of Kir-Moab.

" Eh, bah goom, we are thaät," I said. " Haäv you been expecting oos? "

Father Dunn smiled a little secretly.

" This way," he motioned us. The mission-house was close at hand.

" Maänchester? " I asked, but with a sense that really that was hoping for too much.

" Liverpool," he said.

All that distance away, in the capital of the Moabite kings, on the fortress outpost of the Latin kings of Jerusalem, I felt it could be accepted as almost the same thing.

A few Arab Christian lads gathered round us. They unloaded the car and took our things into the house. The empty stone stairways sounded less forbidding than if no Father Dunn were there to tread them. We passed a room on our left hand, warm with a glow of lamps, and crowded with books.

" You've got nice time for a hot bath," said Father Dunn and went into his room. We went over into ours, plain and clean and pleasant. A youth lit a fire of *ar-ar* wood in the bathroom, under a Horseferry Road geyser. We bathed, and went down to supper. Father Dunn was there already, and his colleague, a bearded Maronite priest. Steaming plates of lentil soup were already waiting on the table. Grace was said. We got down to it. Then Father Dunn looked at us slyly over his lifted spoon.

" I'm sorry about the fish," he said.

" Fish? " I asked, puzzled. " What fish? "

" Your Akaba fish. It hasn't come up here yet." His face still looked as simple and rustic as before; but his eyes less so.

I choked.

" It has! " I cried. " It has! At least the smell of it has! When will we get rid of that fish? "

He laughed gaily.

" It'll swim the Jordan with you. You'll smell it on the docks at Haifa! Oh, what a country! "

" *What* a country! " we echoed fervently.

" We've come about Moses! " said Jim, coming to the rescue.

" Ah, so you say! " He wagged his finger at us. " You're not going to forget Suleiman's hair-restorer? "

" I—I—— " I stammered.

" But what on earth came over you at Shobek? They're quite nice people, really."

It was rather terrifying, the straggly little beard, the innocent blue eyes, the paralysing omniscience. A woman came in and set down the main dish before him.

" I wish you wouldn't look so worried," he chaffed us. " Everybody knows everything in Transjordan. Listen! Don't say anything! Can't you hear them whispering in the desert? That's how it is! I hope you like this *pilaff*. You won't mind the herbs, will you? Give them more vegetables," he said in Arabic to the serving-woman. " Yes, she is! " he went on. " Isn't she? Like Ruth ! "

He saw that my eyes were fixed on the woman, her dark and lovely face, the jet-black hair combed back smoothly from a central parting, the rich plaits hanging in front of her shoulders down to the waist. She was like all the pictures that have ever been painted of Ruth, the Moabite woman, standing amid the stooks of alien corn.

" She is! " I said.

" She is one of our people, of course. We have over three hundred to look after; as well as the schools, which are just as much for the Muslims as the Christians."

" Do the Muslims send their children? I understand they're pretty fanatical round about Kerak. Didn't I read that a great many of the local Christians couldn't stand it, and trekked off en masse to Madebah ? "

" Oh, no. That was just because a Muslim tribe stole a little girl from a Christian tribe. There's not much to choose between them. Is there, Father? " He conveyed the substance of the conversation in French to his colleague.

" Fanaticism is just a recent innovation round here," the other sighed. " The only difference between them used to be that the Muslims were circumcised and the Christians were not." Then he relapsed into his soup gloomily. He left when the meat came. He was imposing some half-fast on himself.

" Oh, yes, the Muslim children come right enough," reverted Father Dunn. " But we don't think it wise to thrust religion down their throats. All we try to do is teach them by example."

" It's not quick work, I suppose? "

" We've got time."

" How long would you say it takes to make a convert, Father? " asked Jim. He likes things cut and dried.

" Oh, I should say about five generations," smiled Father Dunn. " One generation while the first hatred wears off. Then a second while they begin to think we might be human, like themselves; during that time they begin to accept what we have to give them in the way of services and schools. Then a third while they begin to think our religion's not so bad, either. Then a fourth while it dawns on them it is, in fact, better than theirs. And then, hey presto, in the fifth—the trick's done.

"Anyhow," he summed up, "what do five generations more or less matter in Kerak?"

"Well, how many generations have you been established here?" pressed Lucas. "Are you beginning to see results?"

"We are a mission of the Latin Patriarchate of Jerusalem, which was founded in 1099. It lasted only a century, because the Muslims recaptured Jerusalem. The Patriarchate went out of existence for the time being. Centuries passed, but we were patient. We had time. Six and a half centuries went by, and at last His Holiness set us up again. That was in 1847. We could have waited another six and a half centuries. Or sixteen and a half. What's time, to us in Kerak?"

His voice, during this recital, had been quite grave. He pointed to Jim's empty plate.

"Time," he said, "for a second helping." His voice was not less grave. "And you?"

"Oh, me," I said with a start. The girl's plaits swung forward as she stooped to fill Jim's plate. "I was going to ask about Ruth."

"Please."

"Abdullah Bey Rihani showed us a village called Ru-ath on the road south from Tafileh. He said there was a tradition that that was where Ruth came from. But that's Edom, of course. Do you know anything about it?"

"Oh, the frontiers of all these countries kept on changing the whole time, didn't they? Though the wadi Hasa must always have been rather a difficult frontier to play about with. But to this day women from these heights go down into Palestine for the gleaning, as Ruth did long ago, with her mother-in-law, Naomi. They come down this way, by the wadi Kerak to the Dead Sea, where the peninsula of Lisan juts out west and north. They say that in the summer you could sometimes walk dry-shod from that western point over to the Palestine shore; it has been done within living memory, some say. Perhaps it has. I don't know. Anyhow it used to be easy to get across, before the War. A little steam-boat used to go over for letters and vegetables and things from the port of Kerak. That's between the peninsula and the shore here. It would be a good thing for Kerak to fit one up again for the tourist traffic. It would be very useful for us at the mission here, too. I suppose if Lawrence hadn't scuttled the Turkish navy——"

" Lawrence! " I interrupted, a little startled. "Oh, yes, of course! Lawrence! "

He screwed up his eyes contemplatively.

" I think I see. Lawrence in the steps of Moses, eh? "

I lifted my hands in surrender.

" You're still in the steps of both of them," he continued.

" The whole way," I said, " the whole way down to Jordan."

" But he came here this way rather secretly. Lawrence, I mean, not Moses."

" Perhaps Moses did, too, and he didn't like the look of the place. There probably was a strong fort up here at that time, too. Every hill-top seems to have had its Moabite fort."

" Lawrence doesn't seem to have been at all frightened by the people round here. He came as a deliverer, of course, not a conqueror. And he had a lot of money, too. So had the Israelites, of course. They took a lot away from Egypt, didn't they ? "

The voice was not quite kind.

" They had to pay out a lot for bread and water," I pointed out.

" That's true," he agreed. " But reverting to Lawrence, he was very mysterious about that journey to Kerak, wasn't he? He said extraordinarily little about it. Yet there are people in Kerak to-day who'll tell you they saw him and talked to him. Perhaps they saw Moses, too, and talked to him." He shrugged his shoulders. " What about your beds?" he said suddenly. " You all look as if you need it. Or will you have a little air first? "

We had a little air first, the sharp air of Moab coming in fresh and cold from the tangle of valleys. . . .

We had nearly finished breakfast, when Father Dunn came dancing in. There *was* a sense of dance about his movements. I saw now why his soutane looked like a ballet-skirt when the wind lifted it.

" Hello! " he exclaimed. " Sleep well? " He rubbed his hands together jovially.

" *Did* we! "

" There's a visitor for you this morning! "

" A *visitor*? " We looked from one to the other blankly. " A *visitor*? "

" Don't look alarmed! " he begged us. " Finish your breakfast? "

" Police or anything? Papers not in order? "

" I saw to everything last night. Please, *do* finish."

We finished, and followed Father Dunn into the sitting-room. A handsome and distinguished old Arab sat waiting for us. He was a study in *grisaille*, all except his skin, which was as pink as a boy's. Under a grey European overcoat, his white *abba* swept down to his black shoes. He wore a white headcloth, bound with a treble black rope. He had bushy grey eyebrows, thick white moustaches and a white beard. He had intelligent black eyes. His hands were beautifully kept.

He sat there with an air of authority, as if his being there mattered to us a good deal, much more than ours to him.

" May I present Abdullah Akashe," said Father Dunn. " These are friends from England. They, too, are endeavouring to trace the journeys of the Nebi Musa." He spoke in Arabic.

I looked up. " The Nebi Musa? Has this gentleman some ideas then——"

" If it wasn't for Abdullah Akashe, you would have made a very different journey through Transjordan, I can tell you that."

" How do you mean? "

" You wouldn't have made those three efforts to get to Khirbet Feinân, anyhow."

" Khirbet Feinân, Khirbet Feinân," the old man repeated, nodding his head vigorously. His eyes flashed under the bushy brows.

" Khirbet Feinân? " I asked. " What has the old man to do with that? "

" He happens to have discovered it, if any man can be said to have discovered it. It was he who pointed out the similarity between the two words, Punon and Feinân, to Musil, the Austrian scholar, who then told the world about it."

" Is that really him? "

The old man, understanding the question, nodded again, put his hand over his heart, and bowed.

" It was I."

" He was Musil's guide. He told him a lot about a great many other places, too."

" But he's responsible for Khirbet Feinân, you say? Oh, tell him how grateful we are! You're quite right. It would have been a different Transjordan if not for him."

" Forty years ago," said Abdullah Akashe. " I was a young man, and strong, like this one." He pointed to Jim.

" In a sense," I said to Lucas, " he was our real host up on Jebel Dana. Quite as much as that old Sheikh Zaheb."

" Do you think we might ask him what he thinks about our route, Father? " asked Lucas.

" That's what I brought him here for," the reply was. " It's a long time ago, of course, since Musil and he went out hunting; but he's still very much alive, you see."

We explained how we had come from stage to stage. The old man tugged at his beard, interrupting us now and again with sudden shouts of approval,

" Well, that takes us as far as Kerak," I said happily. " What we'd really like to ask him is, what happens now. I mean from the brook Arnon, and after."

" All that was well done, by Allah! " the old man was saying. " Allah took their feet and set them rightly."

" But this is fine! " we congratulated each other. " If *he* doesn't know, who should? We've been going right, after all, and the whole way, too."

" No wonder he approves," said Father Dunn, a trifle cynically. " If one man living is more responsible than any other for the way you came, it's Abdullah Akashe! "

" Yes, yes! " agreed Abdullah Akashe. " By the Prophet's beard they have done well! "

" And where, ask him, did the host cross the brook Arnon? Did they make more or less due north after they crossed the brook Zered and then tackle the two huge precipices, going down and going up? Or did they swing further out east, and cross by the upper reaches, where it wouldn't be any trouble at all? "

" They ask this," said Father Dunn. He repeated the question carefully, but Abdullah would not let him get to the end.

" What? " he burst out. " Were the Israelites madmen? Of course they went out east, towards the great desert. Not alone because the wadi Mojib is deeper than the wadi Hasa, but because, when they crossed Hasa, they came up into the land of their blood-brethren. It was written there must be no fighting, and this side of Mojib there was none. But had they sought to cross Mojib northward from here, where it is deep, their enemies would have ranged themselves along the tops and broken their heads like egg-shells with great stones."

I turned to Lucas.

" That settles it," I said. " We go east, as you said all along."

" Well," said Father Dunn drily, " you haven't much alternative. You'd have to go east anyway, if you want to make use of your car. They haven't yet joined up the road north and south of Mojib. Oh, excuse me." He turned to Abdullah, who had addressed him. " He regrets he must take his leave now. He has business in the courts."

" Will you please tell him it has been a great joy to us. Also that next time we meet, we must eat a sheep together in Khirbet Feinân."

The old man smiled a little wistfully, and shook his head, pointing to his grey beard.

" *Ma es salaam!* " he said. " And peace be with you ! "

We went out into the town, Father Dunn and the three of us. It seemed to me that we saw all the five generations in operation, as Father Dunn had outlined them for us the night before. I pointed this out to him.

" Well, hardly," he compromised. " The Kerak mission only goes back some sixty years, hardly five generations. But you'll find two or three here, ranging between a dirty look and a nice smile." So it was, we found.

There were quite a few dirty looks from the Beduin who had come in from the desert, and a nice smile or two to redress the balance. Father Dunn smiled back nicely to every-one equally. You had the feeling he would smile back nicely on a stake in Ludgate Hill, if someone felt it would be a good thing to burn him there.

It is an old town with an old name, and its exhibits, so to speak, go back as far as the Flood and forward as far as a handsome new police-station. For Noah himself is on view, or rather the tomb of Noah, a small white-domed *weli* beside the Italian hospital. Perhaps there has been some confusion between the two mountains of Ararat and Kerak, though it is not stated that Noah died on Ararat, either.

However, Kerak is certainly more a Moabite than an Armenian city. It is referred to in the Bible by several names, Kir of Moab, Kir-heres, Kir-haraseth, which, in the com-mentaries on the Aramaic version, become K'raka or Krak. It is as Kir-haraseth that the place blazes so luridly in the Biblical tale, during that dreadful moment when King Mesha immolates his son on the sacrificial pyre. But it was a sacrifice made to good effect, it seems. For (it will be remembered) in horror at the sight the Israelites closed their ranks and re-turned to their own land. They seem even to have left some prisoners behind, for a great gash is pointed out under the western wall, where Mesha set them to build an underground approach to the city. Whether the work was done by Mesha's prisoners or not, it is certainly credible the work was done by captive Hebrews after one or another of the frequent Moabite-Israelite wars.

Nothing is recorded of the city for many centuries after that time. The Assyrian had his way with it, and the Beduin after him. The Hebrew, not yet dislodged from the hilltops of Zion on the further side of the Dead Sea, smiled in his beard. Had it not come to pass, even to the very letter, as Isaiah had foretold: " And the fortress of the high fort of thy walls shall he bring down, lay low, and bring to the ground, even to the dust "?

But in the time of the Greek domination, the place and the name of it have risen from the dust again; Karaka is one of the most prosperous cities in Arabia Petraea. Christianity easily gains a foothold there. The men from the desert that have worshipped one or another of a hundred black fetish-stones, turn to the Cross, to which some of them have remained faithful these sixteen hundred and more years, so that it can be said of certain of the Transjordan Christians they are among the oldest of all. In the fifth century, Karakmoba is the seat of a bishopric. There is incense in its churches, and Christian pomp in its streets.

Then suddenly the Islamic flood comes roaring in from the Arabian desert. Even again the huge fort of the walls of Karakmoba is laid low. The Crusaders prospecting east and south from recaptured Jerusalem find but a stone or two standing together on this incomparable strong place, where they determine to build a fortress that shall ensure the Holy Land in their possession for all time to come.

So they set to work duly, and build well, even imperishably. But they have no roots there, it is they who perish after one brief century. Saladin lays siege to their citadel and conquers it for Islam, and makes it even stouter than before. It remains to this day the vastest of the monuments of that age.

Wc

We wandered among the ruins of the citadel for some time, feeling small and strange in the huge vaults, and small and dizzy on the brink of the towering ramparts. It seemed to me the place had a legendary air, the men who built those chambers and walked in those vast courtyards, must surely have been more than life-size. The castle went back before Saladin and Fulkes of Anjou, before even Mesha and Moses. The antediluvian Giants had built it, sometimes called the Emim and the Anakim. Here were the barracks of their soldiers, where they spread out their mattresses on their fearsome bedsteads of iron. They needed walls so stout as these, so that they should not collapse under their titan shoulders, as they leaned against them.

We went back and had lunch. Father Dunn consulted his colleague. We found with pleasure he could spend the rest of the day with us. Which would we consider more profitable, he asked, to go out into the country or go down into the Dead Sea?

From Jim and Lucas the answer was, of course, quite automatic. " The Dead Sea! " they said. " We'll bathe! "

I said nothing. I had already bathed in the Dead Sea, on the western shore, some years ago. I knew that the Dead Sea is far lovelier to look at than to bathe in. But that was not the reason I said nothing.

" What are you looking worried about? " asked Lucas.

" About going down to the Dead Sea. Oh yes, I know we'll go. But ought we? Or at any rate ought I? "

" Why not? " asked Father Dunn, a little puzzled.

" Isn't it a little premature? Ought we to be going down to the lowlands so soon again? Surely it wasn't till after the battles were fought that the host went down to the plains of Moab? "

There was a certain amount of consternation among the camp-followers.

" It's like this, Father," I said apologetically. " We've had a sort of Mosaic justification for every journey we've made so far, even the incidental excursions. It's been our thin red line. You can see how unwieldy it would all have been, unless we'd clung to that as a principle."

" I see that," said Father Dunn. " But this isn't an incidental journey."

" No," I agreed sadly. " There's no excuse for it, pleasant as it's going to be. There's no excuse for not pushing on straight over the Arnon and going into battle with the Amorites."

" But you're forgetting. Quite a lot happened in the plains of Moab. This is Moab. The plains might be down there, below the wadi Kerak. Why not? "

" Oh no," I said firmly. " The narrative is quite clear on the subject. 'And the children of Israel journeyed, and pitched in the plains of Moab beyond the Jordan at Jericho.' You can't get away from that. Beyond the Jordan at Jericho."

" Yes, yes," he admitted. " That's quite true. But a great deal happened in the plains of Moab beside the fighting. Do you remember? Let me look up the text now. ' And Israel abode in Shittim, and the people began to commit whoredom with the daughters of Moab: for they called the people unto the sacrifices of their gods; and the people did eat, and bowed down to their gods.' Do you see? "

" I don't quite see."

" I mean that the text mentions a special place where all that happened, Shittim, the place of acacias. I can show you some very handsome Shittim down there," he brought out, his eyes twinkling. The others were jubilant.

" You can't get away from that! " they announced.

" That's quite true. Nobody can prove that Shittim is actually *not* down there," I admitted.

" The picture's not by any means out of date," said Father Dunn. " It's a very relaxing place, down there. It always has been, all the way back to Lot." He was still turning the pages of the book of Numbers. " Yes, here it is, the passage about Balak! ' And Balak the son of Zippor saw all that Israel had done to the Amorites. And Moab was sore afraid of the people, because they were many: and Moab was distressed because of the children of Israel. And Moab said unto the elders of Midian, Now shall this multitude lick up all that is round about us, as the ox licketh up the grass of the field. And Balak the son of Zippor was king of Moab at that time.' "

" What do you get out of that? " I asked a little apprehensively.

I surprised, for the first and last time, a look of cunning on his face. He had the expression of a smart sixth former at Stonyhurst getting the better of one of the older professors.

" That refers to a time, doesn't it? " he said, " when the Israelites had crossed the Arnon and beaten the Amorites? "

" Yes? "

" But they hadn't yet gone down to the plains of Moab beyond the Jordan at Jericho? "

" Why not? "

" Because the hills above the plain at Jericho were still in the hands of Balak. I mean Beth-peor, or Pisgah, where Balaam stationed himself to curse the people of Israel."

" That's true. They had crossed the Arnon but had not yet gone beyond Pisgah."

" But the country beyond Arnon was the land of the Amorites at that time, wasn't it? Why should the king of Moab be so worried about what was going on in Amorite country? "

" You're suggesting they came back into Moab for a time? "

" Why not? Wasn't it a habit of theirs? "

" Because they were not at war with Moab, and could rest up for a bit after the heat of the battle——? "

" They did, didn't they? "

" —So they came south of the Arnon again. And the king of Moab got rather frightened about it," I hurried on. It was really rather ingenious. " So he sent for the prophet, Balaam, thinking it would be safer to curse the Israelites than to fight them."

" Exactly," he grinned. " And while that was going on, the Israelites were down in the plain there, in Shittim. You can't get away from it, can you? It is as clear as crystal."

" But Balak could actually *see* some of them——" I began to protest.

" *Some* of them," he conceded airily.

Jim had already taken his seat in the car. There seemed to be nothing to do but follow suit.

" In any case, it's a beautiful journey," said Father Dunn. " The road isn't so good, perhaps. But it's not worse than it was in the time of the Israelites."

But the Israelites did not descend to the plains of Moab in motor-cars. It was one of the most dreadful roads I have ever travelled on. Some days later, the report of an official surveyor was quoted to us: " Uniformly bad and sometimes very dangerous." That " sometimes " should have read " always." Do I exaggerate? I hardly think I do. But I had been wandering in the wilderness for nearly forty years, and perhaps my nerves were less stolid than they had been.

They had not got so far as surfacing the road at all, but the recent rain had made things much worse than they might have been. To begin with, the road was extremely steep. It had to descend over five thousand feet in what seemed no distance at all. No attempt had been made to bank up the turnings. If anything, the road sloped down, rather than up, towards the abysses. Sometimes the elbow of the road had broken clean away, like a dog-biscuit. Sometimes a sweet little waterfall dripping down a pocket of the cliff made a morass where the car plunged about help-lessly for a few seconds, till it found some surface to bite into again. The road, of course, had no width. Now and again, going down and coming up, we met a herd of animals whom we managed only with the greatest difficulty to induce to trust themselves to the vertical slopes below. What would have happened had we met a car, and a strong-minded one, I dare not contemplate.

It was, of course, extremely beautiful, that descent through various strata of flora, from the early spring of the high moorland grasses, by way of the full spring of sea-level, to the tropical summer-time of the sunken Dead Sea Garden. High up, great tracts of anemones licked the slopes like tongues. Lower, fields of blue iris were like spilled pots of paint. A little lower, broom flared like a political meeting with torches. On the plain figs and bananas were ripening, the green grape-clusters were swelling, oranges and lemons glowed among their leaves. The afternoon sun was kind to the limestone cliffs and polished the basalt boulders like bronze. Below, the Dead Sea lay like a stone pavement.

We had been descending for some time when the impassive Jemil gave tongue. I did not get what he said.

" Tell him to repeat it! " I asked. Jemil said little, but what he said was usually worth saying.

" He says the Prophet has been this way," explained Father Dunn.

" Which one? " I asked.

" You'd better not ask *that*," counselled Father Dunn.

" No, no," I said, hastily. " Of course not. But what is he referring to? When did the Prophet come to Kerak? "

" When did the Prophet come to Kerak, Jemil? "

Jemil pointed to a hollow full of asphodels, but refused to say another word. Then Father Dunn suddenly remembered.

" Oh yes, of course. They say that the Prophet once ate too many eggs, and was sick. And wherever he was sick, these flowers grew. Yes, I remember now."

" I don't like that story, but it's less grisly than the Greek account of asphodel, when you come to think of it. What's that cairn for, please? " I shut my eyes as we negotiated a bend with less than an inch to spare.

" That's as far as the last car got that took this road." He chuckled. He liked to see me shut my eyes, and hear me suspend a sentence till a peculiarly nasty bit of road was over. He was like a schoolboy having a good time. Once, when we skidded, and one wheel revolved in empty air over a vast canyon, he crowed with delight.

" We're only a thousand feet up. We'd drop that in no time."

There was not only the schoolboy in his gaiety. There was something of the saint, too, the man on the best of terms with death, whether it chose to carry him off with a cancer or in a motor-car accident.

" I'm sorry I haven't got my own car still," he said wistfully. " We'd have got down in no time."

I heard later that his car never had any brakes and that if he had any passengers, he never kept his eye on the road. His passengers had his undivided attention. It was interesting to realize that the journey might have been even more terrifying than it was.

I found, a little incredulously, that we had reached the plain intact, and by road the whole way. There were no foothills worth speaking of. We were trundling along through tropical undergrowth, with great jungly leaves scratching the sides of the car. Every now and again a stream came hissing up about our axles. A few goat-hair tents were spread about the drier reaches, and one or two dishevelled-looking pavilions with torn mosquito-wiring over their casements sweltered in the lush greenery.

" Now and again," said Father Dunn, " one of the Kerak worthies builds himself a little place down here, to have a good time in. But it doesn't last long. The air gets him down. How will those do? " he asked. He pointed to a large clump of feathery trees. " The Shittim, the acacias! Of course there are lots more acacias dotted about——"

" They will do as well as any," I thought. " So will these streams. It is all much as I have pictured it, the place of the whoredoms with the daughters of Moab."

We got out of the car into the steamy air, and walked over the fleshy foregrowth towards the shore, where, beyond an intervening bight, the long black headland of Lisan nosed forward, parallel to the shore.

It was all as I had pictured it, or as the Talmud tales had pictured it for me. Here the tents were spread, even as Balaam had enjoined it upon Balak, king of Moab. For Balaam had been much chagrined that having been commanded three times to curse the host of Israel, he had found it in no wise possible to do other than bless them. Wherefore he set gins for the host of Israel, and duly they were snared in them. And rising one morning from their slumbers in the plains of Moab, behold on the confines of the camp were tents of Moab pitched overnight. And rubbing their eyes, and walking thither, they saw that by the door of each tent sat an old woman, and each held fine shifts of clean linen in her hand. " And would you buy linen? " they asked of the children of Israel. " Go then, within. For there is much store there, comely linen from Beth-shan." For well was it known among the enemies of Israel that on that woeful journey, linen had become scarcer than gold, for linen wears out and gold does not wear.

So thinking no harm soever, the Israelites went into the tents; and behold in each was a goodly array of linen, tended by a fair maiden, perfumed and anointed, with dark eyes smiling, and great ear-rings. And the Israelites would have withdrawn then, but the maidens soothly bespoke them, saying : " Why do ye fear us, oh stalwart ones? Are we not also the children of Terah? Be then, we bid you, a thought more brotherly. Eat with us, and are ye not thirsty? Drink with us also. And then we shall do our trafficking with shifts of linen; but it shall not cost you dear. Nay, nay." And they smiled in the cover of their painted hands.

So they ate and drank; and the maidens said : " How shall we know your measures for your shifts of linen saving ye remove also those old clouts ye wear? " And their wits were but dim now, and they cast their clothes off, and lusted for those smiling ones. And these said : " Worship ye our gods, first, Chemosh and Peor." Which they did also. And lusted with them, and it was abominable, in Shittim, down by the Dead Sea.

And, as it is written, the Lord said unto Moses, Take all the chiefs of the people, and hang them up unto the Lord before the sun, that the fierce anger of the Lord may turn away before Israel. And Moses said unto the Judges of Israel, Slay ye every one his men that have joined themselves into Baal-peor.

For now were not the children of Israel on the very threshold of the Promised Land? And was it not kinder to the whole host of Israel, that these rotten ones should be consumed that the plague might not corrupt the whole harvest?

These streams, too (I told my friends), that go hurrying across the plain down into the Dead Sea—it is very dangerous to drink of them, for one is the " Well of Lewdness," which was in Shittim, and from this water the children of Sodom drank. It was accursed, therefore. And no man drank of it again, until the Children of Israel wandered here, thirsty after the first battles. Wherefore, they were disposed already to this unchastity. Do not drink of it (I said). It will lose its dire cunning only on the Last Day, and only then will go back into its source again, and dry up from the face of the earth.

We sat down by the edge of the Sea, and wondered at it a little. The smell of it was rank, there was a dirty scud over the shallow water close in, and the driftwood on the dun gravel we sat on was black and oily. Yet, from far off, no water looks lovelier than the water of the Dead Sea, kingfisher blue, turquoise blue, lazuline blue, as the caprice of light is. All sin is like that, murmured Father Dunn. Very gay from a distance, but a sad thing close to.

But the air was hot, and the water was liquid, at least seventy-five per cent of it was. So the two others stripped and bathed, and foolishly, though I have already bathed in the Dead Sea, I followed them. You do not, of course, bathe in it, so much as skid on it. It was while we were trying, completely without success, to dry ourselves, that Father Dunn reminded us of another validity the Dead Sea excursion had for us.

" He didn't come here himself," he said, " so far as is known. But his brain came here."

" You mean Lawrence? "

" Yes, Lawrence. This is the port of Kerak."

It did not look much like a port now. It has not yet recovered from Lawrence. This is the tale told in his own words.

" He (Abdullah el Fair) chose out some seventy horsemen, of the Beersheba Beduin. They rode in the night along the shelf of track between the hills of Moab and the Sea's brim as far as the Turkish post; and in the first greyness, when their eyes could reach far enough for a gallop, they burst out of their undergrowth upon motor launch and sailing lighters, harboured in the northern light, with the unsuspecting crews sleeping on the beach or in the reed-huts nearby.

" They were from the Turkish navy, not prepared for land-fighting, still less for receiving cavalry: they were awakened only by the drumming of the horses' hooves in the headlong charge: and the engagement ended at the moment. The huts were burned, the stores looted, the shipping taken out to deep sea and scuttled. Then, without a casualty, and with their sixty prisoners, our men rode back praising themselves."

We reminded each other of that good tale. Also, how Lawrence, who had been offered a military decoration for his text-book battle at Tafileh, had mockingly suggested the award of a naval decoration for this action at Kerak.

" He would have liked my car," said Father Dunn thoughtfully. " Particularly on a road like that one from Kerak. He didn't like brakes. He worshipped speed. He made a god of it. It got him in the end, as God always will, however you worship Him."

I recall several formidable moments of doubt and terror in my experience of motor-cars, but none to compare with a certain moment on the return journey to Kerak. Those others at least retained the element of doubt, however trivially.

There was no vestige of doubt about this one. We were over the precipice, all four wheels of us. Presumably there was a miracle. For, it will be deduced, all four wheels resumed the road again.

A number of such moments succeeded each other on a descent I once made from the cloudy citadel of Andritsaena in Greece, to the town of Megalopolis in the plain below. There was one on a descent from Manchester to Stockport, when the wheels of the car got caught into the tram-lines some thirty yards from a tram-car, and the tram-car was coming full-speed for us. There was one on the top of a public motor-bus en route for Jaca in Spain. We turned a corner at breakneck speed, and on the wrong side of the road, to avoid a car coming from the opposite direction. My head was pillowed in a strong leather case, bound with hoops of wood. A foot or two away a giant branch thrust across the air, at the exact height of my skull. It caught the strong leather case and cracked it like a nut.

But it was more ferocious on the road from the Dead Sea up to Kerak.

A superb sunset was in process, behind us, slightly on our left. I will not dilate on that sunset. It was, I say, superb. So was the pale-blue pink-flushed marble of the Dead Sea, lying like the foundation pavement of some terrific temple of Chemosh. Even Father Dunn was impressed, and he has seen a good many fine sunsets over the Dead Sea. I, too, was impressed by it, as sunsets always impress me. I was also impressed by another phenomenon in the region of light. The sunset in the hinder parts of the sky seemed to have drained from the forward parts every vestige of colour and to have flattened everything, but everything, into a browny-grey monochrome. I perceived with some displeasure, as we came towards a bend, that there was no difference in tint between the thin strip of road and the wide chasm of air beyond it. Jemil was not driving by sight now, he was driving by contact.

It was, I say, a fine sunset. It went on for a long time, as sunsets in these regions go. I regret to record Lucas completely lost his head about it. He got more and more woolly-witted and uttered sharper and sharper cries of ecstasy.

Now Jemil was pretty hard-boiled about sunsets like these. He had seen many more than Father Dunn. But that ecstasy was something he had not met before. Perhaps he thought it was not merely a sunset, but the eve of the Day of Judgment, and the whole sky behind was already streaming with archangels. He was sitting at a left-hand steering-wheel. The abyss lay below us on our left. We were approaching a hideous bend. Suddenly, he caved in. His hands left the wheel, he fumbled at the door-handle, and flung the door open. Then, thrusting his body half out of the car, and slewing it round from the waist, he gazed back into the sunset, to look into the matter of those archangels.

I shut my eyes. I was quite calm. I flatter myself that in moments of final apocalypse, I always become calm.

" Phew! " said Jim. " That was a close thing! "

That *was* a close thing, I reflected dispassionately. Then it no more *is* a close thing, or not so close. We are still alive, I concluded. Perhaps we will continue so for some time still.

Some fifty yards further a fox sat morosely on its haunches by the side of the road. He looked like the genius of the place, whose sombre delight it was to see men and their machinery go crashing over the precipice, below his den there, on the section of the road he presided over.

Not this time, old fox, I murmured. And as for you, oh fireflies, dancing before the bonnet of the car, first on the few feet of road, then out over the great chasm, as if to lure us there—dance another dance, oh fireflies. You will not have us over this side of Kerak.

At least, I don't think so. But if you do, oh fireflies, that's all there is to it.

From that moment a queer sort of resignation came over me. Resignation? It was more a sort of fatalistic tranquillity. The mood extended itself to the others. If I ceased to be a poltroon, Father Dunn ceased being a playboy. We met on common ground, we became philosophers. To philosophers it imports nothing, if death suspend their philosophizing, either by hemlock or old age or motor-car accident. If they are one sort of philosopher, they believe they will elsewhere continue the argument, if another, they do not.

We discussed Heaven and Hell and Purgatory. Purgatory is not a Jewish conception, and Hell hardly more. I was made in my childhood to have far more terror of Dr. Crippen than of Satan. I have a tolerance, despite myself, of the conception of Heaven. To the conception of Hell I have a complete intolerance. To Father Dunn, on the other hand, Hell was a far more real concept than Kerak, or Satan than any of us there.

Skirting the viewless precipices, we debated the soul's future, with special reference to Hell. It was as if we were truly suspended in some limbo, beating hither and hither, right and left, right and left, as if it had not been pronounced yet whither we were to be committed. I would have none of Hell, bringing against it those simple arguments which every Catholic priest, I do not doubt, is familiarized with in the very infancy of his studies. What of the omnipotence of God? How else are not God and Satan equal? How far, if not the whole way to deliverance from Hell, extends the efficacy of Jesus?

Far off, like the lights of the Heavenly City to souls rising from Purgatory, flickered the lights of Kerak. Still close beside, on either side of us, soared the unscaleable basalt cliffs of Hell.

It cannot be, said Father Dunn, in a voice gentle as a hare-bell and terrible as the horns of doom, it cannot be that there is no Hell. And as he spoke, I perceived it was only the husk of a man I had been acquainted with till then, a small Liverpool Irishman, with bright blue eyes, a straggly pointed beard, a simple rustic face. The man was St. Augustine and Aquinas, Origen and Tertullian, and his lips their mouthpiece.

It is for these reasons, he said, that it cannot be that there is no Hell; which he then gave me, winding me tight in the silken cocoon of his reasoning, tight, and tighter still.

There is a Hell, my numb brain conceded. How can it be that there is no Hell?

There is no Hell, my heart said pitifully. There is no Hell. There is no Hell.

CHAPTER ELEVEN

§ 1

NEXT morning we were up early, with the maps and books spread before us, to consider the whole question of the rest of our journey. From where we were on the tops of Moab, the heights of Jerusalem were already visible to the naked eye. That was north and over the river westward. But due north of us were other heights, not visible to the naked eye, for the great plateau rolled between. But these, which were the heights of Nebo, already cast their shadow over us; there was the end of all these journeys. There were many battles to fight before we attained it; but even as the wanderings had been dim and long, so were these battles to be bright and swift. Sihon, King of the Amorites, Balak, King of Moab, Og, King of Bashan—if the Lord has sharpened His sword, how shall their shields prevail?

What way then, to the battles, and to Nebo beyond the battles?

First, we must cross the Arnon, for it is only beyond the Arnon the battles begin. How we should cross the Arnon Abdullah Akashe had helped to decide for us. We had played with the idea of taking the Roman road straight north from Kerak to the bank of the wadi Mojib, then of climbing down and up again. But we had decided instead to take the road due east across the plateau, so as to cross the wadi Mojib by its shallow upper reaches, where the host had crossed before us, as it seemed logical to conclude. The eastward route into the desert, moreover, seemed to have the authority of the earlier itinerary given in Numbers. " And from thence they journeyed to Beer: that is the well whereof the Lord said unto Moses, Gather the people together, and I will give them water." It is not likely the host would have lacked water again, unless they had gone over into the desert again.

Were we then to make for Beer, having crossed the Arnon by the upper reaches? But which Beer? And in what region ought we to look for it? Northward from these same upper reaches of the brook Arnon, say the scholars, and something like a day's march away. That seems fairly reasonable. They thereon point out a wadi-bed rich in water, some twenty kilometres north—the wadi Themed, itself the upper reach of the main wadi that flows into Mojib from the north. Where now from Beer? "And from the wilderness they journeyed to Mattanah," the text says. But in that same wadi, the scholars continue, is a heap of ruins now called " el Medeineh." Does that not sound strangely like Mattanah?

Yes. That is as substantial as most of this route-finding; but that is all the help that extant ruins give them towards establishing this section of the journey. From Mattanah the host journeyed to Nahaliel, the text says, of which nothing more is known than that it means the " wadi of God." From Nahaliel they journeyed to Bamoth, but that merely means " high places," and Moab is dotted with them. The next stage from Bamoth takes us to the scene of the final fighting: " to the valley that is in the field of Moab."

But surely by now the journey is not a journey any more, in the sense it has been till now. The places listed are now the names of battles, which would have been scattered irregularly over the countryside. If Moses, having crossed the upper Arnon, now intended to attack the Amorites, would it not have been unwise to leave the strong places unsubdued in his rear? Might he not, therefore, have marched immediately westward again in order to take Dibon-gad, and thus inflict on the Amorites a vital defeat at the outset of the campaign? At Dibon-gad he would be a few kilometres north of the Arnon. He would then turn swiftly on Aroer, so that he might be able to proclaim with pride: " From Aroer, which is on the edge of the valley of Arnon, and from the city that is in the valley, even unto Gilead, there was not a city too high for us: the Lord our God delivered up all before us.

" And they journeyed from Dibon-gad, and pitched in

FAMILY IN MOAB

Almon-diblathaim." Perhaps, as I have suggested, by the way of the victory at Aroer. Now is there any place designated for this Almon-diblathaim? There is, if not irresistibly, Musil—or was it our friend, Abdullah Akashe?—identifies it with a heap of ruins now called "el Dlelet el Gharbiyeh," some twenty kilometres north of Dhibân on the old Roman road (which was the Nabataean road before that, no doubt, and the Moabite road before that). Further, the place is only a little north and some ten kilometres west of the putative Beer and Mattanah in the wadi Themed. Clearly, we would be in the thick of it all, on that road from Dhibân.

All the more as that road goes on to Madeba and Heshbon, the largest places, then as now, in the land between Arnon and Jabbok, Mojib and Zerqa, the land that Sihon, King of the Amorites, had but lately captured from Moab, the land that Moses now proceeded to capture from Sihon. It is clear that two of the major battles of the campaign must have been fought for Heshbon and Madeba, the two place-names with which the taunt-song quoted earlier begins and ends: " Come ye to Heshbon. Let the city of Sihon be built and established . . . Heshbon is perished even unto Nophah, which reacheth unto Madeba."

We could not do better then, than to make for Diban-gad, and take the road north to Madeba; all the more as it was only at Madeba in all that countryside we could be fairly sure of decent lodging for the night. The police-post could do at least as well for us as El-dji, and we knew there were one or two Christian missions there, that sometimes offered hospitality.

And from Madeba, whither? We should not be far from Heshbon, and must certainly go there, still with the noise about our heads of the Amorite battles. And then? The text goes straight on with the tale of the conquests:

" Thus Israel dwelt in the land of the Amorites. And Moses sent out to spy Jazer, and they took the towns thereof, and drove out the Amorites that were there."

But there seems to be some confusion. If Israel dwelt in the land of the Amorites, how came it there were still Amorites

Xc

to drive out from Jazer? If Jazer was somewhere within the region dominated by Heshbon and Madeba, we need do no more than transpose the two sentences. If it was not, perhaps it was a pocket of Amorite territory not conquered in that first Heshbon-Madeba campaign, but in the one that followed it, against Og, King of Bashan. At all events, there is a place called Khirbet es Sar, which has been identified with Jazer, some eight miles west of the city now called Amman, and in those days called Rabbath-Ammon, one of Og's chief cities.

We would occupy ourselves with Jazer when we reached Rabbath-Ammon, and the battles against Og, of which it is written: " And they turned and went up by the way of Bashan: and Og the king of Bashan went out against them, he and all his people, to battle at Edrei. And the Lord said unto Moses, Fear him not: for I have delivered him unto thy hand, and all his people, and his land; and thou shalt do to him as thou didst unto Sihon, king of the Amorites, which dwelt at Heshbon. So they smote him, and his sons, and all his people, until there was none left him remaining: and they possessed his land."

At Amman, as I say, we would occupy ourselves with Jazer and Edrei, whether that second is to be taken as identical with the modern Deraa, and how we should go thither. Well, then, must we go direct from Heshbon to Amman? Not quite. One episode intervenes.

" And Balak the son of Zephor saw all that Israel had done to the Amorites." In other words, calamity has befallen Sihon, but not yet befallen Og. " And Balak the son of Zephor was king of Moab at that time. And he sent messengers unto Balaam the son of Beor, to Pethor, saying, Behold, there is a people come out from Egypt: behold, they cover the face of the earth, and abide over against me: come now therefore, I pray thee, curse me this people; for they are too mighty for me: peradventure I shall prevail, that we may smite them, and that I may drive them out of the land."

And Balak prevailed upon Balaam, who thereon came out of the land of the Great River (which is the Euphrates) and stood upon the top of Peor to curse the host of Israel; but the Lord would in no wise endure him to utter curses against Israel, and in their stead blessings came from the lips of Balaam. And this top of Peor where Balaam stood, is the same place as that Mount Nebo, called also Mount Pisgah, where later Moses was to come, and die there.

We will go to the top of Peor from Heshbon, we decided, and stand where Balaam stood, between the battle against Sihon and the battle against Og. We must keep from our mind the shadow of Moses, and of his death. He has not yet come this way to die. We will go, still in the traces of a living man, to Rabbath-Ammon and to Edrei. Thereafter we will go down into the plain of Moab beyond the Jordan at Jericho, and there will be fought the last of all the battles, against the Midianites. And now at long last the time is fulfilled, the land of the inheritance waits, the hills beckon, the rivers call out to them. And the mantle is fallen upon Joshua, and Joshua prepares to assemble the companies. But at the sight thereof, a sorrow deep as the sea possesses the heart of the leader, who is to lead no more. " And he besought the Lord at that time, saying: Let me go over, I pray thee, and see the good land that is beyond Jordan, that goodly mountain, and Lebanon. But the Lord hearkened not unto him, and he turned away from the host, and climbed up that mountain again, to Mount Nebo, the top of Pisgah." And thither we would seek to follow him. And that will be the end of the journey, if it turn out so.

But it did not turn out so. There were no strangers to vex the silence and challenge the secrecy, far-wandered from their own place and his time.

§ 2

Father Dunn had been called away during the course of these consultations. He returned just as we were folding our maps away. He looked pleased. He had something of interest to tell us.

" Og, King of Bashan," he said, a little cryptically.

" Yes ? "

" It says he was all that remained of the remnant of the Rephaim . . . the giants, you know, the builders of the citadel here."

" And his bedstead was a bedstead of iron," Lucas quoted.

" He kept it in Rabbath-Ammon," Father Dunn continued. " So does this one usually. But he's got it here with him to-day."

" *This* one? Who? "

" Kirkbride is here. He says he spoke to you when you rang up the Residency at Amman from Suez."

" Do you mean the one Lawrence writes about, the big fellow? "

" That's the one, the last of the Rephaim. He had quite a lot to do with Lawrence. He was in with him to the end, at Damascus. You can't get away from Lawrence."

" No, we can't get away from Lawrence. Where is he? How long is he staying? "

" He's just come up from Tafileh and is going back to Amman. He knows what you're doing, of course. You go the same way for about half the journey. He wonders whether you'd like to go in his car, one or two of you."

" *Would* we! Where is he? How soon is he leaving? "

" Do you hear that horn? There he is! He's in a bit of a hurry. He had to stop off to see one or two people. Your things are already out there! "

We bade hasty farewells to the Maronite priest, the Moabite maiden, the mission boys, and hurried downstairs. The last of the Rephaim stood beside his bedstead of iron, which looked better upholstered than that of his ancestor, Og, King of Bashan. He was in khaki, wearing a headcloth. He was resting on his gun, one hand clasped round the barrel. He was perhaps not so tall as he looked, but he looked enormous.

" How do you do? " he said. " It was you telephoning from Suez? Why didn't you speak up? "

" Speak up! " I protested. " I'm still hoarse! "

" Had a good time? Nice to have a chat about things! Get in, will you!

We shook hands with Father Dunn, Lucas and I got into the back, Jim got in with Jemil. Kirkbride got into the seat beside the driver, nursing his gun between his knees. His gun seemed to be just as much part of him as Abdullah Bey's horse was part of Abdullah Bey.

We put our heads out of the window, and saluted Father Dunn. Father Dunn saluted back, his rustic face shining ingenuously, his blue eyes twinkling. The chauffeur started the engine, put in the clutch, and we were off.

" Oh by the way," said Kirkbride, turning suddenly. " You've not brought any of that Akaba stuff in the car, have you? "

" Akaba stuff ? "

" Fish ! "

Conversation was not brisk for a good many minutes, while we wound down into the ravine, through the groves of fig and olive, and up on to the stony flanks of the eastward hills. I had leisure to recall Lawrence on the subject of Kirkbride. He had met him in Tafileh, at the beginning of a " connection profitable to us, and creditable to Kirkbride." He found him a " taciturn, enduring fellow." He was only a boy in years at the time.

I wanted to talk to him about that " profitable connection." I felt almost I had a right to. Was it by purest blind chance we came up so perpetually against the traces of Lawrence, found ourselves rubbing shoulders with his associates? It was, I suppose ; even though twenty years have gone by since he went campaigning. But what are twenty years in the desert? Perhaps, without knowing it, on the journey hither from Akaba, we had sometimes addressed, or been addressed by, Arabs whose associations with Lawrence had been far closer than Kirkbride's or Peake Pasha's, who had slept in his tent with him, gone out with him on some of his most perilous assays.

But now Fate had decided we should be close-confined for several hours with Kirkbride, the " summary " as once Lawrence called him, Kirkbride of the " ruthless revolver," which he knew so well how to use in that little brush with Abd el Kadir's Druses at Damascus. It was a pity, wasn't it, he should still be Kirkbride " the taciturn," all these years later? There was much I should have liked to ask him, about old wars and new wars, Moses and Lawrence. After all, hadn't he himself gone out raiding in this very countryside, where the earlier one had gone before him, and the later beside him?

And I *did* ask him about those wars. I didn't even have to ask him. We fell to talking about them quite naturally. How could we fail to? He wasn't taciturn any more, as Lawrence had known him. At least not with us, on that journey east to the station at Katrani and north to the station at Khan es Zebib. I suppose, during that first half-hour, he was getting his ideas into shape about the things and people he had been inquiring into in Kerak.

" Cigarette? " he asked.

" English? Fine! Thanks! "

" Which way do you think they came? "

He could mean only the Israelites. He did not need to consult us on which way the troops of Feisal and Lawrence went.

We told him our ideas. We had a long and animated discussion about various encampments, certain miracles. It was a thing we had noticed with excitement throughout the whole journey, the extraordinary vividness and presentness of the Israelitic tale to people living in these parts. You had the feeling it might not have happened three and a half thousand years ago, but only a generation ago, and you could still find the debris of their passing in their camping-places, the charred sticks of their fires, the discarded pots and pans of their field-kitchens.

I had mentioned this thing to Father Dunn.

" What do you expect? " he said. " These are the same people. They move from pasture to pasture the same way. They come up against exactly the same problems. Listen. Two of my Christian half-nomads came up to me only a month ago. The ox belonging to one killed the ox belonging to the other. They were fairly sensible. They knew they could start a nice little blood-feud about it, which would go on from animals to humans, from this generation to the tenth generation. So they came and saw me instead. I remembered exactly the same problem is dealt with in Exodus: ' If one man's ox hurt another's, that he die, then they shall sell the live ox, and divide the money of it; and the dead ox also shall they divide.' And that's how I arranged it," he smiled. " They were as pleased as Punch. I was, in fact, Moses."

The countryside was becoming gradually barer, as we came closer to the great flint desert.

" If they came this way," said Kirkbride, " this is about the only place round here they'd find to water their beasts." He pointed out a line of palm trees, a tract of greenness, a little to the north. " El Lejjun, they call it, corruption of ' Legion,' do you think? " A mile or two further we came up to a big herd of sheep and goats and camels clearly making for el Lejjun from the south-west. Their herdsmen were spread over a large area.

" Of course those people are moving across peaceful country," said Kirkbride. " At least what is now peaceful country. But they can't lose their old habits. That's exactly how the old Israelites will have trekked forward, spread out like that. There would have been an armed vanguard in front and armed men on both flanks to protect the main body. In between, the rest would have been spread out for miles with their cattle. They would never move without sending out their spies to examine the possible water-supply, and according to their reports draw up their plan of march.

" Of course we were less dependent on the wells," he said reflectively. " We had swift riding-camels. But we had to keep a lively eye open for where we could get a fill-up."

It was more than I had dared hope for—to hear a soldier in the Lawrence war dovetailing it thus with the Moses war, thinking of one in terms of the other.

" I think it must have been all pretty well dot and carry, their fighting, just like ours," he continued.

" Dot and carry? " I didn't quite get that.

" Oh, you know, now they were fighting, now for long periods they weren't. They tried to stay put during the summer-time." He peered through the window as if to examine more closely the nature of the ground we were travelling over. " They couldn't have gone out much further east than this," he decided. " The grass on these uplands never grows any longer than this, though you'll get a few aromatic herbs coming up later that the cattle don't mind."

" They wouldn't have had much more in the way of water, would they? "

" Not a quart more then than now. Except, of course, in the towns, where they could increase the water-supply by cisterns. There'd be no limit to that, I suppose. Out in these parts a lot of the springs and wells have been examined. They never supplied more water than they do now. And if you dig—you've got to go on digging for three to five hundred feet. The Israelites couldn't quite manage that. They hadn't the gadgets. What do you think about those censuses? " he asked brusquely.

" Well, of course, pure poetry."

" They can't count. They just don't know how to begin counting." His voice was a trifle querulous, as if he himself had deputed to some subordinate the job of making a census of the host of Israel, and the fellow had made an awful hash of it. " I shouldn't be surprised if their numbers weren't any more than ours. You know what awful poppycock is talked about the number of Arabs serving in the Revolt? "

" Yes," I said. " A little more poetry."

" How many were there, would you say? " asked Lucas.

Kirkbride thought for a time. " Well, in the Arab Legion under Joyce . . . You know, of course, it was Joyce who had charge of the whole thing from Akaba? "

Yes, we remembered.

" I suppose Joyce never had more than three thousand regulars under him," continued Kirkbride. " Probably less than two thousand. I mean *regulars*, wearing British uniform and Arab headdress. There were about a dozen British officers."

" What about Feisal's troops? "

" I don't know. There can't ever have been more than ten thousand in the whole shoot, but they were scattered all over the place. Only a few of them would be available for a given action at a given time. In that final show in September, 1918, there were just about six hundred all told. I'm not including the irregulars. As we moved forward, we'd buy up the locals to help in the local actions, and then drop them. They were too tied up with blood-feuds to be of much use a long way from their own villages.

" I shouldn't be a bit surprised," he said, " if it was like that with old Moses. He'd probably have a main body of a few thousand regulars, then buy up the locals as he went along."

" You mean a few Moabites to lend a hand with the Amorites, then a few Amorites to lend a hand with the Midianites, and so on? "

" Exactly. That's the local custom."

" Perhaps you're right. But it seems to have worked the other way. The Moabites and the Midianites seemed to have got together. Then they called in Balaam the Assyrian."

" To do a spot of cursing? Oh, yes, we had some, too. In Turkish. Oh, by the way, do you realize where we are now? " The road had descended into a shallow trough in the plateau, which seemed to descend and deepen from south to north, coming down from a low amphitheatre of hills, arrayed in level limestone strata. The track dipped into the trough, then zigzagged up the opposite slopes.

" This is the beginning of it, eh? The wadi Mojib, the Brook Arnon? "

" That's right. One of the beginnings of it. You'll see how the gorge starts deepening on both sides, when you look back from higher up there."

" Well," I said a minute or two later. " We've crossed the Arnon. Look out now! The fighting begins! "

" I wonder what sort of fighting it was," speculated Kirk-bride professionally. " I suppose their tactics will have been pretty much the same as ours. A sudden sally where the enemy was least expecting it. Then run like the devil."

" I don't know," said Lucas. " It probably was like that. But there's a very careful account of the organization of the host in Numbers. Every man over twenty a soldier; each tribe with its own regiment, under its own captain and its own flag; all the positions clearly fixed in the camp and the line of march."

" Probably more poetry," Kirkbride thought.

We agreed it sounded a little like emotion recollected in tranquillity. Wandering tribes going out to battle do not move in quite such perfect symmetry.

" Anyhow," I said. " They can't have run like the devil. They hadn't any camels, and no horses. Even Balaam, a distinguished magician, couldn't rise above an ass."

" What about their weapons? " asked Kirkbride.

" So long as you don't say they brought the first fire-arms from Egypt, and that was how they swept the board. . . ."

" No," he admitted. " If they'd been coming from China now . . . Of course, they had swords."

" Yes," said Lucas. " The *chereb*. Probably shorter than anything we mean by a sword. Who was it concealed his sword under his garment? That was only a cubit long, I think, less than twenty inches."

" Perhaps a stabbing instrument? They girded it on, didn't they? "

" ' If I whet my glittering sword,' " I quoted from the song of Moses in the plain of Moab.

" There's a good deal in the later books," said Lucas, " about heavy helmets and breastplates and greaves. And shields—a large shield, and a smaller one. It's all in my notes," he said, a trifle apologetically, as if one ought not to be erudite beyond a certain decent limit.

" They can't have had much of that sort of junk left by the time they crossed the Arnon," said Kirkbride. " That is, if they took any with them. But they had spears, of course. They must have used spears."

" And a smaller sort of spear . . . you remember, the javelin. They may have thrown a sort of dart, too, in the narrow places."

" And you read of bows very early on," I recalled, " with arrows carried in a quiver."

" And slings," said Kirkbride. " You should see some of these goat-boys use a sling! "

We were trundling steadily along the track due east again, great fields of black flints spread out endlessly on either side. The others were looking straight ahead of them. I happened at a certain moment to look through the right-hand window.

" Hello! " I said, leaning forward and touching Kirkbride's shoulder. " What's that big bird standing up there? "

He turned his head quickly, and in less than a moment had turned the car round off the track, towards the bird.

" Bustard! " he cried sharply. His gun was already through the window. He had already taken aim. " It's all right! " he turned his head, and smiled. " He won't move! "

We had leisure to study him as we approached, his brown and black striped wings, his black-edged feathers. We did not frighten him in the least, it seemed. We were a machine. He had never seen the like of us before. We could mean him no harm.

At last we got within thirty yards, we were almost on top of him. It occurred to him that perhaps we were not so innocent after all. He spread his wings and rose with a great clatter. A moment later he was kicking incredulously on the ground, bleeding among the black flints.

We stopped the car. Kirkbride got out and twisted the neck neatly, then threw the inert creature into the bottom of the car.

" If we'd have been on foot," he said tersely, " we wouldn't have got within a mile of him. Flies at fifty miles an hour. Great fun to go after him in a car careering along at ninety, and try and shoot him from below. Important the chauffeur should keep his eye on the road, not the bird. Ah well! Good eating! Like turkey! Sorry you won't be there to share it!"

"'Kirkbride's ruthless shot-gun,'" I murmured.

"What's that? What?"

"Lawrence uses a phrase about you," I said apologetically. "Kirkbride's ruthless revolver."

"Tough!" he said.

I thought it better not to remind him of the context, the little affair with Abd el Kadir at Damascus, and cheek by jowl with it, the business of the barracks hospital, where he figures grimly, but with credit. I suppose there are few more horrifying pages in the whole history of war—the heap of Turkish dead and not quite dead lying stinking together in the dormitories, the red galleries in the flesh gnawed by the teeth of rats, the bodies that could be picked up and the bodies that could only be shovelled up, the great hole dug in the yard for the dead by the dying.

"Hello," I exclaimed, a minute or two later. "That *is* there, isn't it? That big blocky looking place?" One is never quite sure in the desert whether one sees what one seems to see.

Yes, it was there right enough. It was the fort of El Katrani, one of the sixteenth-century forts built by Suleiman the Magnificent, to protect the Pilgrim's Way. It was also a station on the Hedjaz railway, the station for Kerak. The railway follows the old track through most of its length. The natives call it the "Tarik-el-Bint," the Maiden's Way, because Suleiman rebuilt the road for the special comfort of his daughter. The Roman track had been used by the pilgrims till then, but the young lady did not like being jolted up and down by the paving-stones.

"Yes, that's the old railway right enough," said Kirkbride. "Dear old pal of ours!"

"The railway," I repeated. "The Hedjaz Railway."

I suppose one does not often talk about a railway in quite such a breathless tone. But it was, after all, a rather special railway, the railway that at one and the same time was the feeding-tube of that Turkish army bottled up in Medina, and the rope that strangled it. And in a real sense the adventures of that railway make the essential skeleton of Lawrence's book and Lawrence's War. It is, I say, a rather special railway.

" Why? Haven't you seen it before? " Kirkbride was asking.

" As a matter of fact, we haven't. Let me see now. We could have seen it at Maan, couldn't we? But we didn't. We've been a long way from it, ever since."

" Not that you can call it a *railway*, exactly. Pain in the neck to everybody concerned, ever since it started. The amount of trouble they took to build it, the taxes, the graft, the cholera——"

" The amount of trouble *you* took to unbuild it," I interrupted.

He smiled.

" They had quite a lot of that sort of thing from the start. They pretended it was a holy railway, but, of course, the soldiers wanted it. They thought it would be a good way of keeping down Arabia. But it didn't work out like that. They always knew it could never pay its way, but they hoped to make a good bit out of taking the pilgrims to Mecca. Unfortunately the pilgrims didn't want to be taken. The nastier it is, the more marks in heaven. And the tribes en route hated losing their blackmail. Poor show from the beginning. No money coming in from anywhere. Peake tells you about it in his book. He says the Turkish government used to sell decorations right and left to raise funds. Regular tariff. Pasha so much, Bey so much. The market in Pashas slumped. So they had to raise money any way they could. They had a house tax. They sold the skins of all animals used for sacrificial purposes. Poor railway. Ibn Saud is cleverer than that. He doesn't want it in his country at any price. After the mess we made of it, they patched it up as far as Maan in 1919, and then for a couple of years it went as far as Medina. Then there were big rains in 1925, and no train has been able to get further than Maan since then. That's all right by Ibn Saud. He's not grumbling. Here we are, anyhow. Let's get out and stretch our legs, shall we? "

We got out and walked about for a few minutes. It was very bleak with those gritty and sandy flats extending endlessly in every direction. The fort looked sullen and clumsy, as if it did not quite know what it was doing there. There was an enormous reservoir, surrounded by derelict rooms the Turkish soldiers had once occupied. There was a water-tank. There was a single forlorn hen, clucking because she had, or had not, laid an egg. A few goat-hair tents spread their shabby roofs beside the line.

We got into the car again and lurched off.

" Cheerful place, isn't it? " asked Kirkbride. " One train a week, if it's lucky."

" This wasn't quite on your beat, was it? That culvert there, for instance. You didn't pay it any attention, did you? "

" No," he said. " Not that one. But plenty like it. You can always tell those we tackled—you can see the new masonry. The jobs we did were usually either north of Amman or south of Maan. The country round here is very bad for camels, as you see; simply tear their feet to pieces."

" Was it fun, all that raiding? "

" Not bad," he conceded. " But it had its drawbacks. Practically nothing to eat or drink, very cold at night, but above all, no medical attention. You might easily be away days and days without any chance of seeing a doctor. That was the nightmare—bad wounds in a raid. If you got popped off—there you were. Chap I knew looked at an unexploded charge; large sliver of rail stuck in his skull; got carted about for a week on a camel. Recovered—but blind, of course. Would have been all right, if seen to after a couple of days.

" Another thing got you down a bit. You might be away for a month. Then, when the picnic was over, you came back to your base. Bad show. No base there. I remember once, after a couple of stiff days, dead tired, we saw a fire in a wadi.

Didn't dare approach, though our tongues were as dry as cinders. We went on for another half-day. Found out later they were our own chaps. I must say, I like my cup of coffee last thing at night. Mark you," he said hastily, as if one might be taken to exclude the other, " I like my cup of tea in the morning, too! That's where old Lawrence and I didn't see eye to eye. He was a small fellow. He didn't worry about breakfast. He'd set off on a raid without any. Now I've got some stoking up to do. Six foot four in my stockinged feet. I wanted my breakfast. We had one or two dust-ups about it. Finally we compromised. Lawrence went off without breakfast, I'd stay on and have some, then I'd ride like hell and catch up. Funny fellow, this Lawrence. Bit mad, you know. Carried his modesty to extremes, if you ask me. Just another sort of vanity. Could only see his own side of the question. But Lord, what a brain! And how tough! Stout fellow! " he summarized.

" Oh! talking about this breakfast habit," he reverted. " It once saved my life. I'd gone out with a detachment of the regular Camel Corps and two hundred rifles, and we'd blown up a bit of the line. Now normally, as I told you, we'd cut and run. But we'd got it into our heads the Turks couldn't be along for some time, and we were absolutely dead beat, so we thought we'd doss down for an hour or two. At dawn a nice armoured train comes up with a gun or two and a couple of thousand troops. The Arabs start screaming like a pack of madmen. ' Shut up! ' I shouted. ' I'm not going to pack up before I've had my tea! ' So we sat there in a sort of pit under the line making tea. Consequence was, the Turks didn't take the least notice of us. Thought we were workers on the line or something. It was those two hundred rifles that got it—just shot to bits. When we finished our tea, we spread out and walked off."

(A hazy idea went through my head of a fellow playing bowls on Plymouth Hoe. " Shut up! " the man shouted. " Spaniards? They can wait! I'm not going to pack up before I've had my game! ")

" We had another bit of fun soon after," Kirkbride continued. " Turkish H.Q. at Deraa heard of the raid, and sent over a German 'plane to strafe us. It dropped a bomb and managed to knock out six camels, but not a single man got touched, as it happened. Then all of a sudden the engine konked out; the fellow had nothing to do but come down prettily at the head of the line. We roared with laughter. It looked so funny. The chap came out shaking like a leaf, but as he hadn't pipped anybody, nobody pipped him. We just put him on a camel, and off he went. Apparently he'd never been on a camel before. A few hours later he'd had enough of it. ' I would rather be dead ! ' he said. His face was like paste. ' Please kill me ! ' "

" Deraa ! " I repeated. " You said Deraa ! "

" Yes, why ? "

" Oh I don't know. It's all a little uncanny. Deraa was pretty well the climax in this show, wasn't it ? The last big show before Damascus. It was just the same with the Israelites' campaign, when Og and all his people went out to Edrei. Same place as Deraa, of course. But the Israelites were making for Jerusalem, so to speak, not Damascus. . . . Hello, where are we ? " The car had stopped at a place where the railway line got quite excited for a minute or two. It became double, and even had a side line for shunting.

" This is Khan el Zehib," said Kirkbride. " You'd better be turning off here, or you'll be going along to Damascus, too." We got out of the car. He stayed in. " There it is, you see ? There's your track. By that sign-post there."

We walked up to the sign-post.

" Dhibân ! " we read, both in English and Arabic.

" That's right," he said. " You'll have no difficulty. I'll not wait for the other car, if you don't mind. Bit of a hurry. Well, good-bye you fellows. Nice to have had a chat about things. Good-bye."

He went off, rather as if he were going north to Highgate, and we west to Knightsbridge.

" Good-bye," we waved after him.

KHIRBET-ET-TANNUR

" That's good-bye to Lawrence, too," said Lucas a little lugubriously.

" Oh no. Lawrence went all the way we're going," I said, " down to the bank of the Jordan. When he went scouting down from Tafileh. You remember? "

He remembered. He sighed briefly. He would have liked to have gone riding into Damascus on the back of a swift-riding camel.

But we had a lonelier tryst, on the top of Mount Nebo.

§ 3

Jemil got out and looked a little doubtfully on that sign-post to Dhibân. It was rather ramshackle and provisional, but then, probably, not many people want to go to Dhibân from Khan-el-Zebib who do not already know the way there. You could not quite make out whether the board wanted you to go west or east.

" *Shemsh!* " we said, hopefully. " Sun! " and pointed westward.

He could not quite make out which strip of the desert was supposed to be the track.

" *Mish quais!* " he said, nodding his head two or three times. We got in and drove off. There was, of course, nothing else to do. For a long time it was only desert, nothing else at all but desert, a little scrub, a great many flints, a sandy patch, more scrub. You recognized the preponderating part of the desert you were not expected to drive over, by finding yourself suddenly in blind little wadis, which you got out of as soon as you could. Jemil sighed. He may have been wondering what he was going to make out of the journey, by the time he had made some allowance for wear and tear.

We had been travelling what seemed a long time.

" You think the way good for Dhibân, Jemil? "

He turned a lack-lustre eye. He hadn't the least idea where he was going. A nice steep bank spread out before us. He

Yc

hesitated a moment, like a horse at a fence, then pressed hard, and took the bank with a flying jump.

"Well done!" I said, not knowing the Arabic for back axle. I disliked the idea of camping out indefinitely in this wilderness with a broken back axle. The Transjordan desert extended a hundred and fifty miles east of the line. There seemed a lot more west of it.

Or was the country now just a little less desolate than before? Perhaps it was. There was a shimmer of grass here and there. Were not these few pale stalks actually barley? We started a few smaller birds; they looked like stonechats and sand-martins. There were a few partridges, too. Far off on the north-west we saw a line of camels.

"It looks," said Lucas, "as if there'd been an attempt to clear this ground some time. I think that's what those cairns are."

"And that line of stones is artificial, isn't it? Like some sort of boundary."

"Hi!" said Jim. "There's a woman!"

The car gave a sudden roar, as if the car, too, had noticed it. We shot forward.

"Hi, *bint*!" shouted Jemil. "This to Dhibân, the way?"

The *bint* uttered a cry of terror, got down on her hands and knees, and tried to dig a hole for herself. The *bint* wasn't going to be helpful. We continued. Sometime later, Lucas suddenly tugged at my sleeve, and pointed north and west.

"What's that?" he cried. "Isn't that a big town over there? Do you see? Any amount of it? And a big sort of tower place behind?"

"But that's all wrong!" I said. "There shouldn't be any town over there!"

"It can't be Dhibân! There isn't anything left of it!"

"Besides, that's straight on the edge of the Arnon. There's no Arnon there, not for miles and miles."

"Let's go and see!" said Lucas. "Jemil, that place over there! Can you get there?"

Jemil heeled the wheel over, and got a mile or two nearer

to it. It was, perhaps, a mile further on. We seemed to have been on some sort of a track till now, for the going became really harsh.

" That's all right, Jemil," we said. " We'll walk! "

" If you don't mind," said Jim. " I'll stay with Jemil. I've got a headache."

" All right. We'll tell you all about it."

They both were glad of the respite. They slumped in their places. They seemed to fall asleep at once.

" You've got that map? " I asked, after a few minutes of heavy plodding. " But what's the good of the map? We don't know where we are. Look at those walls! They're colossal! "

" And those towers! How many of them are there? "

" Yes, it's one of those mysterious ruined towns we've heard about! Which one? "

We were to find out soon enough. But we were not the only ones intent on finding things out that afternoon.

" Hello! " Lucas said suddenly. " What's that over on the horizon to the west? "

It was something moving, something getting larger from moment to moment.

" Over, there too! " I cried. " In the opposite direction! Do you see? "

Men on horseback. They were coming up from several directions simultaneously. A few moments ago not a single human creature had been visible in all that vast expanse.

" What did Rolfe say? " I asked lightly. I was not feeling at all comfortable. " The whole of Transjordan is one vast whispering-gallery. If you put your ear down to the ground, I suppose you'd hear the whisper spreading out in every direction. Don't look a bit nice, do they? " I observed.

They were close enough for us to make out details. The details were mostly fire-arms. They were just bristling with fire-arms.

" Well, we're not doing anything," said Lucas. " Let's just keep on. We'll go and look at those ruins, then we'll go back."

But it wasn't so simple. The ground all round us now was reverberating with the hooves of their horses. A minute or so later, they had dismounted. They formed round us, a group of some fifteen to twenty. There were two or three quite small boys amongst them, not more than twelve years old. They were as heavily armed as the rest. Some of them, at least, had weapons slung over both shoulders. Most had pistols at their holsters. All had large daggers in their belts. I thought in a hazy sort of way: so this is where all those weapons come from, that the guerilla bands use in Palestine. Each man's a walking arsenal.

" *Ma es salaam!* " we both said friendlily.

But no faces could have been less friendly than theirs.

" *Jehudi?* " they asked.

" Here it goes again! " I said forlornly.

" English! " proclaimed Lucas, with less than his usual resonance.

" Peake Pasha! " I cried out; and felt for my wallet. " Oh good God! " I exclaimed. " My coat's in the car! With those papers! "

" Peake Pasha in automobile! " I pointed out somewhat haggardly.

They did not seem as if they had ever heard of Peake Pasha, or, if they had, that they believed he was in the car. Their faces were quite stony.

" Bit grim! " murmured Lucas. He pointed to the car. " We'll go and get papers! " he conveyed. " I wonder if they think we're quite alone," he muttered. " You could never tell there's two other people in that car."

" *Shuff!* " I pointed to the ruins. " Look! " I was proclaiming the innocence of our intentions. We just wanted to look, that was all.

The boniest of them uttered a few clipped words, which we could not make out at all. His eyes were like two cauldrons of pitch. The others moved a step or two forward.

" Shall I offer to take their pictures? " I asked, fingering my camera. There was a slight note of panic in my voice.

"Anything but that!" exclaimed Lucas. There was as much in his.

"Abdullah!" I cried out, suddenly remembering another gambit. "Emir Abdullah!"

They did not seem to believe that the Emir Abdullah, either, was in that deserted car. My memory of the next few minutes is rather dim. So is Lucas's. We both heard the word *Yehudi* again. I remembered very vividly certain stories I had heard and read of travellers murdered by Beduin in these regions, at one time and another. Major Palmer in Sinai. The young Norwegian writer murdered in 1931 just a few miles south of Akaba. What was his name? Really, this was no time to be worrying about his name. It all felt very recent and near.

Nothing could be easier for them than to chuck our bodies into a hole somewhere between those huge stones. I thought so then, and still think so. It wasn't likely we'd be found for a long time. And they'd be gone by then. I do not commit myself to saying that that was their intention. I can only say they looked like it and it felt like it.

I was glad, of course, that Jim was not in it with us. He was a good deal younger than we were. By the time he and Jemil had wakened up. . . . Oh yes, Kulm Holmboe was his name. That young Norwegian writer. He was a convert to Islam, too.

We heard a noise from far off. It was the noise of a car starting up. There was a slight movement in the group surrounding us.

"Jemil!" Lucas murmured. "He's got up! He's spotted something's wrong!"

The others drew back a little at a word from the bony one. It seemed it had been decided to postpone the issue while the new fact was being taken into consideration that there was some other person, or persons, in that car. The car came plunging and snorting forward, like a hippopotamus through undergrowth. It moved very slowly, I thought.

It stopped at last. Jemil and Jim got out.

" Bring my coat with you! " I cried out loudly.

Jim brought the coat. Jemil addressed himself to the bony one and started explaining. It seemed a long time before the others began to give signs that his explanation interested them at all. If they wanted to be unpleasant, the presence of Jemil and Jim need not affect things very much. Jim would have been good enough for any three in the ring, but there is no arguing with a pistol, and not much with a dagger.

I was holding out the Peake Pasha and Emir Abdullah documents.

" *Shuff!* " I exclaimed, thrusting them into the bony one's hands. " You can't get away from those! " I said. But he could, of course.

" You've forgotten to turn the bottom up! " whispered Jim in alarm.

My heart sank. Perhaps by the time his eye had got down so far as that, I could manage to. . . . It was all right, I saw. He couldn't read.

Several of the elder men moved a few feet further away, and held a conference. Then the bony one went and spoke to Jemil. After a minute or two Jemil came up to us and said: " *Quais!* " He put a finger to his mouth and puffed at it. We were to offer them cigarettes. We did so, and they were accepted. It occurred to me we might have tried that before, but probably they would not have been satisfied with cigarettes. A little general conversation went on between Jemil and the bony one. He was the Sheikh Nasr. They were tribesmen of the Beni Sakhr. That was by way of introduction. We smiled at each other a little frigidly. A certain embarrassment prevailed. Sheikh Nasr suggested we should go and take tea with him, but he did not press us, when we pointed to the sun, and said, " *Shemsh!* "

They got back on their horses again, twitched their reins, and galloped off. The reverberations of their hooves became fainter, men and horses dwindled and disappeared. In a few minutes not a single human creature beside ourselves was visible in all that vast expanse.

" I suppose we had better go and see those ruins," I murmured.

" Business as usual," grinned Jim.

" Um er-Rasâs! " Jemil informed us kindly. He had the information straight from the lips of his friends of the Beni Sakhr. The word means " Mother of Lead," " Mother of Bullets," and records, doubtless, some earlier misadventure. An unprepossessing name.

" Perhaps that's all they wanted to let us know," Lucas said. " Nice kind people they looked."

We were less inspired by archaeological ardour than usual, both as we plodded over the remaining distance to the ruins and while we scrambled over them. We were, if anything, more sensitive to the rich profusion of shrubs and flowers that grew everywhere among the tumbled masonry—the small marigolds, the large yellow daisies, the red anemones, the pink and white asphodels, the feathery gushes of wormwood. There were the ruins of several early churches, many more cisterns, a number of intact arches spanning the blocky debris, and complete crypts everywhere. Or they seemed crypts now. They may once have been living-rooms. One had an entire stove, several had their old cement flooring and prepared wall-surfaces intact. Some had hollowed out sills and niches for holding statues or lamps. These had very much the air of the rock-hewn caves of Petra. We thought the substance of the place Nabataean, despite the Maltese crosses and other Christian symbols carved in numerous lintels, which later inhabitants may well have carved in temples and houses already centuries old.

It had been a big place, once, and doubtless a rich one. If it had not been rich, its citizens would not have been able to transport and carve those masses of alien stone. Those towers on the girdle of its enormous walls had something worth guarding to guard. It was a large populace that quenched its thirst in the water of those many cisterns.

What sort of people were they? What did they live on?

What did they live for? Alas, not even the name of their city is preserved. It can only be said that the things they stood for did not seem good to the Beni Sakhr, or whatever nomad tribe it might have been that again, and still again, pulled it apart stone from stone. We had seen the Nebi Sakhr face to face for a short while that afternoon, and we understood a little more clearly how it might have been.

We resumed our journey towards Dhibân, with the sun as our guide. Almost hourly now the brush of spring swept the surface of the high uplands with a new wash of colour. We had given up the hope of getting on to the track again, so we moved on with something of a tank's indifference over hills and streams. Every now and again the totally uninhabited landscape would yield a sudden crop of Beduin, who would hasten up to us to find out what we were all about. They looked very amiable, compared with Sheikh Nasr's contingent. If the way seemed easier across a field of barley, we drove across a field of barley. The Beduin were not perturbed about that. If Allah decreed the stalks should ripen, they would. If it was written otherwise, they would not. The harder the struggle against Nature is, the more fatalistic are its soldiers.

Then at last we began to make out far off the rim of the further bank of Mojib, and to have a sense of the stupendous gulf between. On this side we made out a line of lumpy beacons that went on at intervals till they passed beyond our sight. They had been Moabite beacons in their day, and later Nabataean, and Roman. They had given warning to Moabite kings that Israel was afoot again, and to Roman generals that there was trouble again among those stiff-necked tribes.

We made towards the biggest of these, which was not merely a beacon, but a hill, or two hills, covered over with ruins, softened and beautified by clumps of flowers and cushions of greenery. A goatherd stood between the hills, posturing his goats and chewing a stalk, as goatherds do.

" This place, what is it? "

" Aroer ! " said he.

We were at Aroer, which is, as we could now well see, " on the edge of the valley of Arnon," that Aroer of which Mesha, king of Moab, had engraved upon his stone : " I built Aroer, and made the highway by the Arnon." And we walked over to the lip of the gulf and looked along it, and climbed some distance down it, and sat down there.

It is idle to compare phenomena like the wadi Mojib and the wadi Hasa and the Grand Canyon at Colorado in terms of figures, and say this is the most impressive because it is the deepest and the broadest. Each is a unique experience, compounded out of its own elements of colour and proportion. There is, however, the element of the spiritual significance one rather than another may hold for the onlooker.

In terms of size Mojib is impressive enough. Here at Aroer the distance between the tops is nearly three miles and the height some two thousand feet. On the east a hundred gorges cleave the blunt mountains and meet upon two central rivers of air which encompass a long-backed isolated hill that careers along the bed of Mojib like the hull of a vast ship. Westward the aery tide like a myriad-tinted glacier slides along towards the Dead Sea. Far down twinkles interruptedly the silver thread of the torrent, the " sounding " torrent (as the Hebrew word announces) so soundless here, eased over with the dark green of laurel and arbutus and the paler green of oleander. Along the less steep slopes hurry currents of springtime flowers, the yellow daisies, marigolds and purple irises, and the guttering red anemones. But for the most part the slopes are too grim for flowers, great cliffs of limestone, sharp swirls of gravel and loam.

But Mojib is more than that ; it is Arnon, the limit of the desert wanderings of Israel. On this side here, Israel began her destiny. The original plan was amplified. Not only west of Jordan, but east of Jordan, too, Israel would pitch her tents. " And unto the Reubenites and unto the Gadites I gave from Gilead even unto the valley of the Arnon, the middle of the valley, and the border thereof," said the Lord. And they would be gone thence sooner than the rest of Israel would be gone from the lands west of Jordan, leaving less trace, leaving no trace at all, save in a Book. But that is enough, though one might say that the fragile texture of the stoutest book is poor stuff compared with the incised granite of a Rameses. To which the reply might be made, that the writing is written not merely on pages of paper but on the hearts and brains of men, a more durable stuff than granite; and when that ceases to endure, granite and thistledown are all one to us.

So we sat there, looking down into the wadi Mojib, while certain sounds separated upon the ear, the hoarse cry of ravens, a donkey braying somewhere far off, the bleat of cropping herds, the breathless song-whisper of a small bird and his mate flickering from boulder to boulder. Beside us was an ancient trough, where once, we were certain, a Moabite soldier had come down from the fort above to fill his drinking-gourd, when it had rained and there was water there. There was only an anemone now, lipping the dry edge.

And I recalled, leaning my back against the warm stone, the tale I had once heard of the miracle at Arnon. Now this valley, the tale said, was made by two great mountains, whose summits came so close together that a man on one could converse with a man on the other. But the depth between them was such that to descend and cross the valley and ascend again was a journey of seven miles. And when the host came to the southward bank, they were sore afraid, for they well knew that their enemy, the Amorites, awaited them in myriads, though not even a single one was visible anywhere. " For they are hidden in the deep woods by the waterside," the scouts said, " and they wait in the countless caverns in the hillside to sally forth and undo us."

And a sound of weeping went up from Israel, and lo, there was a miracle not less than the splitting in sunder of the Red Sea. For it happened that the caverns were all on the south-ward steep of the valley, and on the northward side were not caverns but great projections of rock of the same size as those caverns, each to each. And the two mountains came together, so that Israel marched over as it were upon level ground, and in those caverns the enemy were ground to powder by the rocks that fitted there as the hand fits the gauntlet.

And there was singing and dancing to the timbrels, and the host marched forward and went to Dibon-gad and scored there a further great victory.

It was just after we had eaten our lunch in a small crater brimming with marigolds that once more we heard the thud of approaching hooves.

" Oh, Lord ! " I said. " The Beni Sakhr are on the war-path once again ! We're the last of the Reubenites ! They don't want us ! "

But it was not a Bedu in a flowing *abba*. It was a legionary in trim khaki from the police-post at Dhibân.

He looked enormously relieved to see we were unharmed. They had been keeping a look-out for us all day, and at last had sent out scouts to find us.

" It's nice to know somebody loves us ! " said Jim.

Yes, it was a comforting sensation. The events of the day, and the amount of ground we had covered, gave us for the first time some adequate idea of the grand job of policing the Legion does.

" To Dhibân, yes ? " asked the young man, though, of course, there was no real asking about it. " Drink tea ? "

We would be delighted to drink tea at Dhibân. He was a strapping young man, about twenty-two years old. He had joined at the age of seventeen. He hoped to be an *umbasha* some day.

We got into the car and drove north and a little east. They seemed to have planted barley along the whole length of the track, at least it was barley rather than track that was visible to the naked eye. The Roman road, that was doubtless Mesha's old road rebuilt, comes up from the wadi a little further to the west.

Some twenty minutes later the ruins of the town were spread out before us, hazily extending over two hills, surrounded by a wall of Roman, or perhaps Byzantine, masonry.

I tried to find out from the young man where the Mesha stele had been found. He could not tell us that, but he knew a little more about Um-er-Rasâs, which is a city of the Beni Israel, he said. He could also tell us the name of a new white flower, a close-cropping thing, that had spread out like washing over all the ruins. *Kibsi*, he called it. It was almost alarming, the way you could shut your eyes, then open them again, then see a new flower blooming all over the place. The flower-symphony was massing all its effects and all its instruments.

A Bedu had made himself a home out of an intact arched room in a narrow gully we crossed. As we passed, his front door swung open. It was cunningly put together out of pale-blue-painted kerosene tins. He had an eye for colour and for flowers. When we set out on our journey again, he had plucked a gay posy for us. Above the gully a donkey brayed excitedly, as if there had not been so much company in these parts since the battles.

The rest of the staff was gathered at the door of the police-post. There was generally such an air of relief at our appearance, that no one remembered to take any interest in anybody's racial origin. A busy telephoning got under way. No, they were all right. They had not had their throats slit. Not yet.

Tea? It would be fine to have tea. We stroked the tabby-cat asleep on the office-table. We deplored the deed of a murderer whose photograph was pasted on the wall, and pointed out, amid great laughter, the astonishing resemblance to Jim. We received pocket-lighters and only with great difficulty managed to scrape up sufficient revolving-pencils to go round in return.

So far as revolving-pencils is concerned, it was a good thing, we felt, we were making for Madeba, and that Mount Nebo is not far from Madeba.

"Good-bye!" we said. "Good-bye!" slapping each other's backs. They were stout fellows. The donkey brayed in unmitigated grief to see us be going again. The Bedu ran beside the car and handed us our posy with some urgency, as if it was Mesha, King of Moab, had sent it after us.

On the road northward from Dhibân, there are several Roman milestones left exactly where the Roman road-builder put them up, to lighten, or depress, the hearts of the marching legionnaires. At one place five or six had been collected together. They leaned inward towards each other and had the air of talking things over. What's happened to the Fifth Legion? It's about sixteen hundred years overdue now. What on earth will Nerva Germanicus say? (His name was incised sharp and clear on one of the milestones.)

On both sides of the road the countryside is heaped up with ruins which bear names easily identifiable with place-names familiar to us both in the Mosaic story and in the later books of the Bible. If the Mosaic identifications are ingenious, they are not the less likely for that. The later ones are mostly quite definite. The Biblical writers knew the country well. Did not their kinsfolk Reuben and Gad elect to stay there, and did they not inhabit it for centuries?

I think the richest and greenest region we had come upon since we left Egypt was the wadi Waleh, some ten kilometres north of Dhibân. Later it takes the name of Heidan where it makes for its confluence with Mojib, being one of its major tributaries. Earlier its name is Themed, and in that earlier region the scholars have placed the well of Beer, and Mattanah the next station after it.

The water in the wadi Waleh needed no cozening of song or sceptre, as the water of the Beer in the wadi Themed did. Or perhaps they had done their work so well that the fullness of it endures to this day. The stream cascaded clear and cold through thickets of reed and oleander, laurel and willow-herb. The smell of it was English. Opening your eyes on the wild stock and the ragged robin, the flags and the mallows, you might have said: a stream in Somerset. Birds flew between the spires of the reeds, bending them slightly as they flew. Fish slid between the stones. In the still margins of the water, great bullfrogs sat and bellowed lustily.

As we rose zigzagging northwards out of the wadi, we looked back to see vast banks of green sward on different levels, where flocks of sheep and goats browsed, and she-camels moved about very statelily, leading their leggy young, and donkeys skipped about inconsequently, and small red cows went about, jingling their bells.

What wonder at all is it, you asked yourself, that the children of Reuben and Gad elected to stay here, concerning whom it is written: " Now the children of Reuben and the children of Gad had a very great multitude of cattle: and when they saw the land of Jazer, and the land of Gilead, that, behold, the place was a place for cattle . . . they came and spake with Moses . . . and they said: If we have found grace in thy sight, let this land be given unto thy servants for a possession; bring us not over Jordan." No wonder they elected to stay here, with all their cattle, though not without first giving a gauge to the Prophet of Israel: " If ye will arm yourselves to go before the Lord to the war, and every armed man of you will pass over Jordan before the Lord, until he hath driven out his enemies from before him, and the land be subdued before the Lord: then afterward ye shall return . . . and this land shall be unto you for a possession before the Lord."

And it was so, and they inherited this land, leaving in the place-names which now are attached to a heap of five stones or fifty, the ineradicable traces of the Israelitic sojourn.

So at last we sighted the city of Madeba, that looks down from its low hill over the undulating plain, the Madeba they had laid waste in their swift sequence of victories:

> . . . Heshbon is perished even unto Dibon,
> And we have laid waste even unto Nophah,
> Which reacheth unto Medeba.

As we came nearer, the declining sun dusted all the slopes

with a sort of coppery-golden powder, over a dark red soil. The air was full of the sound of bells. Some were ringing on the collars of moving beasts, with a gentle flurry of sound, that might be interrupted as the creature paused to nibble a juicy stalk, then resumed with a quick scatter of notes as it lifted its head again. Others were louder, quite regular, more insistent, like the bells of schools and churches.

They were the bells of both, in fact. As the heart of the weltering ruin of ancient city upon city, a city of churches and missions and schools has established itself, Roman Catholic, Greek Orthodox, American Protestant. The present Madeba goes back no further than 1880, when the Christian Arabs of Kerak, finding their surroundings uncongenial, obtained permission from the Turkish authorities to emigrate en masse to the desolate hillside and start life afresh. The place must have looked not unlike that Um er-Rasâs we had seen earlier that day, and the success of the move would seem to indicate that the same fortune might attend the resettlement of many another derelict city in Transjordan, of which the only citizens now are the owl and the lizard.

It took us some time to find the police-post among the complex of ancient ruin and modern church-foundation; and we had the impression that the spiritual needs of the population, which can hardly be more than two or three thousand, must be unusually well attended to. The police-post, being already assured we were alive, took us across the road without more ado, to a one-storey green-painted wooden bungalow, which looked as if it had been transported in one piece from some Middle Western farming city. And in a sense it had. It belonged to a Mr. Ward, a missionary from the Christian Missionary Alliance of America, who extended to us the warmest hospitality. There, in the midst of the high places of Moab, we sat down to a meal so blissfully American, there were moments I thought myself dreaming, and wondered whether it would be in Des Moines, Iowa, or Oshkosh, Wisconsin, I would awake again. There was clam chowder, or it tasted like that in a miracle of synthesis; also crackers to eat with it. There was a leg of mutton with apple-sauce and red currant jam. There was a salad with a Thousand Islands dressing. And there was lemon cream pie.

Our host and his wife were of a winning earnestness and kindness, but it was not easy to overcome the strangeness of it all. Two Arabs came in after dinner and took coffee with us, but did not succeed in swinging Madeba back into the orbit of Moab again. One was a Muslim, a sardonic gentleman. The other was a Christian, the local doctor, a pleasant gentleman. But the second was addressed as " Doc." The first was presented as " the sheriff." When I went to bed and took my things off, I found myself looking round for a Servidor, to hang them in.

Early next morning we went round the small town, and later in the day to Hesbân, or Heshbon, as it is simpler to call it. For the evening of that same day, the pleasant doctor arranged to accompany us to the hill-tops where Balaam stood, seeking to utter curses, and only blessings came.

Of the early town of Madeba nothing but potsherds remain, the town that Moses captured from Sihon, King of the Amorites, and razed to the ground; the town that Reuben and Gad built in its place and Mesha razed to the ground; the town that Israel recaptured under Jehoshaphat, and the Moabites possessed again in the time of Isaiah, till the Assyrians came, and did as all those hosts had done before them. And thereafter the Nabataeans came, and Du-shara succeeded Chemosh and Jehovah; then the Romans came, and Astarte followed Du-shara. Then at last the Cross came, and the Crescent later. But the extant relics of early buildings in Madeba are mostly of the early Christian churches, of a time, somewhere between the fifth and sixth centuries, when a good school of mosaic-makers flourished here among the church-builders of Madeba. They were not among the great masters of their craft, but one of their works, or rather the fragment of it that still survives, was of extreme interest to us, that had followed so far and deviously in the steps of Moses, Lawgiver and Conqueror. This was the famous

KERAK CASTLE

Mosaic Map of Madeba, which even in its present greatly diminished state, remains one of the most important documents in the science of palestinology. The map covered a good deal of the floor area of one of those early churches, and extended so far, it is reported, as to include on the east Babylon, and on the west, Rome. In 1896, a new church was built on the site of the old one, and the children of the cement-mixers and brick-layers were given the free run of those jolly little cubes of stones, till nine-tenths of the mosaic was wiped out. The surviving tenth is now well protected by a wooden balustrade and a collection of floor-boards, which are solemnly removed for the stranger, in the presence of the assembled township, and after a great ringing of bells, which would seem to be an indispensable element in any act of worship or study in Madeba.

The place-names in the map are given in Greek, their dominant tradition is rendered in the form of a graphic symbol. I say that the map was of special interest to us because, down in the Arabah, at a place corresponding exactly with that Khirbet Feinân we had been at such pains to visit, the mosaic-makers had recorded the existence of a town they called Phaenon. Alongside this Phaenon they had composed the image of a rod encompassed by a serpent, the rod of Moses and the bronze serpent he had set up that the plague of serpents might be cast out. It did not prove beyond the possibility of doubt that that old city of mines and martyrdoms stood where the Israelites had encamped at Punon. But it proved that the tradition went back for at least fifteen hundred years, a long time before Musil and his young guide, Abdullah Akasheh.

Heshbon is some seven or eight miles north of Madeba on that same Roman-Nabataean-Moabite road northward to Amman, half way between the two rivers; well-chosen, therefore, by Sihon, king of the Amorites, to be capital of the country he had lately wrested from Moab. But whether Heshbon fell before Madeba to the onslaught of the Israelites,

Zc

or Madeba before Heshbon, cannot be established. It is written that Moses " sent messengers out of the wilderness of Kedemoth unto Sihon, King of Heshbon . . . but Sihon would not let us pass by him . . . and came out against us, he and all his people, unto battle at Jahaz." Now Kedemoth, a word which does not occur elsewhere, means the " east parts," and seeing that it is expressly spoken of as " the wilderness," it would seem that Moses would be over on the east side of the plateau, when he sent forth his messengers, having gone that way to turn the upper reaches of the Arnon. Jahaz, however, where the decisive battle took place, is implied in the Mesha stele to be near Dibon, the first encampment cited in the Numbers itinerary after Iyim, on the border of Moab. They are beyond disentanglement, these encampments and battle-grounds. It can only be said: drawn to fulfil his people's doom, Moses came this way, to Madeba, to Heshbon, and came back again and died close by, on the summit of Mount Nebo.

I must confess that I felt a certain amount of trepidation as we approached the ruins of Heshbon, stretched out upon the ridge of its long hill. The Wards had warned us against the people who had taken possession of the ruins, and had possession of the adjacent lands.

" They will chase you out with stones," they had foretold lugubriously, with something of the accent of Isaiah foretelling woe in that same town: " On the tops of their houses, and in their streets, every one shall howl. . . . And Heshbon shall cry, and Elealeh: their voice shall be heard even unto Jahaz."

" They will chase you out with stones," they had said. " If nothing worse."

I thought it would be a pity if something worse happened. We had got away safely from Um er-Rasâs, and that was away over towards the Kedemoth, the eastern parts of the wilderness. It would be sad if something worse happened so near Peake Pasha in Amman and journey's end in Nebo.

But I should say at once the people of Heshbon were as friendly as any we had met. I think they took a fancy to us, because one of us picked up all the pieces of pottery in sight, another plucked all the flowers in sight, the third stroked the noses of all the animals in sight. I suppose there had been a lot of digging for treasure lately, for none of the sites visited by us was so richly littered with scraps of ancient pottery. There has been more digging by the westerners among the Transjordan ruins during the last few years than in the previous two thousand, and the rumour has gone about that it is treasure of gold coins and jewels they are digging for. Every ruin has its own treasure, guarded by some dreadful *djinn*, a black snake or a large negro, or whatever it might be. If you can but utter that word, the *djinn* must clothe himself with flesh; is then at your mercy. You can slay it. The treasure is yours. They think in these parts that the natives of Tripoli have an especial talent for this sort of magic. Perhaps, because we came from even further west than Tripoli, they thought us even more potent.

At all events, they saw me lift one potsherd and another, and study it and drop it again, and on one or two occasions put it in my pocket. The consequence was that the whole village delightedly gathered potsherds for us, which we were compelled to stuff into our pockets lest we hurt their feelings, and before we had ended, our progress among the fallen pillars and empty cisterns was very weighty. The trophies included the hoop of a bucket and the top of a petrol-tin, which may have been offerings in the way of irony, for the donor had been to Venezuela; but we accepted them with the same dignified pleasure as we accepted the fragments of Roman glaze or rouletted sigillata ware. It seemed, at all events, a pleasanter sort of discomfort than to be chased from Heshbon with stones.

I admit there was a moment of doubt when three brawny young men came charging up from some far-off invisible field, brandishing knives, and hallooing for all they were worth. Their shirts were tucked up inside their belts, revealing

their drawers, and a sort of Russian knee-boots they were
wearing. Both drawers and knee-boots were drenched, as
it seemed, in blood, as if they had just been doing a dance
on a few pulped infidel bodies, and were quite ready to do
another one. They looked very much, in fact, as if they had
just stepped out of the corps de ballet of some very much more
sanguinary *Prince Igor*. I suppose it was those Russian boots.

But their intentions were not at all unfriendly. They had
been pounding ochre and wet sand together, to make a paste
to mark their cattle with their family and tribal signs. (Perhaps that was why the soil looked so lurid, there was so much
ochre about.) They had come to join the fun. They wanted
to collect potsherds for us, too. But we were already over-
weighted with potsherds. And Lucas was plucking flowers.
So everyone set to work and stuffed our arms with posies.

No, it was not stones they flung at us in Heshbon, but
flowers. I think that our host from Madeba spoke of the
stone-throwing of Heshbon out of direct experience, an idea
that took firmer hold of me when I repeated to him the
dictum of our host in Kerak.

"There are missionaries in these parts," I said, "who
think that five generations is time enough to redeem a soul from
Islam. Do you, too, think that time enough? Or too much?"

"And what did the Lord say unto Satan?" the reply was,
the eye going dark, and the mouth grim. "'Is not this a
brand plucked out of the fire?' And what will remain of a
brand, brother, if you leave it in the fire for five generations?"

His fervour was not of the waiting sort, neither for a day,
nor for an hour. He had undergone for his faith dangers
far more summary than to be attacked with stones. I think
both those missionaries are the stuff of which martyrs are
made, but one would die singing a hymn in a loud voice, and
the other would die seeking to confute his executioner with
a piece of delicate casuistry.

The history of Heshbon is similar to the history of Madeba,
excepting for the recent episode which has made a Christian

town of Madeba again, as both were in the Byzantine days. But Heshbon sounds lyrical and lovely on the ear, as no other place does in the whole land. Why? You ask, and in the same moment remember. Of course. There was a great king once, Solomon was his name. He loved a shepherd maiden, a Shulamite, and sought to win her with his wealth. He wooed her with songs also, singing: " Thy neck is as a tower of ivory; thine eyes like the fishpools in Heshbon, by the gate of Bath-rabbim." But he could not win her. She went back to Shulem again, to her own lover, a shepherd lad.

No one can tell you now where the gate of Bath-rabbim was, in the circuit of the walls of Heshbon. But the fishpools are there to this day, great basins hollowed out in the rock two and a half thousand years ago. They have long been bone-dry now. It is a long time since the fish dawdled in the stored waters, and the girls of Heshbon stood on the margins feeding them with crumbs.

§ 4

It was at this stage of the Mosaic story, as we had worked it out, that the strange episode of Balak and Balaam occurred.

Balak, the King of Moab, " being sore afraid of the people, because they were many," sent messengers to Balaam the prophet, requesting him to come and curse them, that they might smite them, that they might drive them out of the land. And Balaam consulted the Lord, and the Lord said: " Thou shalt not go with them; thou shalt not curse the people, for they are blest." So he bade the messengers of Balak be gone, he would not curse the people of Israel. But they came again, with richer inducements, and once more Balaam consulted the Lord, who said: " Rise up, go with them; but only the word which I speak unto thee, that shalt thou do."

So Balaam saddled his ass, and went with the princes of Moab.

Now, we are told that it was in a place called Pethor, which was by the River, that Balaam lived at that time; the River

they cannot but have heard of these proceedings with jubila-
tion, and perhaps, without excessive animosity. For Balaam
had taken a lot of persuading to come to Nebo, and he had
made it quite clear he would only be able to utter the words
the Lord put into his mouth. Moreover, after the episode of
the ass, he had pointed out with some justice he had not known
the angel of the Lord stood in his way, and was entirely
disposed to go back where he came from.

However, his heart seems later to have hardened against
Israel, for we read of him as joining with the kings of Midian,
and being slain with the sword along with the rest of them.
But even that does not quite seem to explain the Talmud's
invincible hatred for him. Not only does it make Balaam the
villain of the whole Pharaoh story, but it insists that he was
none other than that Aramaean Laban who had sought to
compass the death of Jacob. It was he who had instigated
Amalek to attack Israel on the journey through Sinai. It
was he who now on Nebo sought to curse Israel. It was he
who induced Israel to commit whoredom with the daughters
of Moab.

So the Talmudic writers arranged an adequate end for him.
Seeking to escape by sorcery his doom in the plains of Moab,
he flew high into the air, passing through five different layers
into a thick darkness; but fortunately the general Phinehas
knew a spell wherewith to cleave it, and Balaam came hurtling down again on to the plains of Moab. But even yet, his
cunning managed to blunt the edge of every weapon with
which it was sought to despatch him; till once again Phinehas
bethought himself of an arch-sword in his armoury, whereon
was engraved on each side a serpent, and these words under
the serpent: " Slay him with that whereto he belongs—
through this he will die."

And so he was slain at last. But even now the Talmudists
will not give him peace. His body was not buried, and his
bones rotted, and from that rottenness sprang seven sorts of
serpent, the most noxious of all their kind; even the worms
that fed on him waxed fat and became serpents. And the

sorcerer that came after Balaam took these serpents and with
their heads, their bodies, their tails, wove their three different
sorts of enchantment. And one of the questions that the
Queen of Sheba asked Solomon was regarding these enchantments: " What are those three words, by which these three
enchantments may be withstood, Solomon? "

And Solomon answered her forthwith, being so wise a king.

Along a line extending unevenly for some two miles at about
twice that distance from the Madeba-Heshbon track, the
main plateau dips a little and rises again in a flinty limestone
ridge. Its general line is north to south, though it sends out
a short spur westward, to a point called Jebel Siaghah. On
that side the ridge falls sharply in a complex of wadis towards
the northern end of the Dead Sea over against Jericho. It
rises into several distinct summits, the two most important of
which are marked on the map as Jebel en Neba, the " mountain's back," and Jebel Siaghah. Jebel en Neba is also the
common name for the whole ridge. No doubt has ever been
entertained that this Jebel en Neba is the Mount Nebo of
the Scriptures, called also Mount Pisgah. Even if Nebo-
Pisgah had not been named, and its position over against
Jericho specified, it would have been clear that it could not
have been elsewhere that Balaam went, and Moses after him.
There were " the high places of Baal," whence Balaam saw
the utmost part of the people. The debris of them, and of
high places that go back for half an æon before that, are there
to this day. There is the " field of Zophim," of " the
watchers," whither Balaam climbed a second time, his first
utterance having so gravely displeased Balak. The Zophim
still endure in the name of a valley north-east of Nebo,
" Safa," a singular form of that same word. It is only from
the top of Nebo that Moses could have had some such vision
as the text describes. There it was that the Lord buried him,
" in the valley in the land of Moab over against Beth-peor,"
in a sepulchre unknown to this day, the whole mountain
being his headstone, and the sparse grass his winding-sheet.

The boy took a cigarette. Then Dr. Zahran walked over to the man. "I am doctor, and Arab!" he said. "From Madeba! Why do you look so strange?" He managed to get the better of the man's suspicions. The face softened. "Call the other one over! My friends wish to hear him sing."

"Saleh!" the man called. "Saleh!" the small boy followed. Then the voice of some invisible goatherd joined in, "Saleh! Saleh!" The rocks echoed the cry. At last he came over. He was a handsome lad, in his white headdress bound with black ropes, his blue and white striped *abba*, his great brown sheep's pelt slung over his shoulders. The smaller boy wore a cloth half-jacket, a *bamir*; he had picked up an old pair of boots somewhere several sizes too large for him. His flute was about twelve inches long, with six small stops cut in it, and a larger one. It seemed to have been cut quite recently. Both had long, curved daggers at their belts, in brass sheaths embossed with coloured stones.

They sang two songs for us. One was addressed to Al Kata, the sand-grouse.

> *Oh fast-flying Kata,*
> *Is there one amongst you,*
> *Who will lend me his wings,*
> *So that I may fly to her I love?*

The other seemed to be a warning sung by the dwellers in the west, the sown or half-sown land, to the strangers from the east, the high desert.

> *You who are riding on a camel,*
> *Do not come to the place which is ploughed land.*
> *The grazing place is in the East,*
> *In the place which is not ploughed.*

I suppose song can hardly be reduced to simpler elements than that. It was as if the wind itself had found words, or the reed spoke, without human lips on the mouthpiece.

"Ask them," I said, "if they know any song about the Nebi Musa?"

The boys shook their heads. Saleh kept his eyes on the ground. His self-consciousness was returning. It suddenly got the better of him, and he dived back among the fleeces of his flock.

" They know no songs about Nebi Musa," said Dr. Zahran. " They say they did not know there was any Nebi Musa."

" No, no! " I exclaimed. " That can't be true? "

He looked at me curiously.

" Why not? "

" You remember it is written: ' no man knoweth of his sepulchre unto this day'? It would be too ironical, if the very shepherds who walk on the roof of it, don't even know his name. I can't let myself believe it! "

" They are very primitive, like five thousand years ago. Perhaps they hardly hear yet there was a Nebi called Nebi Mohammed."

" Please. Will you ask the older man? "

He asked him. The older man shook his head. There was a note of querulousness in his voice as he replied.

" He also say he has heard of no Nebi Musa. He ask why should he hear of strange Nebis, has he not enough to do with his own sheep and goats? " He paused, then he resumed in a different tone. " Of course what he say is not true at all. He knows well about Nebi Musa. Perhaps he has himself been over to the tomb of Nebi Musa over there, on the Palestine side. You know the Muslims in these parts, they say he do not die here on this side of the Jordan. They say he die there, in the hills near Jericho, looking over the Dead Sea? And the angels make him a tomb, the outside white, the inside black. And the people make a big celebration there one whole week. You know of it? "

" I do," I said. " I was in Jerusalem one Easter, when the procession was starting off for Nebi Musa. I thought it very strange. The Bible is so very clear on the matter."

He shrugged his shoulders.

" So it is. He know, that older one. He think it better to say no."

" Why? "

" No is always safer than yes. Is not that true? Probably he think there is much treasure here. The Franciscans dig up a church here. He thinks for treasure. Other people ask can they dig here. He thinks for treasure. So he thinks he will dig himself some day. He will find the Word, the abracadabra, and he will have it all for himself. *Ma es salaam!* " he called out to the retreating goatherd. He turned to us again. " Where shall we go now? The little museum the Franciscans make of the things they dig up? Or over there, straight forward to Mount Siaghah, where Moses stood and looked all round before he died? "

" If we go there, let it be the last thing. Yes, of course we will go there. But I should like to feel Balaam has been up the mountain and gone down again. Moses is alive still. He's out there in Bashan, making for Edrei. Let's go to the high places of Baal first."

So we moved southward along a lesser ridge running parallel with the slightly higher sky-line. The hills were folded in stony hollows. You could hardly hear the bells of the herds at all, they were so far off, or they were not moving. We climbed again and came out upon a broad, levelled place. It was not easy to walk over, there was such a confusion of stones. Then you saw that the stones lay there in no confusion. They were arranged. Here they were collected in cairns, there they were spread in a great circle, there they lay in parallel lines as if to mark the precincts of a shrine.

" Do you see," said Dr. Zahran, " there is a track there, coming up from further south? "

" Yes. It looks as old as the stones."

" It was made specially for Emir Abdullah when he came here a few years ago, so he should camp here a few days. Look! " He stooped and picked up a rusty long-handled roasting implement. " In this the road-makers roast their coffee."

" What did he come up here for? "

" Perhaps those kings you talk of also come before him—

Balaam, and Sihon, and Og. What he should come for? Perhaps to pray. Perhaps to look over to Palestine, and wonder shall he be king there some day." He stopped. "You hear a foot? Yes, someone is coming."

We turned to the sound of a faint scrabbling of stones coming up the slope from the west. It sounded like an animal approaching, but it was not, we soon saw. It was an old man, his clothes hanging in loose tatters. As soon as he saw us, he made as if to go back again where he came from.

" Where are you going, Arab? " Dr. Zahran called reassuringly. " We're friends! Come closer! "

He tottered toward us, shaking in all his limbs. Within two or three yards of us, he came alongside one of the stone cairns. He stopped and picked up a stone. Then he added it to the cairn, and turned, facing westward a moment. Then he turned again and came up to us.

" You know why he do that? " Dr. Zahran whispered.

" No. Why? "

" Wait, I ask him. You will hear."

We heard the name of the Nebi Musa on the old man's lips. He pointed far off across the valley. With the other hand he rubbed his lumbago, or rheumatism, or whatever it might be.

" You see? He cannot go himself to the Nebi Musa, so he puts a stone on the heap. Perhaps it will do good. Last month, he did it for his son. His son got up again next day, well and strong. Very bad for my business," smiled Dr. Zahran wryly. " How you say, not fair competition."

" Ask him has he heard tales of Nebi Musa in these parts. He is so old, he almost goes back himself to Nebi Musa's day."

Some words passed between them. The old man shook his head. No, he had heard no tale of Nebi Musa.

" Just an old miracle-worker on the wrong side of the Jordan. Nothing left of him but that." I sighed.

But the old man was speaking again. He had placed his skinny hand on Dr. Zahran's forearm and was speaking with some urgency.

" Yes, yes, he remembers something. It comes back to him.
You see, he is so old. His brain not working quickly."

And this is what the old man remembered—on the top of
Mount Nebo, the tale of a dream, and of another dream. It
was not himself that had dreamed them, but an old man of
his tribe, a sheikh of the Ghneimat. And this sheikh being sick
in the back as our friend himself was now, was minded to go
over to the tomb of Nebi Musa, beyond Lot's Sea there, over
in Al Qoods. And he was going thither the next day, or the
day after. And in the afternoon, while he lay asleep in the
heat of the day, a holy one appeared and said to him :

" Old man, what is this thou sayest thou art minded to go
across to Al Qoods to cure thy sickness at the tomb of the
Nebi Musa? It is on this very mountain where thou now
sleepest he is buried, in a valley I will show thee."

And he rose, and the holy one took him to a valley, and
there was a whole multitude gathered there, for there was the
tomb of the Nebi Musa, there, and not in the other land across
the river. And in that instant the sheikh awoke, and went to
that valley, which he remembered clearly from his dream.
The valley he found with no trouble at all; but the exact spot
where the tomb was he could not find again.

" He showed me, too, that valley," the old man said. " It
is there southward . . ." Then he stopped, and changed the
subject hurriedly, looking at us cunningly out of the corner of
his eyes. " And once again that sheikh went to that valley,
shortly before he died, and he lay down there and dreamed a
dream. And in that dream it was not the tomb of the Nebi
Musa he saw, but the Nebi Musa himself, lying as if he still
lived, but sleeping. And above his head, right and left of him
were two Books, and in his hand a great quill, an eagle's
feather, wherewith he had written them.

" So he told me with his own mouth," the old man said,
" and died soon after. It is a long time ago, a hundred years
ago. I was only a boy then. And he told me and Ahmed,
my cousin : ' Seek and ye will find,' he said. ' For there is
surely much treasure where the Nebi lies.' And often when

WADI MOJIB

we were young, we would go and dig there, having a spade hidden away where no one knew. But after we had raised the spade three times, we could not lift it from the ground again. It was like a tree with roots. The magic had fallen upon it.

" It is a hundred years ago," the old man repeated. " I was only a boy then." He looked at us with a sudden flicker of hatred in his eyes, as if it were we who had stolen his boyhood from him.

Then his voice became very honied. " I could show the strangers that valley," he said, and, as he spoke, cupped the palms of his hands. " Perhaps they bear the Word with them. And then they can bring a spade. And for them the spade will not be heavy. Yes, would the strangers wish to see that valley? "

" Would you wish to see that valley? " Dr. Zahran repeated.

" Please," I said, " let us go along to the summit of Mount Siaghah now, while there is still light."

I could not bring myself to explain why I felt it would be so perverse and impious to go with that old man.

So we went along the lower crests again till we came to Jebel en Neba, and walked along the ridge between Jebel en Neba to the further top westward, which is called Mount Siaghah. Here was the platform, it is said, where Moses stood, and the Lord showed him all the lands to be possessed of the children of the host of Israel, all their lands to the hinder sea; and the south, and the plain of the valley of Jericho, the city of palm-trees, under Zoar. It was not possible that with the body's eye he saw *all* those lands, though he might see much of some, and some of all; or that he saw the hinder sea, the Mediterranean, for the hills of Palestine are between. But it was not only with the body's eye he saw.

At this moment, the middle parts of those Palestine hills were a deep violet, with a red scarf of cloud swathing their summits. In the gulf between, and far below, the Dead Sea

AAC

lay like a sheet of pale green glass. The Jordan lay heavily
on the hazy plain, like a chain of brass loops. Jericho drowsed
among its palm-trees like a scatter of ivory petals shaken
from a pear-tree. The slopes of the wadi on our right hand
just north of us were a deep rose, with a swirl of golden cliffs
along the tops. That is wadi Musa, called also el Hamra, the
red one. Midway in the wadi Musa, the falls of the Ayun
Musa hung like a song, or a thought, transfixed deathlessly
in mid-air. The hills north and south of the wadi Musa, the
hills of Moab and Gilead, were throbbing in a just perceptible
pulse of colour, from lilac to crimson, from crimson to pale
rose.

Slowly the red scarf of cloud swathing the Palestine tops
became grey, the pale green glass of the Dead Sea became
grey glass. The pulse of colour in the Transjordan hills
throbbed more faintly, then died away. Only the falls of the
Ayun Musa did not change, as a song does not, or a thought.

We turned and went eastward again to Jebel en Neba, and
descended towards the spread tents and the folded flocks.

CHAPTER TWELVE

§ 1

FROM Madeba we went next day to Amman. There were hills with ruins on them beside the road, one of them being the ruins of Elealeh, now called El Al, one of those fenced cities with folds for sheep, which the children of Reuben rebuilt for themselves after the conquest of Canaan.

But we could not induce ourselves to be interested in the children of Reuben and their cities. They belonged to the tale that followed the death of Moses, and since we had stood upon Mount Nebo, on the roof of his sepulchre, our imaginations were too worn to go on further journeys. It was true we had gone to Mount Nebo to go about among the places where Balaam had stood prophesying. We had done that, but it was impossible that the memories of the lesser figure should not be submerged in the memories of the greater. We knew that Moses was dead, that our journey was over.

But we did not admit that to each other. We would continue the journey in his footsteps as we had planned it, to Edrei, to the plains of Moab, once again to Nebo. The spirit would be in it no longer, the spirit having been extinguished in a valley in the field of Moab, over against Beth-peor.

So it was on that journey from Madeba to Amman that all the histories were flattened out intervening between Moses and our own day. Only that thing could stir us which was at once a thing of the immediate moment, or a thing older than the host of Israel—a suddenly starting bird, a flower we had not as yet added to our register.

So it was in Amman itself. We wandered about duly and looked at the Greco-Roman theatre and the fragmentary Forum and the Sassanid castle, but remotely, tiredly, as one might look at the châteaux of the Loire, or the brick churches of Stralsund. Yes, our eyes that had looked down on Akaba from the Ras el Negeb and on the carved mountains of Petra and on the lunar remoteness of Selah, were a little tired by now. They would have been quickened by the one monument contemporary with Moses which might have been visible at Amman, the iron bedstead of Og, King of Bashan. They were, in fact, quickened by the spectacle of the immediately contemporary Amman, the Damascus pewter at the ironmongers, the tennis-parties at the house of the Resident, the postcards in the general stores, the strikers and their tyre-slitting implements outside the garages . . . this last most of all, as I will tell shortly. But everything in between lacked lustre to our light-dimmed eyes.

Of course there was no not going to Amman. That was the way to Edrei, to-day called Deraa. It might be the way, later, down to the plains of Moab, perhaps the very way Moses and his host had taken. It would be pleasant to bathe in a great deal of hot water, and order dishes to our liking from a bill of fare. And we had arranged to pick up our letters in Amman.

We found a great many letters waiting for us when we got there, for we had been in the wilds for a long time now. A number were concerned with our journey in general and, more often, Moses in particular. We gathered that some reference to our journey had been made in the Press after our departure. We were interested to find what different types of mind are preoccupied with the Moses theme, a theme which had possessed us for so many months in spirit, mind and body. It is for that reason I propose to quote from a few of these communications, with a minimum of comment.

From a friend in Vienna we learned that Sigmund Freud had been at work on a psycho-analysis of Moses, that, as usual, he was being very secretive about it, but the result of his studies would be presented to the world in a few months. Dr. Freud had established that Moses was an Egyptian noble and not a Jew at all; that he was a supporter of the heretical

Pharaoh Ikhnaton, who tried to introduce a helial monotheism into Egypt in the fourteenth century, B.C., and that he thereon placed himself at the head of the Israelitic Exodus, preaching a sort of Egyptian monotheism, to be cemented by the Egyptian rites of circumcision and dietary taboo. He had, further, established that the Hebrew word for God, Adonai, was derived from Ikhnaton, and that the name, Moses, was an Egyptian word.

The final considerations seemed to belong to the domain of etymology rather than psycho-analysis. We did not feel that, as reported to us, the earlier conclusions were very revolutionary.

A friend enclosed a spiritualist magazine, containing the first article of a study of Moses from that aspect. We acquired the others subsequently. I quote a few passages.

" The Bible is a Spiritualist book, written by Spiritualists for Spiritualists about Spiritualists."

Regarding the miracle of the Burning Bush: "Moses seemed to have been a little startled by the ' flame of fire ' which did not consume the Bush. It may have been his first experience of a psychic phenomenon. . . . When his guide, Yahveh, saw that he was sufficiently intelligent and balanced not to fear but to investigate, Yahveh spoke to him in a perfectly natural way, calling him by his name ' Moses.' The place was probably the site of an ancient sanctuary, the psychic atmosphere of which provided helpful conditions for the psychic phenomena known as materialization and the direct voice."

Regarding the Pillar of Cloud: "By day it was an ectoplasmic cloud which screened off the Israelites from their enemy and also screened off the radiance of Israel's guide."

Regarding the Lawgiving on Sinai: " The Ten Commandments were given to Moses in the ' direct voice ' and were then psychically written down by Yahveh on two tablets of stone. . . . Spiritualists are familiar with these phenomena. They are the phenomena of the séance room. The ' thick cloud ' of ectoplasm was there; the psychic light, ' the fire,' was there;

the trumpet was there, and the ' voice ' of the trumpet was heard."

A lady who stated quite frankly she was an ardent feminist, wrote inquiring whether we would help her to redress one of the wickedest injustices in history. Moses was a woman, not a man. Would we help her to establish that fact? She had herself seen the original documents in which the feminine words, " woman," " she," " her," " hers," had been crossed out and the masculine words, " man," " he," " him," " his," had been written in their place.

A letter was there from a political theorist. It declared that Moses was the first Trades Union Leader; he had been dissatisfied with the rate of pay received and the number of hours per diem worked by the Israelites in Egypt; he had therefore decided to transport the Israelitic working classes to a more progressive area.

A letter had been forwarded from a leading figure in " The True Law Party." It reminded me I had met its author at a party in London. I might remember him, it stated, by the fact that I had insisted on shaking hands with him when he appeared disinclined to do so. He tried not to, he explained, because of the Mosaic laws about touching or being untouched when unclean. The letter accompanied a pamphlet stating the objects of " The True Law Party." My attention was drawn to page twelve of that pamphlet, to the bottom of the page, in which the possibility of the Ark being in Mount Nebo was mooted.

The author had been there looking for it a few weeks earlier, he stated, but he had not been allowed to excavate because the Franciscans have a concession to excavate over the whole mountain. The Franciscans were doing no excavating at the time, because of the strike, he continued, although he found the strike and present troubles were not enough to stop him. He wished I could help him to get a permit to excavate, because it would be a marvellous discovery, he said, and one likely to bring an end to the troubles in Palestine. There was a postscript to the effect that the writer believed that unless I had the enclosed views on Mosaic Law, especially the laws about land, I would find difficulty in following in the steps of Moses whenever Arabs were about.

Here follow a few of the measures promulgated in the Pentateuch, and to be introduced, the True Law Party hopes, into our modern constitution. They are culled from the pamphlet referred to.

" The following crimes are to be punished by death :
 Continued disobedience, etc., of children.
 Smiter of parents.
 Owner of an ox known to gore, which kills anyone.
 Presumptuously disobeying ruling of final court.

" Regarding Sex and Marriage:
 Polygamy to be legal ; but any honeymoon must last a year.
 Certain relations by blood not allowed in same nudist colony.

" Regarding Land and Property:
 It is forbidden to put grapes of a neighbour's vineyard into a vessel.

" Regarding the Four Yearly Festivals:
 Three times a year all males to go to Palestine.

Finally : " Regarding the Resulting Imperial Policy:
 The law commanding that any persons within our gates who worship false gods should be put to death is very necessary in India and colonies where there is heathen worship. An ultimatum to the Hindus to leave their false gods and worship within a year (or less if they can all learn of the ultimatum before a year has passed) ; and then a descent upon those who refused, with death penalties, would clear up the terrible muddle which now exists in India and relieve some of the most terrible suffering any outcast poor people has had to undergo. The English rule would be heartily supported by Mohammedans in India in producing this excellent change, for they are enjoined by their bible, the Koran, to exterminate worshippers of any other than Allah (the one God)."

§ 2

Next morning we duly presented ourselves at the Residency, for it seemed only courteous to hand over, even if belatedly, the letter we had brought with us from London. But we had hardly advanced a step over the threshold of the Resident's ante-room, when the smell of the fish of Akaba came wafting gently towards us.

" Do sit down, won't you," said an official. " The Colonel will only keep you a minute or two."

We sat down. There were a number of mineral specimens in a cabinet against the wall. I wanted to ask about those mineral specimens, for I recognized a good many rocks that had been puzzling us throughout the journey. I did, but later. In between, the water waved, and the fish floated.

" Talking about the fishing-industry in Akaba——" began the official. But indeed, we had *not* been talking about the fishing-industry in Akaba.

" Of course, we knew from the beginning it was all nonsense," continued the official.

" You mean, that we were going to go partners or something with that fellow—what's his name now. . . . Of course it's all nonsense ! " I started hotly.

" Perfectly. We'd had a letter about you from Jerusalem. We knew all about you. But you know how things get about in Transjordan."

" Don't I just ! " I said grimly. " That explains what happened in the hotel this morning ! "

" What happened ? "

" Oh a great bouncing Arab came up to us and said he'd heard we were financiers; would we take shares in the concession he was getting to run the Baths of Herod as a Dead Sea spa. I said all we were interested in was the Nebi Musa. He said the Nebi Musa had bathed in the Baths of Herod. He had a stone to prove it. So had Pharaoh."

" Excuse me," said Lucas. " About that fellow Rolfe. Has he a dog's chance of getting anything going in Akaba? "

" Not a hope! One firm has already sunk ten thousand pounds in it. It's no go. There are too many governments concerned in it, this one, and Palestine, and Saudi Arabia, and Egypt! How on earth are you going to get all those fellows seeing eye to eye? Particularly Saudi Arabia. If they catch fishermen who shouldn't be fishing their waters . . . I've heard say they apply the Shari Law good and hard straight away. I don't vouch for the story."

" The Shari Law? What part of it? "

" Chopping hands off at the wrist. I certainly know they were doing it in Mecca till only a few years ago."

" I should hate to see poor old Rolfe sticking out a pair of stumps where his hands used to be," murmured Lucas.

" He won't get as far as that! " smiled the official.

" No hope at all, eh? "

" Not a hope in ten thousand. Hello! That's the Colonel's bell. The Colonel's ready to see you. Will you go in, please? "

It was a very amiable interview.

It may have been a postsentiment rather than a presentiment, but as I look back on it now, I seem to have known with certainty as we made our way back to the hotel, that we would find Rolfe waiting for us when we got there.

And it was so. A Rolfe does not enter a life and pass out of it before he has somehow woven a design, completed a pattern. There he was, Rolfe of Akaba, sun-tanned, full of life and bustle. He wore a pair of flannel trousers as before, an open-necked shirt, and no hat. His small attaché-case was on the floor beside him. He had just come, just half an hour ago, from Jerusalem. He had only intended to wait another minute or two for us, before dashing off to the Air Force, where he had a date. Immediately after that, he was rushing off to the Residency. Then he'd be back again, and we'd have a few drinks, and a good long yarn.

He lifted his attaché-case, and was making off, when I put my hand on his arm.

" Just one thing," I begged. " Do let us know. How is it going with that fishing business in Akaba? "

" Absolutely O.K. ! " he said. " Got 'em all in my pocket, all of 'em! Signed, sealed, and delivered! We'll be putting up the ice-plant in a week or two from now! Well, so long, chaps! Just a matter of putting a stamp on it! See you soon, chaps! "

We did not see him again.

§ 3

We wandered about the shops for an hour or two that evening, for we find shopping a pleasant thing to do, even when we have not been wandering for some months in shopless deserts. They were attractive shops, too, the jewellers with their beaten silver brooches and bracelets, the greengrocers with their glowing pyramids of Jaffa oranges, the rug-sellers, the ironmongers—above all, the ironmongers, with the domestic utensils they make in Damascus out of some shining alloy of tin and pewter.

But in addition to their normal wares, nearly all the shops were selling picture-postcards. Not merely views of Amman and birthday-greetings. You could get those, too, if you looked round for them. No, it was a rather more bellicose sort of picture-postcard they were selling. In practically all of them one individual occurred, a tall, well set up Arab, with a small moustache and close-cropped hair. In those postcards where they were visible, you saw he had a mouthful of fine white teeth. He usually had his bandolier round his shoulder, often his rifle. Sometimes you saw him mounted, sitting astride an embroidered saddle-bag on a gaily caparisoned mare. Sometimes you saw him taking aim from behind a rock, in what was evidently an ambush. Sometimes you saw him taking the salute, while a whole battalion of Arab soldiers defiled past him, their rifles on their shoulders. Now and again you saw

him relaxed, sitting in high ceremony in a chief's tent on a pile
of rugs.

He was evidently some leader greatly loved in this region;
perhaps his fame went further than that in the Arab world.

It was Jim who asked what the name of the leader might
be. I had not asked. I had an idea I knew his name already.

"That is Fawzi Kawkaji," said the pleasant little man
behind the counter. "Would you like?"

"I would like that one, please," said Jim, and took it, and
placed it, so that it should not get bent, in a book he was
carrying.

That postcard shortly emerges again into this narrative.

It should be explained here that Fawzi Kawkaji is a Syrian,
the leader of a guerrilla band of Iraqis, Druses, Syrians, and
Palestinians, who were giving the British authorities in
Palestine a good deal of trouble at that time. I confess that the
ostentation of those Kawkaji postcards in every other shop-
window of Amman puzzled me. I could not help wondering if
the authorities would have been so complacent, if the postcards displayed a defiling of troops and a firing from ambush,
in a Transjordanian, not a Palestinian, setting.

"I shouldn't look so thoughtful about it," Lucas counselled.
"I'm quite certain that when the Israelites conquered
Canaan, they had to put up with any number of Moabite
Kawkajis."

"Yes, yes," I agreed with a sigh. "As you say, it's all in
the picture."

§ 4

There was another letter we felt it even more imperative
to present, our letter from Sir Ronald Storrs to the ruler of
Transjordan, the Emir Abdullah. It was a little late in the
day to solicit his assistance " to visit hills and valleys trodden
by the Prophet," but we felt our journey would lack a sort of
completeness if that letter were not delivered, a letter which, as

I said earlier, played so integral a part in our journey, as almost to make us a company of four rather than three.

The Emir Abdullah had chosen among the cities of his Emirate to live in Amman, and to make it his capital. It is not known whether his Biblical predecessor, Og, King of Bashan, made Rabbath-Ammon (as the place was called in his day) his capital. But it is quite clear he lived there, for had he not, it is most unlikely his bedstead of iron would have been there, as the third chapter of Deuteronomy reports it was. It does not sound like the sort of furniture a prince carries about with him as he moves about his principality; we hear a good deal, for instance, about the beds Queen Elizabeth slept in, but never that she carried them about, and her bedsteads must have been considerably lighter than the King of Bashan's. The scholars, in fact, state that the bedstead was not a bedstead, and it was not of iron; that those words are better translated " a sarcophagus of basalt." If that is so, it is clear the object would be all the more a permanent fixture.

In presenting ourselves to the Emir Abdullah we hardly hoped he would invite us to inspect what sort of a couch he slept on, whether it was an iron bedstead or a basalt sarcophagus. But was it possible, just faintly possible, that as we were ushered into the audience-chamber, a door might be open and it was the door of his bedroom, and we could satisfy ourselves on the matter? It seemed almost impossible, but we would keep a weather-eye open. And apart from anything else, he was the only living analogue to the princes Moses had met on his journey to the River Jordan. There was no Balaam, King of Moab, any more. There was no Sihon, king of the Amorites, any more. But there was a king, or almost a king, again in Rabbath-Ammon. He had been well acquainted, moreover, with our other conqueror, the Englishman, Lawrence. How worthy a link between the two conquerors in whose steps we had journeyed!

We knew beforehand that the Emir Abdullah was no sort of a match in size with Og, King of Bashan. The Talmudists let themselves go about the size of Og. We learn, for instance, that when Moses, in the grey of a certain morning, set out to invest Edrei, he recoiled with dismay, for it seemed to him that the inhabitants had built up during the night a great new wall to protect it. But as the sun came up, and he looked closer, he saw it was only Og, sitting on the old wall, with his feet touching the ground. He was of a formidable appetite, we are informed, needing not less than a thousand carcases of oxen and a thousand measures of liquid per day. He had teeth, it seems, in proportion. In his earlier years, he had been a servant to Abraham, for he was none other than that Eliezer whom Nimrod had given as a gift to the young patriarch; and it happened that Abraham was one day compelled to shout at his servant for some trespass, and Og started back in fright, and one of his teeth fell from his mouth, and from that tooth Abraham fashioned the bed he always slept in.

His death, as might have been anticipated, was curious. It took place at this same battle of Edrei. So furious was he at the sight of this puny Hebrew that dared to come out to battle against him, that he tore up by the roots a mountain three parasangs high, and, swinging it round his head, marched out to hurl it upon the camp of Israel, and so obliterate it. But even as he did so, the Lord conjured a myriad myriads of ants that perforated the mountain, so that it slipped down from his head about his shoulders. And as he sought to rid himself of this mass of earth and rock, his teeth came out left and right and impaled it, so that he could not move and see. And in that moment Moses took an axe twelve cubits long and leapt ten cubits into the air and hacked at his ankle. So the giant was brought down and died. Truly that body was a large thing, and the bones of it, as we learn from Abba Saul. For once, he tells us, he hunted a stag, and the stag fled before him along the thigh-bone of a dead man, and he pursued the stag for three parasangs along the thigh-bone, and still did not manage to catch it. That thigh-bone was the thigh-bone of the King of Bashan.

Og, it is clear, was a giant. He was the last of the legendary race of giants, the Rephaim, close kinsmen of the Nephilim, if they were not identical with them, who were on the earth " in the beginning," and married the " daughters of men." The ancestry of the Emir Abdullah is almost as legendary, but has the advantage over Og's in that it is carefully documented, being minutely recorded on the great roll of the Prophet's family, and preserved, till lately, at least, in the Sherif's archives in Mecca. He was the second son of the Sherif Hussein, the guardian of the Holy Places in Mecca and Medina; in the direct descent from Mohammed, therefore, by his daughter Fatima, and Hassan her elder son. Bedstead or no bedstead, it would be a great privilege to be received by him.

His palace is an unpretentious stone structure built for the Emir on one of the hills overlooking Amman. It is set back in a small grove of firs and cedars. It is sturdy enough, yet it has a transitional air, like the Emir's own fortunes. He is, after all, a direct descendant of the Prophet. He considers himself more amply than some of the chroniclers do, one of the major architects of the Revolt in the Desert. When Winston Churchill, at that time Colonial Secretary, met him in 1920, he had marched up with a force of zealots from Arabia, and was claiming the complete autonomy of all the Arab countries. He was threatening to march into Syria and drive out the French. It was under such circumstances that the Colonial Secretary suggested making him the Emir of Transjordan, on condition that he accepted the British Mandate. Abdullah held his hand. He has marked time with patience and address ever since. It is already proposed that he should become king of the Greater Transjordan which is to include part of Palestine. He still marks time. He did not have the fire of his brother, Feisal, nor of his associate, Lawrence. But that fire has burned them both out, and Abdullah survives. He has not the iron rigidity of Ibn Saud, but it is the rigid thing that breaks, the supple thing that bends. He will perhaps outlive Ibn Saud. He will not always remain in the stone villa screened by firs and cedars, that looks down on Amman.

We waited a moment or two in an antechamber, spread with pleasant eastern rugs and with a good many low coffee tables standing about. Then a rather cadaverous dignitary appeared, and conducted us into a much more western drawing-room, with lace curtains over the windows and ranged round with straight-backed chairs and intermittent divans upholstered in brown-purple plush. It was the archetypal sheikh's "best room," the room that every sheikh in the sown and half-sown land strives to make for himself. He was sitting in a corner in an armchair, full of smiles and well-being. He wore a brown silk *abba* with silver edging, over a brown *kibr*; at his belt, a dagger in a brightly-jewelled sheath, on his feet a pair of elastic-sided boots. He was much as Lawrence had seen him. "His eyes had a confirmed twinkle; and though only thirty-five, he was putting on flesh. It might be due to too much laughter. Life seemed very merry for Abdullah. He was short, strong, fair-skinned, with a carefully trimmed brown beard, masking his round smooth face and short lips." He had put on a little more flesh since then, and there were a few strands of grey in the brown.

He read the letter from Storrs and, smiling, slapped it with the back of his hand.

"What a beautiful Arabic the man writes," he said. "He is writing a book now, I hear. He should write it in Arabic!" He spoke in Arabic, the dignitary interpreting. It is stated he knows English almost as well, but by abstaining from it, gathers a good deal more than he might if he admitted to it.

He asked about the journey, and had we been well treated. We told him something of our salient adventures, and said that we had been well treated everywhere. Then a not altogether inconsequent train of thought brought the memory of Um er-Rasâs into my mind. I felt I would like to have Um er-Rasâs in the conversation; not because I wanted to complain of our treatment there. Indeed, there was nothing to complain of. But I had some curiosity about the place.

" Does his Highness know Um er-Rasâs? "

There was a moment's shocked silence. I felt certain his Highness had understood the question quite as well as the dignitary. Then the dignitary said, in a somewhat clipped voice: " Please, his Highness knows *everything*."

I was hardly more fortunate on the subject of miracles. I brought up the question of the Burning Bush, and said I had seen a natural phenomenon which bore an astonishing likeness to a bush burning and not being consumed. I think the dignitary misconstrued the remark into an attempted explanation of the original episode on scientific grounds. The scion of the House of Mohammed was rather distressed. He objected to the introduction of Science into the world of Faith. Science deals with the world of the five senses, Faith with the world behind the five senses, and independent of them. Had we not heard of the Professor who had dug up some corn in an old site, and pronounced the corn to be a thousand years older than the Invasion? And then, digging a little further, he had found a layer of sardine-tins? Were not these two thousand years older than the Invasion?

We drank coffee in the emiral white china, neatly touched with a small gold crown. We smoked the emiral rose-tipped cigarettes. We talked about this and that, nothing of moment. I had a feeling I would like this conversation to have led somewhere. His personality and ambitions were, after all, a matter of some moment in the present disposition of Near Eastern affairs; more, for instance, than Og's, King of Bashan. I breathed the name of Lawrence, which was bound up with the fabric of our adventure.

" I hear he has written well," the Emir said, and left the subject at once.

It was clear I was to be treated as the descendant of a line of Jewish scholars, who for that reason proposed to write a book on a great Jewish character. Exactly that, and nothing more.

Which was as it should be, completely in the spirit of all our undertaking. Neither Weizmann nor Mufti, but Moses.

ANEMONES BY DHIBÂN

But it was a little saddening to feel that even though the Emir himself had been made privy to the midnight secret of my Jewish blood, I must still venture hardly beyond the Nabataean epoch in any consideration of the relations between the Jews and their neighbours. We would be leaving Transjordan soon. Why, I would like to have meditated, why, that perpetual, that ominous question: " *Inta yehudi?* " Why? What did it portend?

" And what did the travellers think the most beautiful thing in our country? " suavely asked the Emir.

" Anemones! " Lucas answered promptly, and scored heavily.

Abdullah beamed all over, caressing his jewelled sheath.

" Anemones beautiful, beautiful, beautiful! " he repeated. Then he lowered his voice. " Her cheeks are like anemones on the banks of streams." It seemed like the turtle-dove voice of one that quotes his own verses.

I grew a thought more insistent, thinking that a reference to the Winston Churchill arrangement might lead the way to a consideration of more immediate inquiries and commissions. But the stone dropped into a deep, deep well. I did not hear it fall. And I dropped no more stones.

We did not stay, rather we were not permitted to stay, many minutes more; but during those last few minutes the fun became fast and furious. We told each other funny tales and ghost stories. He told us a particularly good one, though we got it a little tangled, until we induced the Resident to disentangle it for us. It happened in the Emir's house at Mecca, which was next door to the prison. It was a very hot night, so he was sleeping upon the roof; but the uneasy clankings of the chained prisoners and their sleepless groans disturbed him so much that he went down to his bedroom. He usually had someone sleeping in the antechamber, and he took it for granted someone was there that night. He fell asleep, but after a time he was awakened by the sound of the pigeons flapping away out of their dovecot. That disturbed him. Something must be wrong, he thought. He shouted to the attendant in the antechamber. There was no reply. He shouted again. There was no reply. He grew frightened, his scalp tingled. He felt he must do something about it. He screwed up his courage, got up and walked along the passage. At the end of the passage, a small stairway led up to a room where coffee was prepared. He was sure, quite sure, he saw a dim shape appear at the door of the coffee-room. Quite terrified now, his hair standing on end, he climbed the stairway and walked into the room. No one was there. Trained assassins are fleet of foot, and very silent. How came it there was no attendant there? How long had there been no attendant? Still facing the door of the coffee-room, he walked backward, down the small stairway. On the fourth stair, his foot met something. He and the thing uttered a loud cry simultaneously. The thing was the women's cat, he realized, as he slid off into a faint. It had managed to get out of the harem somehow.

We were allowed to leave. It had been a most agreeable interview. But we had got no further, we realized, in the matter of the bedstead of iron. We would have to give it a miss.

§ 5

Jim had not accompanied us on this visit to the Emir Abdullah, preferring to spend his time less pontifically, wandering round the town. When we rejoined him in the hotel, he looked quite put out. It seemed as if something odd had happened to him.

This is what it was.

He had been walking up and down for quite a long time, he said, and was rather tired of it. He was away in the back end of the town somewhere. He pointed vaguely out toward the west. There happened to be a ramshackle little café there, so he went in and sat down, and ordered a cup of coffee. He thought for a moment or two there was nobody in the room with him, and then he saw that a bundle of rags in the corner wasn't really a bundle of rags at all. It was an Arab. A rather dopy Arab, he thought, by the look of him.

Anyhow, he wasn't very interested in that Arab, or in his coffee, either. He doesn't like Arab coffee. All he wanted to do was to ease his legs. He took his book out of his jacket pocket, thinking he might as well read a page or two. But as he removed his book, the postcard he had put in it to keep it straight had fallen out. That postcard, you know, with that fellow, the one that did all the shooting up.

Anyhow, as far as he could make out, that was a sort of a signal or something. At all events, that dopy old Arab in the corner started talking at him nineteen to the dozen. He thought he was talking English, but he wasn't. Even his Arabic was rather funny, for he had practically no teeth, and he was dopy, anyway. But he, Jim, did recognize one or two words, or so he thought. He heard the word " guns " come up several times, and perhaps the word " bullets," but he could not be sure of that. This went on for several minutes, and he got quite hot in the neck. It looked as if the Arab had been expecting someone, and that postcard had mixed things up, somehow.

Well, about five minutes later, another Arab came in, an altogether different type of fellow. Apart from his headcloth he was wearing European dress. He was very natty. This second Arab just looked round sharply for about two seconds, as if he was taking things in. Then he rapped out a couple of words. Something like " Shut up! " and " Get out! " And the first Arab came all over queer, and they both marched out plenty quick, and that was the end of it.

" Funny, wasn't it? " said Jim. " Gave me quite a turn, you know! "

§ 6

We had said good-bye to Jemil not many minutes after our arrival at the Philadelphia Hotel. After being paid off, he had asked us for a *shehada*, which had surprised us somewhat; we had had a feeling that the men of Maan are too dour in their self-esteem to value the recommendation of other townsmen. We were a little sad to see him go off with his little pink blanket over his shoulder, for he had been devoted and intelligent; nothing had been too much for him. I think he felt it a bit, too. But none of us allowed a shade of emotion to soften his features. It would not do to compromise the stern self-discipline of Maan. We saw him sitting on the kerb during the next two or three days, waiting to pick up a passenger for his home town. Then we saw him no more. We were glad he got away before the strike ringed the city with a girdle of nails and broken glass. It would have been painful to see his four tyres fluttering round the steel rim and the crack and dazzle of a bullet-hole through his windscreen.

We had let him go for several reasons. In the first place, his car had had about as much as it could stand. Then we had a feeling we had kept him from his own world long enough; he would not show it, but he would be pleased to be going back. Then we did not know where we ourselves were, how we were to shape this final section of the journey.

There remained only one point now of which we could say definitely: the text states, or at least, implies, that Moses went there. This was Edrei, where " Og the king of Bashan came out against us, he and all his people . . . And we smote him until none was left to him remaining."

We could go to Edrei, then, if the scholars are right in identifying it with the modern Deraa, a strong position on the ravine that forms the southern boundary of the Jebel Hauran, the Druze country. Or we could go a few miles further north, to the ruins still called Edra, a name nearer to the original word . . . a strange place, writes Dr. Smith, " without water, without access, except over rocks and through defiles all but impracticable . . . ruins nearly three miles in circumference, with a strange wild look, rising up in black shattered masses from the midst of a wilderness of black rocks."

Edra seemed the sort of place that would stir us. On the other hand, Deraa is more bound up with the Lawrence saga than any other place on the Hedjaz railway. It was the clue of all his fighting for Damascus, a good place to have them meet for the last time, and go their ways—Moses and Lawrence. That would stir us, too. However, we need not choose between Edra and Deraa. We could combine them.

Unfortunately, there are difficulties about the identification, that need not be analysed at this stage. So much so, that certain scholars tend to place Edrei not at Deraa, but at Zora, near the south-west corner of the Leja, which, however (we are discouragingly told), " helps little."

Still, we were used to difficulties and to taking them in our stride. What was to happen after Edrei-Deraa? As I have said, that is the end of the specific place-names in the Mosaic story. There is one other, it is true, in the following passage: " We took the land out of the hand of the two kings of the Amorites that were beyond Jordan, from the valley of Arnon unto Mount Hermon . . . all the cities of the plain, and all Gilead, and all Bashan, unto Salecah and Edrei, cities of the kingdom of Og in Bashan." But it is not implied there was a battle at Salecah, or that Moses was himself there; it is merely a point to mark a frontier. (The place, incidentally, is identified with the modern Salkhad, some forty miles east-south-east of Deraa.)

After Edrei-Deraa, then, there is no alternative but to make for the plains of Moab, and the last battles against the Midianites. When we got to Deraa—if we got to Deraa—we could at that point decide how to make this stage. It would be good, no doubt, to go down to the Jordan plain, as soon as might be, rather than back along the tops of Gilead; no one knows how far north of the Jericho line the battles in the plain extended. Then, having come down as far as the Jericho country on our side of the Jordan, one thing only remained . . . the ascent to Mount Nebo, however that might be done, should it be done at all.

And then the strike came, the strike I have already mentioned, which Jemil managed to escape, and we did not. It was, in some ways, a happy strike, a strike we are grateful for. It cut a line straight through the speculations of the scholars and our own doubts, as a knife cuts through cheese. It gave a dramatic finality to the last stage of the long journey, uniting round itself, or cutting off brutally, all the loose ends. It reproduced for us, as if it had been specially engineered at great trouble and expense, the exact mood of the Israelites ploughing through danger and ambush to the brink of Jordan.

We had heard vague rumours about a strike almost as soon as we got to Amman. It seemed that the wholesale dealers in petrol had had notice from the combine that controls the commodity in Transjordan to put up the price of petrol. Or perhaps they had done so already. It did not seem to concern us much. But apparently motor-car people in Amman and round about did not like the change in price, that is to say the people who let out cars on hire, the garage-proprietors, as well as the owners of single taxis.

As I say, it did not seem to concern us much, during the first day or two. There was a great deal it was possible to do, and we preferred to do, on foot—going round seeing places and people and shops and so on. Then it began to get awkward, as we wanted to get further afield; but in one or two cases the notables we wished to see sent their cars for us and the strikers were shy about knocking their cars about. Then rumours began to go round it was going to be all right in a few hours. The motor-car people had achieved contact with a supply of petrol at the old price—bootleg petrol, so to speak. It would be all right. They would compel the combine to rescind the new scale of charges.

But a few hours passed, and another few hours, and it was still not all right. Contact had not been achieved with the bootleg petrol. In the meantime disturbing rumours began to come in from all over the place—disturbing to us, I mean, who wanted to get moving again, and to anybody else who wanted to get moving. The strikers had totally forbidden the sale of petrol at the new price. That meant they had called a halt to all transport by petrol. We did not know how that affected movement by government machines. Probably not at all, they had their own supplies of petrol. But it affected everything else. Transport by petrol was stone-dead. Anybody that defied the ban, the strikers let it be known, was for it.

It was very inconvenient, of course, for a great many people. They felt they must get from one place to another. Rumours began to come in of cars with all their tyres slashed to ribbons, of goods stacked up in the roadway and burned. There were tracks of glass and nails across the roads, and armed strikers in ambush behind rocks. There had been shooting.

We had done all we had intended to do in Amman. It was time we started off. It was manifestly clear we would have to revise our plans radically. We could not get to Deraa by car, and would have to cut it out. It was not at all certain, anyway (we consoled ourselves readily), that it was the Edrei of Moses. We could get there by the once-a-week train on the Hedjaz railway. But that did not appeal to us. That was not because neither Moses nor Lawrence had got there by train, but because, somehow, to travel by train on this journey seemed wrong, while we had no compunction about travelling by car. A car is a donkey, a horse, a camel, *in excelsis*. You are, within certain limits, its master. There are no limits to the mastery of a train over you.

Moreover, if we went to Deraa, we would have to go directly on to Haifa by rail, where we intended to take a Messageries Maritimes boat for Marseilles. That would mean cutting out Jerusalem, and we did not wish to do that. There is a certain appropriateness about going by way of Jerusalem, after a journey in the steps of Moses. Also, we wished to interview certain scholars in Jerusalem. There was one further objection, and a serious one, against going to Deraa and Haifa by rail. It would cut out the plains of Moab, over against Jericho, and the battle against the Midianites. Obviously, Deraa must be ruled out.

Well, supposing we could get straight down to the plain by way of es-Salt to the bank of the Jordan. And then? We were beginning to feel more and more doubtful about that final ascent to Mount Nebo, in the wake of that man about to die. We had felt no such thing about the ascent to the top of Sinai, in the wake of a man about to receive a Covenant. The Sinai ascent is all carefully worked out for you; thousands of steps are cut in the rock for you. There are chapels all the way up, and one on the summit, too, for you to say a prayer at if you have a mind to.

But there is no such ascent to Mount Nebo from the plain of Moab. No chapel on its summit marks that sepulchre which no man to this day knows of. It is, I think, one of the most fortunate errors in the history of shrine-making, that the Muslims built that mosque of Nebi Musa over against Jericho, neglecting Nebo.

Yet can it have been an error? If it had been an error, it would have been so glaring, it would have missed the point so monstrously. Read this again: " And I besought the Lord at that time, saying, O Lord God, thou hast begun to shew thy servant thy greatness, and thy strong hand: for what God is there in heaven or in earth, that can do according to thy acts? Let me go over, I pray thee, and see the good land that is beyond Jordan, that goodly mountain, and Lebanon. But the Lord was wroth with me for your sakes, and hearkened not unto me: and the Lord said unto me, Let it suffice thee; speak no more of this matter."

No, the setting up of Nebi Musa's tomb on the west side of Jordan cannot have been an error. They must be right who state that it was set up as a counter-attraction to the Tomb of the Holy Sepulchre in Jerusalem . . . a doubly fortunate institution, that has saved much bloodshed in Jerusalem, and kept Nebo inviolate.

No stairway leads up to Nebo, I say, and no shrine is there. The bareness and austerity of those rolling hills—how much grander a monument it is than the most elaborate tomb of the Pharaohs, the chairs and the couches, the gold and the enamel, the armouries and the wall-paintings! How much grander a tomb, how much more impervious to desecration! For it is hard to desecrate grass and stone, wind and sky.

We would get down by es-Salt to the bank of Jordan, and pause a moment before the hither end of the bridge. In that moment much would happen. We would prevail in a last battle. Moses the Conqueror, finding One to conquer him, would lay his hands on Joshua, the son of Nun, that he might be full of the spirit of wisdom. And Moses would go up to the top of a mountain, and have a Vision there, and utter in that extreme loneliness his last praises of the Lord. And he would die there, according to the Lord's word, and there in the plains of Moab there would be thirty days of weeping among the children of Israel. And thereafter the host would go over to the land promised them.

And we would go with them. But we would have to find a way to reach there first.

That did not seem as if it was going to be at all easy. The *sortes Virgilianae* were definitely against us. For, sitting disconsolately in an armchair in the corner of the lounge, I picked up *Tancred* and this was the passage that came out towards me: " ' A man cannot go to Jerusalem as he would to Birmingham by the next train,' continued his lordship. ' He must get something to take him.' "

That did not look at all good. A motor-car was the only thing that could take him, but a motor-car was not to be had, as it is phrased, for love or money. It was really dangerous for everyone concerned, the chauffeur, the passengers, the car. We had appealed for their help to a number of notables, but they could not do anything, or would not accept the responsibility. Their regrets had been coming through successively during the last hour or two on the telephone. Among others we had appealed to Peake Pasha. He had asked us to give him a couple of hours, but he was not at all hopeful. The couple of hours had gone by.

Sitting in another armchair in another corner of the lounge, Lucas was also studying the *sortes Virgilianae*. He had picked up the one English book in the hotel, a novel called *The Knave of Diamonds*, by Miss E. M. Dell. Suddenly he uttered a cry of derision. It was obvious he had drawn a lot, too.

" Listen to this ! " he exclaimed, and read : " ' The car ran smoothly on through the night like an inspired chariot of the gods. There was no sound of wheels. They seemed to be borne on wings.' " He snapped the book to, and flung it at Jim's bottle of stratified coloured sands from Petra that had started running into each other. Jim had brought it out to see if he could do anything with it. " That's about the only sort of car we're likely to get ! " he snorted. " Borne on wings ! Pah ! "

We smoked, and kicked our heels, and smoked, and were very bored. We were afraid of picking up any other book, for fear we might draw more lots. Peake Pasha was a long time getting through. Of course he was not going to get through. He had far too much on his hands, what with gun-running and strikes, and one thing and another. We did not want to go outside. There was a lot of wind and sand blowing about, it was *khamsin* weather. You could hardly see across to the Greco-Roman theatre. And we did not want to see across to the Greco-Roman theatre. We had seen enough of it.

We did not want to go outside, but we did not want to stay inside, either. We had seen enough of that hotel-lounge, the last day or so. It was a difficult situation.

Then the telephone-bell rang.

" Beake Basha ! " the man at the telephone called.

We raced over.

" Is that you, chaps ? " the almost Berkeley Bar accents came out to us.

It was us.

" Have you got your kit ready ? "

It had been ready packed for days.

" I've got a fellah here. He's a Palestine fellah. He's *got* to get back to Palestine to-day. Message come through. Wife sick or somethin'."

" Yes? Yes? "

" Will you be ready in five minutes? "

" Good *Lord*, yes! "

" No hangin' about or anythin'? "

" Good *Lord*, no! "

" Your responsibility, mark you! And his! "

" We don't mind *that*! Oh I say, Peake Pasha, we can't begin to thank you——"

" Just to make sure, I'm sendin' over a bit of an escort. First bit of the road's the nastiest! Take care of yourselves! Good-bye! "

He rang off.

I turned round, radiant.

" And we shan't be strike-breakers, either! " I exulted. I had had some compunctions about that. " Poor fellow! Wife sick or something! If it hadn't been for us, he might have had to wait weeks and weeks before he got to her! "

" I take it," said Lucas, " we're fixed up? "

" Yes! Here in five minutes! "

" Then let's shunt the stuff out! Sorry about that bottle of Petra sand, Jim."

Jim looked sorry, too. It had come a long way, without the Nubian sandstone running into the grey limestone, and the green diorite running into both.

Exactly five minutes later a large car drew up outside the front door of the hotel. The proprietor would have preferred the car to be a little less well-polished and palpable, for he was not quite sure how the strikers would feel about it. They were standing about all over the place, looking ominous. However, a big car cannot pretend it is not there. The next best thing was to get it loaded up as quickly as possible, so that it might move away at the first possible moment from the windows. In an astonishingly few seconds all our luggage was in. It was like a brilliant piece of scene-shifting, with the curtain only down for a second or two. Every member of the hotel staff acted as scene-shifter. Jim got in front beside the driver, Lucas and I got in behind, and we were just about to drive off, when a large group of women and children unloaded itself into the car, like a coal-scuttle unloading itself into an enclosed stove.

We had seen that family of women and children about for some days; we had heard them, too. They were relatives of our hotel-proprietor, who had come back lately from America. Though Arabs, they did not like Arabs. They did not like Jews, either. They found everything goddam-awful. They had Milwaukee accents, I think. They had been very unfortunate. They kept an hotel in Jericho, and somehow had not heard about the strike. So two or three mornings ago one of the husbands thought how nice it would be to take a trip to the Amman relative. They set out and had a clear journey to es-Salt about half-way. Then they were informed there was a strike on. It was too late to turn back there, and anyway, they thought, the strike might be over by the time they got to Amman. Outside es-Salt, strikers stopped them with guns, but seeing all those women and children, they did not shoot. Instead, one of them got up on a mudguard and rode with them the rest of the way. A kilometre or two outside Amman, he got off, because the police forbid people to ride on mudguards. Then another group took them in hand. They were asked to get out of the car, and half a dozen strikers got to work on their tyres. It was nice to know those curved Mecca daggers were not there for fun. They had a long walk before they got to the hotel, and were quite footsore when they arrived, as they only had thin houseshoes on. The children started crying, too. They had not stopped crying since.

As I say, we had heard and seen them about the place; and there they were, all of them, and the car was quite crowded already. It all happened very quickly, with several sorts of noise going on, imploring husbands, cajoling hotel-proprietors, squalling children. And what could we do? I

am forced to confess we did not want them, we deplored
them. But were we the sort of people to drag helpless women
and children from a car that was to be protected by a police-
escort? We were not. And the chauffeur was in a great
hurry. So somehow or other the doors were closed in on us,
and he started up. A little distance ahead the escort was
waiting for us. It consisted of a motor-truck with a tough
wire cage all round. It looked oddly like the sort of thing
a farmer sometimes takes his pigs to market in, excepting
that it would be a rope net, not a wire cage. And these were
not pigs, but armed policemen. As we let in our clutch, they
let in their clutch, and we set off. It had all taken no time
at all.

It was a queer way (it occurred to me) to set off on the
last stage of a journey which had begun after much fore-
thought and with some ceremony.

Even if Moses went down to the plains of Moab from somewhere in the direction of Deraa, it is quite possible a goodly
contingent of Gaddites and Reubenites went down from
Rabbath-Ammon to the river by the very road we were taking.
If that is so, it was a pity we could not see more of it. Our
view was almost completely blocked by women, children and
kitbags, and the escort car in front kicking up a smoke-screen,
perhaps deliberately, which our chauffeur hugged grimly the
whole time. In addition to all that, there was a good deal
of rolling mist about. Visibility was bad that day.

We had left Amman by the old road, which circumvents
most of the town. It was thought there would be fewer
strikers that way. We soon joined a fine new macadamized
road, and were speeding across very handsome country, from
what we could see of it. It was a pity, I complained to Lucas,
what we could see was so little. Well, there's one good thing
about it, he said. And what is that? I asked cynically. We're
almost bullet-proof, he replied. What with women and
children in front and at the sides, and kitbags behind us,
nothing short of a hand-grenade can stop us.

There seemed to be some comfort in that thought. I moved

up the bulkiest ruck-sack to cover the back of my skull, which had been feeling a little exposed for some time. I caught a quick glimpse of the wind threshing the barley-stalks against the hill-sides. Then I lost it again. A little time later we saw two armed policemen on horseback. That seemed almost an extravagance of assurance. Everybody saluted. We passed them. Then the road was grey and empty again, the road grey, the landscape and sky grey, our hair and mouths going grey, everything grey: a kilometre further, at a bend in the road, there was a stranded lorry. It had been carrying wooden boxes of some merchandise or another. Some of the boxes were still in the lorry, some still on the road. The driver was sitting ashen-faced on a heap of stones by the roadside, his face in his hands. He seemed past caring where his wooden boxes were.

At about eight kilometres from Amman our escort suddenly stopped. Hello, I said to myself, is this a drawn battle? Where are those Midianites? We must turn back at this point, the escort said. We would find the road patrolled by mounted policemen from now on.

They turned back and we went on alone. It was astonishing how alone their departure made us feel, despite all those women and children. Some distance further, we saw a car behaving in a suspicious manner. It was in the middle of the road, and moving very very slowly. The chauffeur stamped on his accelerator, and managed not to fall into the gully beside the road. The children clapped their hands and thought it great fun. Some distance further, at a sharp bend, three or four fierce looking men got up suddenly from among some rocks. They took as good a look at us as the chauffeur would let them. Then they settled down among the rocks again.

" Look what comes of travelling with us women and children ! " said the women.

" I think they know I from Palestine ! " said the chauffeur.

The children clapped their hands.

" I wonder where the next lot of mounted policemen are ! "

I said, and moved the kitbag into position again behind the back of my skull.

We saw a police-post beyond us, and a small town on a hill, shrouded by the mist. The road bore away from the police-post, turning due south. We had for some time been going south and east. That place is es-Salt, we were informed; we had covered about half the journey. The place is said to be the ancient Gadara, but this seemed no moment to undertake an inquiry into the matter.

A handful of policemen came out to us from the police-post. There has been shooting along the road, said they; if we wished to go on, we did so at our own risk. We preferred to go on. "I will come in with you," said one of the policemen, and opened a door. A child or two and some of the luggage fell out, but they were restored, and room was found somehow for the policeman, too. He looked very businesslike, with a rifle, revolver, and handcuffs. He was a curly-haired friendly sort of fellow, very well set up, as they all are. He told us that the strikers had littered the road with broken glass about a kilometre from Amman, but the police had had word about our car, and they had got it swept up.

As we turned the first bend beyond the village, we saw a cordon of men stretched out across the road. The chauffeur went straight for them, and the policeman stuck his gun through the window very menacingly. They did not like the look of either, so they scattered.

" It might have been the Amorites," I said, turning to Lucas.

" Amorites? " he asked, looking rather blank.

" Yes. They wouldn't let Moses through, so he went straight for them."

" Oh yes, the Amorites ! "

I had a feeling he would not be displeased to get away from Amorites, and Moabites, and Ammonites—and Midianites, too, for that matter. But he still had to put up with the Midianites.

" What would you have done," I asked the policeman, " if they would have stopped us? "

" I shoot them all dead," said the policeman, " if there is a hundred of them."

The children clapped their hands more excitedly than ever. "Oh please, shoot, policeman!" they cried. "Please shoot!" Growing up as they are in the Palestine of our day, they find life rather tame without a little shooting once a day, at least.

We heard the sound of a car moving round a corner towards us. Everybody tensed up expectantly. It was a very decrepit omnibus, which had determined to run the gauntlet. There were at least fifty Arabs in it and on it, clinging to the bonnet, the mudguards, wherever it was possible to hold on with a couple of fingers. The omnibus had heard us the same time as we had heard it. The driver was dickering with terror. He took both hands off the wheel, and spread them out, as if to say: " All right then, shoot, if you have the heart! " The eyes of all the passengers were starting out of their heads. Then they saw the barrel of the gun sticking out of the window. A general wail went up, male and female. Then it was perceived we were a policeman; the wail subsided; a shrill huzza went up in its turn.

About a kilometre further we saw the rust-red skeleton of a car beside the road. Is that what happened, I asked, to the last car that took this road without a policeman?

" Turkish car burnt in war! " the policeman corrected me.

" Looks like Midianite car burnt in war," I reflected. We were getting nearer the Midianites.

The road continued to descend deeply. Somehow the mist had been excluded from the ravine. For some time we could see quite well what was going on in the landscape. We had left the upland barley-fields behind us. We were in a lovely flowery wadi now—the wadi Sheib, they said. The smell of rushing streams came fresh to our nostrils. Wormwood spurted around us. There were anemones—no Transjordan without anemones—purple orchids and dark-blue irises. There was full-blossomed white broom, oleander not yet in blossom, and great meadows of mauve stock tremulous in the misted sunshine.

MEN OF HESHBON

Still the steep descent continued. Beside the road a board announced " Sea Level." We turned a shoulder of the wadi and over the slope of the diminishing hills on our left saw the Dead Sea like a sheet of tin heated from below by great fires. The mist was again beginning to close in on us. We were in the foot-hills. We were in the fringe of good land between the foot-hills and the sterile waste. Bananas lopped over top-heavily, fat branches of fig coiled in and out of the mist like snakes. The lamps of oranges burned for a short time and were extinguished.

We were in the Ghor now. The black goat-hair tents spread out along the sweltering rifts. They seemed innumerable, like the bivouacs of an army, disappearing north and south into the mist. It was very hot and steamy. I could hardly see my friends, nor the huddled women and children, nor the policeman with his gun resting on the rim of the window. The car closed round on me like the walls of a cave. The floor of the cave was fissured and rumblings issued from it and sharp spurts of vapour. The confused cries of men grappling together, the clank of sword striking sword, the fortunes of the battle shifting with the shifting mist.

For Midian! For the Black Stone of Midian!

For Israel! For the Lord which is neither stick nor stone!

The cries of men falling back, the cries of men rallying again. And does Midian triumph, and shall Israel fail on the threshold of the land, the heritage?

Whose voice is this, louder than them all, clear as the voice is of a man about to die?

" Vex the Midianites, and smite them ! "

Smite them! the echo comes. For Israel! For the Lord which is neither stick nor stone!

And it was with Midian as with Moab and Ammon. And Israel prevailed, and abode in the plain.

" Now I go down," said the policeman. We had stopped at a police-post in a small village. " It is hot, yes? " He mopped his forehead with his sleeve. " You come soon to Allenby Bridge. All good now, yes? "

Ccc

" All good," we agreed.

He got out and shook hands all round.

" Good-bye," we said, and thanked him warmly.

" Cigarette-lighter," he said, " to light cigarettes! Please take! "

We thanked him again. So went our last revolving-pencil.

" Shall we get out a bit and stretch our legs? " asked Lucas.

" Not here," I begged. " We can only be a kilometre or two away from the bank of the river. Let's just wander about there for a few minutes, when we get there."

We went on. The mist had lifted a little, but it revealed little, only the mangy desert acacia, the snail-starred scrub.

" And Moses went and spake these words unto all Israel. And he said unto them, I am an hundred and twenty years old this day; I can no more go out and come in: and the Lord hath said unto me, Thou shalt not go over this Jordan. The Lord thy God, he will go over before thee; he will destroy these nations from before thee, and thou shalt possess them: and Joshua, he shall go over before thee, as the Lord hath spoken. Be strong and of a good courage, fear not, nor be affrighted at them: for the Lord thy God, he it is that doth go with thee; he will not fail thee, nor forsake thee.

" And Moses wrote this law, and delivered it unto the priests the sons of Levi, which had the ark of the covenant of the Lord, and unto all the elders of Israel."

And this being done, he arose and spoke the words of a certain song in the ears of the assembly of Israel:

> *Give ear, ye heavens, and I will speak;*
> *And let the earth hear the words of my mouth:*
> *My doctrine shall drop as the rain,*
> *My speech shall distil as the dew;*
> *As the small rain upon the tender grass,*
> *And as the showers upon the herb;*
> *For I will proclaim the word of the Lord.*

He spoke of the kindness of God, that had made Israel ride in the high places of the earth, and eat the carcase of the field, suck honey out of the rock, oil out of the flinty rock. And his eye darkened, and thunder was about his forehead, and he spoke also of the wickedness of Israel, and of his whoredom, and the payment that must be paid in the later days.

And making an end of speaking the words of this song, he said unto them : " Set your heart unto all the words which I testify unto you this day; which ye shall command your children, to observe to do all the words of this law. For it is no vain thing for you; because it is your life, and through this thing you shall prolong your days upon the land, whither ye go over Jordan to possess it."

" Here is Allenby Bridge," said the chauffeur.

" Here is Allenby Bridge," Lucas repeated, nudging me.

" Yes, yes. We'll get out here for a bit."

" You've got to get out here anyway," said one of the women, " and show your papers."

" It isn't much of a bridge really, is it? " said Jim critically. He walked up to the bank and looked over the narrow strip of yellowish water. " Not much of a river, either," he added.

" Not much of a river," I said. " Yet in some ways it's broader and deeper than the Thames and the Seine and the Hudson River."

Jim looked a little puzzled.

" And the Rhine, too," added Lucas, quietly.

I looked at him, and looked away quickly. I felt the sort of gratitude which it is better that not even the eye should seek to express.

" And the Lord spake unto Moses that selfsame day, saying, Get thee up into this mountain of Abarim, unto Mount Nebo, which is in the land of Moab, that is over against Jericho; and behold the land of Canaan, which I give unto the children of Israel for a possession : and die in the mount whither thou goest up, and be gathered unto thy people;

Ccc*

as Aaron thy brother died in mount Hor, and was gathered unto his people: because ye trespassed against me in the midst of the children of Israel at the waters of Meribah of Kadesh, in the wilderness of Zin; because ye sanctified me not in the midst of Israel. For thou shalt see the land before thee; but thou shalt not go thither into the land which I give the children of Israel."

And before going up into that mountain, once more and for the last time, Moses turned unto the Lord: "This one thing only, that I may bless the children of Israel before I die."

"Even so," the Lord said; and Moses arose, and uttered his blessings of the people, first all the tribes of them, one with another, then all the people as one tribe, saying:

> " *There is none like unto God, O Jeshurun,*
>   *Who rideth upon the heaven for thy help,*
>   *And in his excellency on the skies.*
>   *The eternal God is thy dwelling-place,*
>   *And underneath are the everlasting arms.*
>   *And he thrust out the enemy from before thee,*
>   *And said, Destroy.*
>   *And Israel dwelleth in safety,*
>   *The fountain of Jacob alone,*
>   *In a land of corn and wine;*
>   *Yea, his heavens drop down dew.*
>   *Happy art thou, O Israel:*
>   *Who is like unto thee, a people saved by the Lord,*
>   *The shield of thy help,*
>   *And that is the sword of thy excellency!*
>   *And thine enemies shall submit themselves unto thee;*
>   *And thou shalt tread upon their high places.*"

And Moses went up from the plains of Moab unto Mount Nebo, to the top of Pisgah, that is over against Jericho. And the Lord showed him all the land, saying: This is the land which I sware unto Abraham, unto Isaac, and unto Jacob, saying, I will give it unto thy seed: I have caused thee to see it with thine own eyes, but thou shalt not go over thither.

Wide, wide, that vision was, all the hills unto the hinder sea, and the south, and all the plain. But can it have been that the vision was not wider than that, outward over space, and forward into time? Foreseeing the Temple on a hill, did he not see the Temple in flames? Did he not see the host scattered to the four corners of the earth, that he had brought up out of Egypt and across the desert with so much travail? Is not all my work undone? did he not ask in sore dismay. Or is not this the fulfilment of the prophecy which alas, I with my own tongue prophesied? Is not this the payment they must pay for their evil-doing—the arenas of Rome, the Frankish ghettoes, the stake of Spain, the Russian pogrom? Did the vision go further, by but one moment of time, to this latter day? And seeing the things of it, the innumerable murder, the long cold calculated murder, not of one man on a stake or one family in a cellar, but of whole cities, of multitudes beyond the cities . . . did he utter one great cry to the Lord, crying: " Enough, enough, Lord! It is paid for! Is it not enough? "

Did his own words come back to him as upon wings:

Thine enemies shall submit themselves unto thee;
And thou shalt tread upon their high places——?

Or did he forget the enemies of Israel in that final moment, remembering only their sorrows:

The eternal God is thy dwelling-place,
And underneath are the everlasting arms——?

And so he died there, as it is written, Moses the servant of the Lord, in the land of Moab, according to the will of the Lord.

And those that came later, learned in the knowledge of cherubim and seraphim, declare that in that last moment three archangels came down with the Lord God from beside the Throne in the topmost heaven. Michael was one of these, Gabriel another, Zagzagel the third. And Gabriel arranged the couch of Moses and Michael spread over it a purple garment, and Zagzagel placed there a pillow of fine wool. And these things done, God set Himself behind the head of Moses, Michael on his right hand, Gabriel on his left hand, and Zagzagel by his feet. And the Lord said: "Cross thy feet," and Moses crossed his feet. And the Lord said: "Fold thy hands and place them upon thy heart." And Moses folded his hands and placed them upon his heart. And the Lord said: "Close thine eyes." And Moses closed his eyes. And the Lord stooped and kissed Moses upon the mouth and drew his soul from him, and bore it away to the topmost heaven, to the footstool by the Throne.

And as for his body, he buried it in the valley in the land of Moab, over against Beth-peor: but no man knoweth of its sepulchre unto this day.

It was Lucas, I found, who was standing by me, and had addressed me once or twice, and I had not answered him. Jim was there, too. I turned to them.

"I'm sorry," I said. "Forgive me. I was thinking."

"I was saying we did right not to go up there after him," murmured Lucas.

"It isn't as if anybody knows where he was buried," Jim added.

That was quite true, I said. I recalled that my father used to say how strange it was that though the Holy Word gives a sign within a sign . . . "in the land of Moab, over against Beth-peor" . . . yet no one has ever been able to find out where his grave is. In later years (my father would continue) the Romans began to get very curious about it. They were convinced there must be a lot of treasure with Moses where he lies buried—exactly like that old goatherd whom we had met up there among the cairns and stone circles. So the Romans sent over to the garrison of Beth-peor, saying: You must find out for us without fail where the grave of Moses, the Hebrew Prophet, is. And the soldiers went about searching for it. When they stood on the top of the mountain, it seemed to them it was at the foot. When they stood at the foot, it seemed to them it was on the top. So they split up into two parties. But those below still thought it was on the top, while those on top still thought it was below.

There is only one way to find out where the grave is, my father pointed out. There is a secret passage connecting the grave of the Patriarchs over in Palestine with the grave of Moses in Transjordan here. But you have to find the Palestine end of the passage, and that is not easy, either.

" Did he say why the grave of Moses was kept so secret? " asked Jim.

Yes, he told us why that was so. For in later years, when the Temple was burned down, if the Jews had known where the grave of Moses is, they would have come and wept there night and day, and implored him to plead with God on their behalf, to restore their Temple. And Moses could not have remained deaf to their pleading. And he would have arisen from his grave, and pleaded with God. And God loved Moses so much, He could not have withstood his pleading, not even He. And the Temple would have been restored to Israel.

" Well, why not? " asked Jim.

" Because the time had not come yet."

" Do you think the time has come now, perhaps? " asked Lucas.

I turned away from the direction of Mount Nebo, and walked back towards the brink of the River Jordan.

" You would have thought so. But apparently the time has not come even yet."

There was silence for a little time, and a faint noise of weeping came out of that silence, and the weeping endured thirty days. And at length the days of weeping in the mourning for Moses were ended.

The car had been on the other side of the bridge for some time. The only sound to be heard now was the water chuckling and tugging among the reeds.

" The men over there are signalling to us," said Lucas.

" Yes," I said. " Let's go over to the other side."

THE END

PARIS—LONDON—PARIS.
1937–1938.

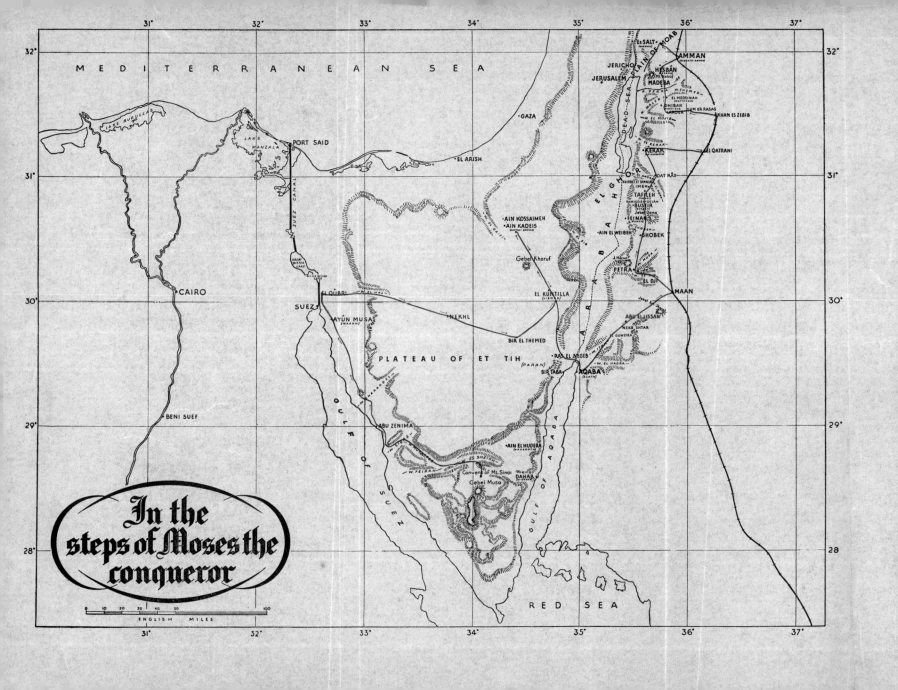

In the
steps of Moses the
conqueror

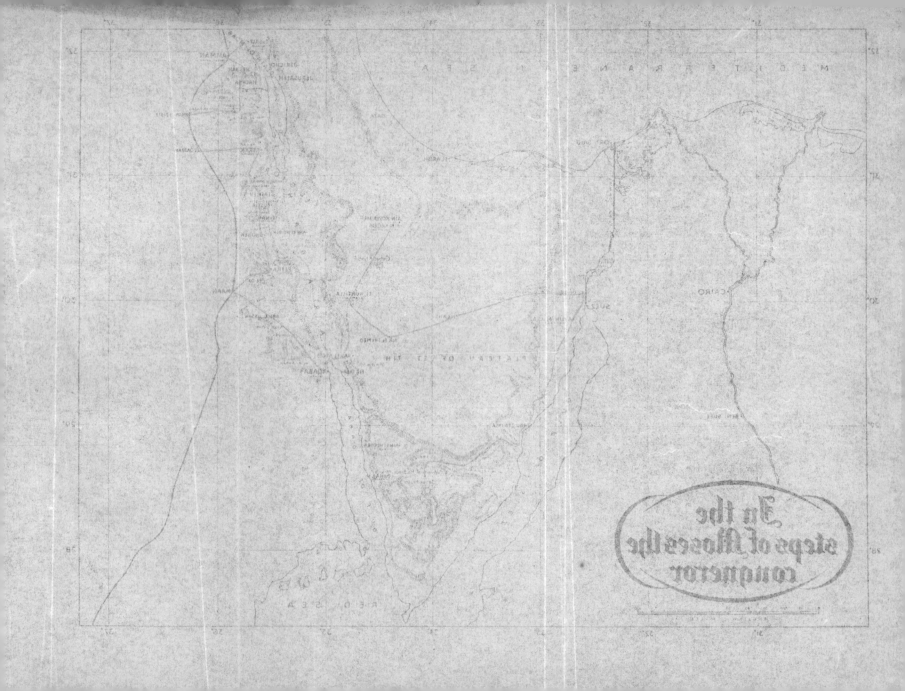

BIBLIOGRAPHY

Aaronsohn, A. Florula Transjordanica.

Bentwich, Norman. A Wanderer in the Promised Land.

Bible, The.

Chapman, A. T. An Introduction to the Pentateuch. (The Cambridge Bible.)

Colenso, J. W. The Pentateuch and Book of Joshua.

Conder, C. R. Heth and Moab.
                Survey of Eastern Palestine.

Doughty, C. M. Arabia Deserta.

Ebers, G. Durch Gosen zum Sinai.

Eckenstein, L. A History of Sinai.

Encyclopaedia Biblica, ed. by Cheyne, T. K., and Black, J. S.

Ginsberg, L. The Legends of the Jews.

Graetz, H. History of the Jews.

Graves, R. Lawrence and the Arabs.

Hart, H. C. Some Account of the Fauna and Flora of Sinai, Petra and Wadi Arabah.

Hastings, J. Dictionary of the Bible.

Huntingdon, E. Palestine and its Transformation.

Jarvis, Major C. S. Yesterday and To-day in Sinai.
                Three Deserts.

Kent, C. F. The Beginnings of Hebrew History.

Koran, The.

Laborde, M. Léon de. Voyage de l'Arabie Pétrée.

Lawrence, T. E. Seven Pillars of Wisdom.

Lawrence, T. E., and Woolley, C. L. The Wilderness of Zin.

Lowenthal, M. A World Passed By.

Luke, H. C., and Keith-Roach, E. Handbook of Palestine and Transjordan.

McNeile, A. H. The Book of Numbers. (The Cambridge Bible.)

Meistermann, P. B. Sinai et Petra.

Meyer, E. Die Israeliten und ihre Nachbarstämme.

Musil, A. Arabia Petraea.

Orr, J. Problem of the Old Testament.

Palmer, E. H. The Desert of the Exodus.
Paton, L. B. History of Syria and Palestine.
Peet, T. E. Egypt and the Old Testament.
Robinson, E. Biblical Researches.
Smith, G. A. Deuteronomy. (The Cambridge Bible.)
        The Historical Geography of the Holy Land.
Smith, W. R. Religion of the Semites.
Stanley, A. P. Sinai and Palestine.
Storrs, Sir Ronald. Orientations.
Talmud, The.
Toffteen, O. A. The Historic Exodus.
Trumbull, T. C. Kadesh-Barnea.
Weill, R. La Presqu'île du Sinai.
Yahuda, A. S. The Accuracy of the Bible.

INDEX